HOLLIS F. FAIT, Ph.D.
associate professor of physical education
university of connecticut

SPECIAL PHYSICAL

second edition

EDUCATION: adapted, corrective, developmental

W. B. SAUNDERS COMPANY / PHILADELPHIA / LONDON

W. B. Saunders Company: West Washington Square,
                           Philadelphia, Pa. 19105

                           12 Dyott Street
                           London, W.C.1

Reprinted May, 1967, and September, 1968

Special Physical Education

PREFACE

The years since the first edition of this textbook was published have witnessed many new developments in medical treatment and in educational endeavors for those in our society whom we call handicapped. One of the most significant of the developments in the area of education has been a program known as special education, which has the goal of providing the kind of instruction that will best meet the special needs and abilities of physically and mentally handicapped children and, by extension, of handicapped adults. In keeping with the dynamic concept of special education, it seems appropriate that the various physical education approaches which have been used to meet special needs arising from physical limitations and deficiencies be incorporated into a single special physical education program.

The author conceives of special physical education as embracing adapted, corrective, and developmental physical education activities and has used this premise as the basis of this new edition. Accordingly, the contents have been reorganized into sections dealing with adapted physical education for the mentally, physically, and socially handicapped; with corrective physical education for body mechanics; and with developmental physical education for physical fitness. Several new chapters present detailed discussions of the skill techniques of numerous games, sports, and activities and the ways in which they may be adapted for many kinds of handicapped players. All of the factual material has been brought up to date, and the latest references for supplementary reading have been included.

Like the first edition, this edition is addressed to students planning to teach physical education in elementary and secondary schools in which a certain portion of the school population will have disabilities requiring special offerings in the physical education program; to those who plan to teach in special schools and hospitals for children with physical and mental handicaps; to those who are preparing for careers in physical education and related areas in hospitals and institutions for persons with physical, mental, and emotional ills. The book is designed to give the prospective physical education teacher, in whichever of these situations he may be employed, a brief introduction to the nature of each of the most common types of handicapping conditions, and the psychological implications for the one who is so afflicted, in order that he may bring to his work with the handicapped the understanding and enthusiasm without which no program can succeed.

The author wishes to express his gratitude to numerous individuals who have given assistance in the preparation of the manuscript. Particularly deserving of thanks are Miss Marilyn Quinlan, instructor in physical education at the Mansfield (Connecticut) State Training School and Hospital, who wrote the chapter on rhythms and dance; Francis Kelley, superintendent of the Mansfield State Training School and Hospital, who expanded and updated the chapter on the mentally retarded; and Dr. Jay Shivers, supervisor of the recreational services curriculum of the School of Physical Education, University of Connecticut, who developed the material on outdoor education. Appreciation for their helpful reviews of the technical discussion in certain chapters is expressed to: Dr. T. Erwin Blesh, professor of physical education, Yale University; James M. Bauer, assistant technical director of the School of Physical Therapy, University of Connecticut; Miss Dorothy L. McLaughlin, instructor in physical therapy, University of Connecticut; Dr. Ingeborg MacKellar, professor of foods and nutrition, University of Connecticut; Richard Miller, occupational and recreational therapist, Norwich (Connecticut) State Hospital; Dr. Donald P. Kent, former director of the Institute of Gerontology, University of Connecticut; Dr. John LeRoy, director of Health Services, University of Connecticut; and L. Paul Murray, medical-social consultant and director of Camp Hidden Valley. Acknowledgment is also made of the valuable suggestions made by Dr. Karl Kline, University of Texas, and Dr. Ernest Gardner, Wayne State University School of Medicine, who read portions of the manuscript for the first edition. The efforts of these individuals in helping the author to achieve an accurate and comprehensive presentation of the material are greatly appreciated, and any errors which may appear in the text are solely the author's responsibility.

Special recognition is accorded Mrs. Gladene Hansen Fait for her careful editing of the manuscript and for the performance of numerous other tasks which facilitated its preparation; Miss Arden Curtis, physical education teacher at Manchester (Connecticut) High School, who compiled the basic skill games for Chapter 16; and Dr. Harriet Kupferer, formerly in charge of adapted physical education for women, University of Connecticut, who assisted in the initial planning of the manuscript for the first edition.

Organizations and publications which made photographs, illustrations, and other materials available to the author are thanked for their courteous and generous service.

Storrs, Connecticut   HOLLIS F. FAIT

CONTENTS

1
HISTORICAL BACKGROUND

Among our population are large numbers of children and adults who differ so markedly in mental, physical, emotional, or behavioral characteristics from their normal peers as to require special help in realizing their optimum potential. An increasing awareness among educators and laymen alike of the needs of these children and adults has resulted in a number of programs designed to give them special assistance in a variety of ways. On the educational level, this has taken the form of *special education* programs, established and financed in most of our states by their legislative bodies. Those in physical education are apt to be more interested in the programs of special education in the public schools than in the other programs, although, more and more, people trained in physical education are finding employment in institutions, hospitals, and special schools where those with special conditions and needs are cared for.

Children for whom special provisions must be made to enable them to achieve optimum development in the educational program are usually identified by the term *exceptional*. Exceptional children have been defined as "those who deviate from what is supposed to be average in physical, mental, emotional, or social characteristics to such an extent that they require special education services in order to develop to their maximum capacity."[1] They may be classified into four groups: the physically disabled, the

---

[1]National Society for the Study of Education: *Forty-ninth Yearbook*, Part II. Chicago, University of Chicago Press, 1950, p. 3.

1

mentally disabled, the mentally gifted or talented, and the emotionally disturbed or those with behavior problems. These classifications are very general and not mutually exclusive. In fact, a child who fits into any one category may very likely fit into one or more of the other classifications. The interrelationship of the physical, mental, and emotional development is such that it is likely that a child with a physical or mental disability will also have emotional problems.

It is essential in dealing with exceptional children to recognize the "whole" child. When in this textbook we consider the problems of children in one of the defined categories, we do so with full recognition that these children may well have other problems arising from the disability, or the special gift, which they have; and that while we are concerned with the instruction of physical activities, we are ultimately concerned with the education of the whole child.

DEFINITION OF TERMS

A number of different names have been given to the special educational provisions made in the physical education curriculum for those unable to profit from the offerings made to the student body generally. Among the names used are corrective, remedial, developmental, modified, adapted, and preventive physical education. The choice of names is determined largely by the emphasis and approach of the special program. The basic intent of all the programs is the same: the improvement of body mechanics and general physical condition through motor activity.

For purposes of discussion within this book, it is essential to establish how the terms normal and handicapped are used. *Normal* individuals are defined as those who display reactions and behavior patterns which are the most prevalent and the most widely accepted by our society. *Handicapped* individuals are those who because of physical, mental, social, or emotional differences cannot display the reactions and patterns of behavior of the normal segment of society. Accordingly, one who has a physical or mental disability but has overcome it to the extent that his reactions and patterns of behavior are like those of normal people is not considered to be handicapped.

The only exceptional students who cannot also be considered handicapped are the mentally gifted. Those who have exceptionally high mental capacities do not require the same kind of consideration in planning the physical education curriculum as other types of exceptional students and so are not generally provided for in the special physical education program. Nevertheless, there are certain ways in which the physical education curriculum may be enriched to make physical education a more challenging and meaningful experience for these youngsters; a brief discussion of these methods may be found in the Appendix.

Corrective physical education and *remedial* physical education are terms used for programs that emphasize the change or improvement in function or structure by means of selected exercises. *Developmental* physical education stresses the development of motor ability and physical fitness in those who are below the desired level. *Modified* and *adapted* physical education programs are those which have the same objectives as the regular physical education program, but in which adjustments are made in the regular offerings to meet the needs and abilities of exceptional students. The purpose of *preventive* physical education is to forestall the failure of normal growth and development. For the exceptional, the program is concerned with preventing other abnormalities from developing, protecting against further injury, and promoting proper use of the body.

Two other labels for special programs of exercises and physical activities should be explained here: *rehabilitation* and *reconditioning.* These terms are commonly used to describe the motor activities programs developed for convalescents in military hospitals during and after World War II and now extended throughout physical medicine and therapy.

It is interesting to note that the word handicap had its origin in an ancient Anglo-Saxon game of chance, "hand in the cap." In the game one player challenged another for possession of his cap in exchange for a cap of his own. A certain amount of money was placed in the cap to be awarded to the one receiving the article of lesser value, as determined by an impartial judge. The hand in the cap was a means of equalizing the chances of the two players, just as in some games today a player of lesser strength or ability may be awarded a handicap, which is a shortened form of the original hand in the cap.

Over the years the word came to be applied to any circumstance or condition which prevented anyone from competing successfully with his peers in social or economic endeavors. Those who were thus prevented from successful competition were labeled the handicapped. It is in this sense that the word is used today, although currently we also include the mentally retarded and emotionally disturbed as well as the physically disabled among the handicapped.

PROVIDING FOR THE HANDICAPPED

Education for all is a basic tenet of our democratic faith, and the opportunity for each individual to develop his potential is a guiding principle of our educational system. In the progress toward equalized educational opportunities for all, the handicapped have not always received due consideration. The establishment of special schools for the handicapped and the introduction of special programs and methods of instruction for the disabled had to wait largely upon enlightened public opinion regarding the handicapped and their special needs.

The first real public awareness of the problem of the disabled in the United States came in the early years of this century, growing out of the tragic consequences of disease and war. In 1916 our country experienced an epidemic of infantile paralysis, and within the next few years the wounded and disabled returned from World War I. An aroused public's desire to help the victims of paralysis and the disabled soldiers forged a new attitude toward the handicapped which spurred legislative and educational assistance.

To appreciate fully the new attitude and its ramifications, one must leaf back through the pages of history and appraise the prevailing attitude toward the handicapped in other times and places. In primitive societies defective children generally perished at an early age as a consequence of their inability to withstand the rigors of primitive man's strenuous existence. Even in the civilized societies of early Greece, the Spartan father of a crippled child was expected to carry the babe to the hills to be left to perish, while the Athenians, whom we generally consider more humanitarian than their Spartan neighbors, permitted such babies to die of neglect. During the days of the Roman Empire, crippled babies suffered a like fate.

Although some handicapped individuals found social acceptance as court jesters during the Middle Ages, the prevailing attitude was one of superstition and fear. Physical and mental disabilities were believed to have been caused by Satan, and the afflicted were held to be sinful and evil. Hence, the handicapped were either harshly treated or carefully avoided.

The humanistic philosophy which flowered in the period of the Renaissance undoubtedly softened the general attitude toward the physically handicapped, but the gain in understanding of their problems did not extend to include treatment, care, and education. Some legislation to prevent conditions which might produce crippling injuries was passed during the Industrial Revolution, but beyond this the conditions of the handicapped were lost sight of in the tremendous technical advancement of the age.

Thus it was not until the 1900's that social awareness of the problems of the handicapped gained momentum in this country. This awareness resulted in the organization of conferences on the welfare of the crippled child and in the opening of schools for crippled children and clinics and centers for their treatment.

World Wars I and II gave impetus to the development of the techniques of orthopedic surgery which had already made important gains through the treatment of crippled children. From the treatment of war casualties, care was gradually expanded to include physically disabled civilians. Accompanying the physical reconditioning of crippled soldiers and civilians came a movement to rehabilitate the handicapped, to help them become useful, self-sufficient citizens again. There developed after World War I what were known at the time as curative workshops, in which patients were taught purposeful activities for their therapeutic value.

Today this type of program is known as occupational therapy, and it has as its goal the rehabilitation of the patient through the teaching of some craft or trade by which he may become at least partially, if not totally, self-sustaining.

Today there are also programs of physical therapy, recreational therapy, and exercise therapy which endeavor to help the disabled reach maximum potential. Physical therapy attempts to correct remediable conditions through a carefully planned and controlled program of exercise, while recreational therapy encourages desirable psychological reactions through the medium of numerous recreational activities such as music, drama, arts, crafts, and games. Physical education programs in hospitals are frequently presented under the name of exercise or corrective therapy and are taught by a physical education specialist who is certified as an exercise or corrective therapist.

Funds for most early efforts to provide rehabilitation services for the disabled came from charity and fraternal organizations, private philanthropy, and community service organizations. A great deal was accomplished through the efforts of these groups, not the least of which was helping to arouse public concern for the needs and rights of the crippled, the blind, the deaf, and the otherwise handicapped. As a result, states began to pass the legislation needed for a more nearly complete program of care and rehabilitation of a heretofore largely neglected segment of our population. Today states own and support hospitals and institutions at which adults and children can secure the kind of professional care and treatment their disabilities require. The states also assume a share of the responsibility for the educational and vocational needs of the handicapped.

Federal legislation had been enacted following World War I to provide certain benefits to disabled veterans; these were supplemented by further legislation in 1943 to increase the scope of aid to the veterans of World War II. The legislation provided for the rehabilitation of soldiers with war disabilities under the supervision of the Veterans Administration.

The first law providing for assistance to civilians with disabling injuries was passed in 1920. Under its provisions civilians injured in industrial accidents and from some other causes were entitled to vocational rehabilitation: they were to be returned to employment where possible. A subsequent law in 1943 provided for physical restoration as well as vocational rehabilitation.

A steady growth of services to the handicapped has been in evidence over the years as the result of private, state, and federal assistance. Services today include research into the cause and cure of mentally and physically crippling diseases; better facilities and increased knowledge in detecting, diagnosing, and treating disabling conditions; vocational rehabilitation and training; job placement or replacement; and, in the case of veterans and the industrially disabled, compensation or disability allowances and pensions. Special hospitals and schools for certain kinds of handicaps have also been established throughout the country. These include hospitals or special homes for the crippled, convalescents, and aged; institutions for the mentally ill and emotionally disturbed; and schools for the blind, deaf, and mentally retarded. Itinerant teachers are financed by state funds to instruct children confined to their homes by disabilities. State funds also assist local schools in providing special classes with adapted equipment and specially trained teachers for the instruction of handicapped children.

These programs of educational and vocational rehabilitation have made it possible for the handicapped to become economically contributing members of society. This is of tremendous importance to them and to society, for as they become self-sufficient the cost of their care is removed from society. Changes in attitude toward the employment of the handicapped over the years have implemented their economic status. Once, only a few of the most skilled could find employment, and then sometimes even these found it difficult to convince employers that they were capable of doing the same job as those without handicaps. For a period of time there was a movement to give partial employment or part-time jobs to the handicapped. Favorable experiences in employing handicapped workers have helped to foster a growing attitude that the handicapped deserve to be given equal consideration when seeking employment and equal compensation for performing the same work as their fellow employees.

In the foregoing paragraphs we have attempted to understand the handicapped individual and his position in society. We have seen how the attitude toward the disabled has changed from complete disregard to a consideration of him as a potentially productive member of his culture who differs from his fellows only in the extent of his disability. The change in attitude has motivated and in turn been given impetus by the work of numerous service and philanthropic organizations[2] and by the legislation of state and federal governments.

SPECIAL PHYSICAL EDUCATION

Although the special physical education program is one of the more recently developed services for the handicapped, it is interesting to note that the basic concept of the program—the correction and improvement of motor functions of the body through exercise—is an ancient one. Pictures and records dating back three thousand years before Christ have been found in China depicting the therapeutic use of gymnastics. In more recent times a system of medical gymnastics was developed in Sweden, by Per Henrick Ling, which was introduced in this country in 1884 and had a wide vogue. It was a system of calisthenics of precise, definite movements designed to produce a healthier body and improve

[2]See Appendix for list.

posture. Because it was believed that exercise of this nature would be highly beneficial to school children, programs of calisthenics were widely introduced in the public schools of that period.

A department of corrective physical education was first established by Dudley Sargent at Harvard in 1879 with the objective of correcting certain pathological conditions. The idea of physical education as corrective exercise for bad postural habits and for the general improvement of health persisted until about the time of World War I. Then, following the development of successful physical therapy techniques for paralyzed and convalescent soldiers, the idea of corrective exercises for students with physical handicaps took hold. Soon many colleges had established corrective classes for students who were unable to participate in the regular physical education program. Corrective physical education for the improvement of posture was de-emphasized generally, but a few schools continued to stress corrective exercises in their physical education classes. The trend today is to provide a corrective program in the physical education program for those who need to improve their body mechanics.

Adapted physical education grew out of the early corrective classes that were established specifically for those with disabilities. Gradually, over the years following World War I, the practice grew of assigning handicapped students to corrective courses in order to protect their condition from possible aggravation. As yet little consideration was given to the idea that the handicapped student could be taught to play modified forms of sports or games or that he might possibly be integrated into regular classes for part of his instruction. By 1930, fundamental changes had been initiated in physical education for handicapped students in some universities and colleges. A recognition of the value of play as an educational tool to implement social, mental, and physical development became the philosophical basis of course offerings to the handicapped. Calisthenics, gymnastics, and corrective exercise were supplanted in the course content by games, sports, and rhythmic activities modified to meet the individual needs of the students. Handicapped students who could participate with safety in some activities of the regular physical education classes began to receive as much instruction as their cases warranted in these regular classes. The worth of this approach in teaching physical education to the handicapped has been proven over the years and is the basis of present-day adapted physical education.

Developmental physical education also had its origin in the early corrective programs which, as conceived by Sargent, had the objective of promoting a generally healthy and fit body. Although this has always been one of the recognized objectives of physical education, it has only in recent years received special emphasis. This was the direct result of the nationwide concern over the low level of physical fitness of American children. The developmental physical education program of today utilizes special exercises and vigorous games to promote optimum health and fitness.

Public schools generally have lagged behind institutions of higher learning in developing special physical education for the handicapped. As late as 1954, less than 5 per cent of the secondary schools had special physical education; however, there has been a recent increase in this number. In a recent survey by the author in the state of Connecticut, 15 per cent of the schools were found to have some type of program for the handicapped, and over 75 per cent indicated plans to initiate a program in the near future. Most of these anticipated programs, however, were to serve the mentally retarded rather than the total range of exceptional children in the school.[3]

Many states have passed legislation requiring local boards of education to provide education in the public schools for the mentally retarded. As these youngsters have been brought into the schools, physical education teachers and special education teachers have had to provide opportunities in physical education for them. With this impetus, considerable progress has been made in establishing adapted physical education programs for the mentally retarded. Physical education for the physically handicapped, however, is becoming available at a much slower pace.

Considerable progress has been made by the colleges and universities which are preparing physical educators for the teaching of exceptional students. A number of schools now have graduate training programs, and many others have increased their course and clinical offerings in this area. Some states now require that all physical education teachers have instruction in adapted or corrective physical education or its equivalent for state certification. Elsewhere, physical education majors planning to teach or do hospital work are encouraged to take such courses. Consequently, the number and the quality of the present-day physical education programs for the handicapped are vastly improved.

[3]Hollis F. Fait: "A Survey of Physical Education for the Handicapped in Connecticut Schools." Unpublished study, Storrs, Connecticut, Physical Efficiency Laboratory, University of Connecticut, 1965.

QUESTIONS

1. Who are the exceptional children?
2. In what ways can exceptional children be categorized? What would be the difficulty in placing a child in any one category?
3. Discuss the terms that are frequently used to describe special classes in physical education for handicapped students. Which terms fit best into your concept of physical education?
4. What is meant by the word "normal" in physical education? How can one determine who is handicapped?
5. Explain how the democratic philosophy supports the concept of physical education of the handicapped, even though the cost of such education for each handicapped child may be considerably more than for the normal child.

6. What was the situation which directed public attention to the educational needs of the handicapped?

7. What have been the prevailing attitudes toward the handicapped in different periods of history?

8. In what ways did World Wars I and II give impetus to the physical education of the handicapped?

9. Discuss the history of financial aid to education of the handicapped.

10. Trace the growth of services to the handicapped.

11. Discuss the change of attitude toward employing the handicapped. What were the factors responsible for this change?

12. At what period did civilized man first conceive of the idea of the therapeutic value of physical activity? Trace the development of this concept.

13. Trace the development of adapted physical education in our schools.

14. In what ways did the recognition of the value of play as an educational tool influence the physical education for the handicapped child?

15. What are some of the aims that a good adapted physical education program of today should strive for?

SELECTED READINGS

Baker, Harry J.: *Introduction to Exceptional Children*, ed. 3. New York, The Macmillan Co., 1959.

Dolch, Edward: *Helping Handicapped Children in School*. Champaign, Ill., Garrard Press, 1954.

Frampton, Merle E., and Gall, Elena D. (ed.): *Special Education for the Exceptional*: Volume I — *Introduction and Problems*. Boston, Porter Sargent, Publisher, 1955.

Heck, Arch O.: *The Education of Exceptional Children*. New York, McGraw-Hill Book Co., Inc., 1953.

Kessler, Henry H.: *The Principles and Practices of Rehabilitation*. Philadelphia, Lea & Febiger, 1950.

Stafford, George T.: *Sports for the Handicapped*, ed. 2. New York, Prentice-Hall, Inc., 1947.

Van Dalen, Deobald B., *et al.*: *A World History of Physical Education*. New York, Prentice-Hall, Inc., 1953.

2
UNDERSTANDING
THE HANDICAPPED

Success in working with exceptional children and adults is dependent upon understanding their special problems. It is significant that for most disabled people the major problems are psychological in nature rather than physical. Ways have been found to reduce, if not actually eliminate, the physical pain of a disability. Many mechanical devices have been created and methods of rehabilitation developed to assist the handicapped person in achieving more normal use of his body. Medical treatment and the careful regulation of diet and activity enable many victims handicapped by functional diseases to lead normal lives in many respects. But regardless of how nearly normal body function and physical performance may be, the presence of the disability creates many psychological problems. Anxieties and fears are created about the condition itself or its effects upon the future. Frustrations are commonly experienced, and the individual's sense of security and self-confidence is threatened. Feelings of guilt are also sometimes aroused by the disability, as when the victim believes that he is being punished by the affliction. Because these problems are frequently more difficult to alleviate than the physical problems arising from the incapacitating illness or injury, their solution often constitutes the major obstacle in the total education of the handicapped.

FACTORS AFFECTING ADJUSTMENT

Satisfactory solutions are achieved through the process of adjustment, a term used to describe the changes which an individual undergoes in order that he may adapt to his environment. Adjustment begins at the moment of birth and is a continuous process throughout life. Certain innate factors, the result of inheritance, influence the kind of adjustment that is made in response to the stimuli of the environment. These factors are intelligence, physical appearance, and temperament.

INTELLIGENCE. The degree of native intelligence determines the amount and quality of the direction and control of behavior. The more intelligent the child, the better able he will be to direct and control his behavior. His greater ability to reason enables him to anticipate the results of certain actions, and he acts accordingly. Because he understands more, he is less likely to resort to undesirable behavior to achieve his ends. Children who are mentally retarded often are able to learn socially acceptable behavior, but in new and unexpected circumstances they are unable to apply the learned behavior.

PHYSICAL APPEARANCE. Physical appearance is an important factor in the development of behavior tendencies because of the responses of others to physical characteristics such as body build, facial features, and obvious deformities. We are aware that even such slight deviations as more-than-average height or weight cause others to respond with a certain amount of teasing or even ridicule. Greater deviations from normal cause more intense responses, even to the extent of casting the one who deviates in an inferior social role. The adjustment of a handicapped individual is often greatly influenced by the nature of the responses of those in his social environment to him and his responses to them.

TEMPERAMENT. Behavior tendencies are also influenced by what is generally called temperament, but which scientific evidence indicates is actually glandular function. Although the precise functioning of all the glands is not presently known, it is known that the personality of an individual is affected if certain imbalances or malfunctions occur in the various glands. For example, less than normal activity of the thyroid gland influences certain metabolic changes which produce laziness, dullness, and depression while, in contrast, an overactive thyroid causes and individual to be very active, tense, and restless.

THE EFFECTS OF ENVIRONMENT

A continual interplay exists between the conditions arising from these innate factors and the conditions of the environment—the attitudes and responses of others. Society tends to react in definite ways to any deviation from the norm. Sometimes the reaction is one of ridicule, curiosity, or maudlin sympathy; in the case of those close to the handicapped person, the reaction is often one of indulgence or overprotectiveness. The combined reactions of those in the social environment toward the one who deviates mentally or physically from the norm greatly influence his adjustment.

Because of his physical appearance or his inability to participate normally in the activities of his contemporaries, the handicapped individual is set apart. If the disability has been present since infancy, the child may for a time live in a fairly normal environment. For the first year or two of childhood, the play activities of the child are self-centered. The very young child plays side by side with other children, but the activities are not usually cooperative ones. Because this is true, he is not required to perform his play activity in the same way as his playmates, and he calls no particular attention to his "adapted" method of play. The methods and mannerisms which are necessitated by his particular disability do not come as markedly to the attention of his playmates during this period of self-centered play as they will when, as a slightly older child, play becomes a more cooperative and competitive venture requiring normal competence in motor performance and verbalization.

While the child may not yet feel isolation from his peers, he may begin to sense the attitude of his parents and other adults in his environment. Overprotective and solicitous parents and relatives may promote an awareness of being different. If the disability is one which elicits shock or pity from adults and curiosity from older children, the child begins to wonder about himself. As he grows older, he becomes more acutely aware of the reactions of others to him. His inability to compete successfully in the play activities of others in his age group sets him increasingly apart from them. His drives for success, recognition, and approval are thwarted. His self-confidence and self-esteem are shaken. A satisfactory adjustment becomes difficult.

We have been speaking of the child whose disability has been present from his earliest years, perhaps even from birth. Many other youngsters, adults, and aged people find themselves confronted suddenly with a disability which prevents them from participating in their former life. A sudden accident in the home, at school or work, or on the highway has changed the course of life for many thousands of those whom we number among the handicapped. Many thousands more find themselves handicapped as the result of crippling diseases such as poliomyelitis or a heart attack. The problems of adjustment present themselves to these victims of accidents and disease with abruptness and sharp intensity. But like the child who comes gradually to recognize his situation, they must make adjustments.

When a person is disabled by injury or illness after his personality traits and patterns of adjustment have been established, the new adjustments which must be made to his handicapping condition will be largely of the same nature as previous adjustments. If his previous psychological adjustments have been good, he will likely, after a time, work out satisfactory solutions to the emotional problems presented by his new circumstances. Maladjusted personalities will probably resort to the same unacceptable means of solving problems which they resorted to prior to this time.

Nearly everyone confronted with a sudden debilitating illness or injury experiences a period of emotional upheaval upon realizing that the former mode of living must undergo considerable change and adjustment. The independence of action which a whole healthy body makes possible may be reduced to partial or total dependence upon others for even the necessities of daily living. This realization coupled with the negative responses of family and friends to the patient's condition may be particularly injurious to the self-esteem. Initial responses to these circumstances may be ones of fear, anxiety, despondency, and self-pity. However, as the rehabilitation begins and the patient is reassured of his adequacy in the performance of many of his former skills and pleasures, he begins to make a better psychological adjustment. The more difficult it is to make satisfactory substitutions for the lost motor skills or sensory perceptions, the greater is the adjustment problem.

WAYS OF MAKING ADJUSTMENTS

Adjustment to the problems presented by a handicapping condition may be made in several recognized ways. The mechanisms employed are not relegated to the handicapped alone; they are used by everyone in seeking satisfactory adjustment. There is, however, a tendency for the handicapped to resort to the use of certain of these mechanisms more frequently and with greater intensity; as a consequence, they become unacceptable means of adjustment. Some of the mechanisms are:

1. *Sublimation* — the replacement of a desire or impulse that cannot be satisfied with one which can be fulfilled.

2. *Compensation* — an attempt to offset some shortcoming or limitation by developing some special talent or ability.

3. *Identification* — the conscious or unconscious assuming of the attitudes, manners, etc., of another admired individual or group.

4. *Projection* — placing the blame on others for one's own shortcomings.

5. *Escape* — an attempt to avoid reality by escaping from it in daydreams or fantasy.

6. *Rationalization* — the substitution of reasons other than the real ones for a certain act.

7. *Repression* — the unconscious inhibition of unpleasant memories. Nonhandicapped readers will recognize their own use of these mechanisms in their endeavor to adjust to their environment.

SUBLIMATION. Most people realize that not all desires and impulses can be satisfied in their original form, perhaps because of social disapproval, personal limitations, or other restrictions; then the original desire or impulse is replaced by another which is capable of being fulfilled. In other words, the mechanism of sublimation is used to achieve adjustment. The handicapped person must necessarily make many more such substititions than the nonhandicapped. His problem is further complicated if his handicap restricts the choice of substitutes.

COMPENSATION.   Everyone uses compensation as an adjustment mechanism, either consciously or unconsciously, to build up or maintain self-esteem. Physically handicapped individuals often develop special talents or abilities to offset their limitations in physical performance. A partially sighted boy, for example, may work very hard to develop a musical talent for playing the piano to compensate for his inability to perform the athletic skills which win esteem for his peers.

IDENTIFICATION.   Identification is a frequently employed mechanism, particularly by children and adolescents, who like to identify themselves with teachers, adult friends, movie stars, and athletic heroes. The handicapped child is particularly likely to identify himself with an individual who represents all the things he is not and cannot be. The danger in overuse of identification is that the activity and achievements of the one who is the object of the identification will provide the identifier with so much satisfaction that he will not attempt to achieve anything himself.

PROJECTION.   Projection might be said to be a negative application of the identification mechanism, for here the individual attributes to others activities and attitudes for which he is himself responsible but which he will not accept. An example of the operation of the projection mechanism in a normal youngster is his explaining his being late for class because his mother forgot to set his alarm clock. It is essentially a means of adjustment in which others are blamed for one's personal failures. A handicapped person unable to make satisfactory progress in mastering locomotion with crutches or prosthesis may lay the blame on the doctors, for fitting him poorly, rather than accepting his responsibility for the failure.

ESCAPE.   Avoiding difficult situations or problems by escaping into daydreams or fantasy is fairly common in all youngsters, not just the handicapped; however, the latter are likely to resort to this kind of escape more frequently. A handicapped person—one who is deaf, for example—finding the demands of his environment too great and his failure to meet them too frequent, is likely to withdraw from social contacts and to escape to a dream world to gain the satisfaction he cannot otherwise achieve.

RATIONALIZATION.   Rationalization is another commonly employed mechanism. When the real reasons for certain behavior cannot be expressed because they are not socially acceptable, other reasons which will be accepted are substituted. The need to substitute a more acceptable explanation for the action usually indicates a self-dissatisfaction with the action and the adjustment. Environmental demands on the individual which exceed his physical and mental capabilities often cause the individual to find excuses for his limitations. Thus, the handicapped who does not measure up often resorts to rationalization.

REPRESSION.   Repression of unpleasantness, of places and people which are feared or disliked, is not a conscious act. It does, however, prompt peculiar behavior, because the individual tries to avoid things, places, and people which call forth an association with the repressed memory. The mentally or physically defective child who was ridiculed at the beach may thereafter exhibit great fear of going into the water. He will attribute his fear and dislike of the water to something tangible such as the water being too cold, but the actual reason, his unpleasant experience with those who teased and laughed at him, will be repressed in his subconscious mind.

A person does not usually make a conscious selection of a special adjustment mechanism; rather, he is confronted by a situation and he attempts to make an adjustment which is satisfying to him. If he succeeds, he is likely to use the same mechanism when confronted by a similar situation. If the mechanism does not actually solve the problem, it is, of course, not an acceptable means of adjustment. It may actually become harmful if it is used so frequently that the individual ceases to try to find a more satisfactory mechanism.

THE EFFECTS OF SPECIFIC HANDICAPS

The nature of the handicap or the extent of disability appears to have no significant influence on the adjustment mechanism which is used. Observations of the handicapped have revealed no definite personality traits inevitably arising from a particular handicap. Nevertheless, subjective observations of handicapped groups have led some authorities to conclude that the problems presented to individuals by a major disability such as blindness, deafness, or severe crippling are so similar for each person that certain common behavior tendencies are observable. Undoubtedly, the innate personality factors influence a difference in adjustment even among those similarly afflicted. An individual who is by temperament an active, aggressive person is more likely to seek adjustment through action and to achieve it in a satisfactory way such as compensation, whereas one who is by temperament quiet and retiring is more likely to seek adjustment in less active ways such as, perhaps, in daydreaming.

WAYS THE TEACHER CAN HELP

The environment of the handicapped individual does, as was suggested, play an important role in adjustment. Because any handicap reduces the social interaction between the person and his environment, the environment cannot make the same contribution that is possible with normal people. Nevertheless, the help and understanding of those in the environment of the one who is handicapped make a tremendous difference in the quality of his adjustment. No one develops a socially acceptable personality and becomes well adjusted entirely by his own efforts; he must have the help of family, friends, teachers, and classmates.

It is in the role of teachers that we are here primarily concerned with the promotion of good environment for the wholesome personality development of the handicapped. Any educational endeavor to help the handicapped make a more satisfactory adjustment must include the promotion of better understanding among the children with whom the handicapped child comes in daily contact in the classroom and on the playground. These children constitute the greater portion of his social environment. If they can be given a greater understanding of the role which society forces on the handicapped, if they can acquire respect for a handicapped person as an individual rather than as a deviate, many of the difficulties imposed by his handicap can be alleviated for the disabled child.

In developing a favorable climate in the classroom for the acceptance of those who are physically or mentally handicapped, the teacher may discuss with the students the reasons for liking and disliking certain people. The importance that is sometimes attached to attractive physical appearance may be pointed out and contrasted with more meaningful personal attributes. In connection with this point, it might be emphasized that performing the best one is capable of is just as admirable and worthy of respect as being the most outstanding performer. Attention should be directed toward the concept that one does not have to play well the popular spectator sports such as football and basketball; success, according to one's ability, in an adapted game of corner ping pong or loop badminton is of no less significance than success in the more popular games.

In addition to helping others understand and accept the handicapped, an educational program should be directed toward helping these youngsters develop skills and abilities to offset their physical shortcomings, and to find satisfactory substitutes for the desires they cannot attain and the activities they cannot perform. In these ways the handicapped may overcome the fear, shame, and social inadequacies which cause them to seek refuge in escape and projection and other unacceptable behavior. The adapted physical education program can make particularly significant contributions to the total educational program by helping the handicapped to develop better motor skills, improved body mechanics, and increased physical fitness. The special contributions of various kinds of activities will be presented in the chapters dealing with the specific types of disabilities.

QUESTIONS

1. What does the term "adjustment" mean?
2. In what ways does one's appearance affect his problems in adjustment?

3. What role does glandular function play in personality development?

4. How will the problems of adjustment for one who is handicapped differ if he becomes disabled later in life, or if the disability exists from birth?

5. Discuss the various types of adjustment problems that may occur at different age levels.

6. Define: sublimation, compensation, identification, projection, escape, rationalization, and repression.

7. In what situations may the use of the adjustment mechanisms be to the advantage of the individual employing them? When to his disadvantage?

8. What is the difference between conscious and subconscious selection of an adjustment mechanism? What implication does this have for the physical education teacher?

9. In what ways, if any, will the nature of the disability affect the adjustment of the handicapped?

10. Why is it important for the normal child to have a proper understanding and appreciation of the handicapped? In what ways can a physical education teacher help promote such understanding and appreciation?

SELECTED READINGS

Cruickshank, William: *Psychology of Exceptional Children and Youth.* New York, Prentice-Hall, Inc., 1958.

Frampton, Merle E., and Gall, Elena D. (ed.): *Special Education for the Exceptional:* Vol. II— *The Physically Handicapped and Special Health Problems.* Boston, Porter Sargent, Publisher, 1955.

Garrett, James F., and Levine, Edna S. (ed.): *Psychological Practices with the Physically Disabled.* New York, Columbia University Press, 1962.

Garrison, Karl C., and Force, D. G., Jr.: *The Psychology of Exceptional Children,* ed. 3. New York, The Ronald Press Company, 1959.

Goffman, Erving: *Stigma.* Englewood Cliffs, N. J., Prentice-Hall, Inc., 1963.

Goodenough, Florence L.: *Exceptional Children.* New York, Appleton-Century-Crofts, Inc., 1956.

Taft, Jessie: *The Dynamics of Therapy in a Controlled Relationship.* New York, Dover Publications, Inc., 1962.

3
ADMINISTRATION OF SPECIAL PHYSICAL EDUCATION

When organizing a special physical education program for exceptional students in the regular school, it is useful to have a rough estimate of the number of children (and the nature of their disabilities) expected to take part in the physical education program and of the number with low physical fitness and poor body mechanics for whom special work must also be planned. In a large school system with an adapted program in existence, the figures available from previous years can be used as a guide in estimating the number to be enrolled. A small school population will not provide a good estimate because the sampling is too small to give a reliable average. On the basis of general population of the country, certain percentages can be estimated which can in turn be applied to the individual school situation.

It is estimated that between 5 and 10 per cent of the school-age population will suffer some type of physical or mental deficiency requiring special education consideration.[1] Some of these, of course, will be in special institutions or private schools. Of those in the public school systems who might be expected to be in special physical education classes, no

---

[1]Estimation based on materials in Arthur Daniels and Evelyn A. Davies: *Adapted Physical Education*. New York, Harper and Row, Publishers, 1965, pp. 4–6.

absolute percentage can be determined, since this is dependent upon the policy of the school regarding the types of exceptional students who are enrolled. However, as a working basis for planning the special program, the statistics presented in Table 1 may be useful.

TABLE 1.   *Estimated Percentage of Exceptional Students Who May Need Special Physical Education*

Low physical fitness	20–25%
Poor body mechanics	50–60%
Nutritional disturbances	1–2%
Visual handicaps	2–4%
Auditory handicaps	1–2%
Cerebral palsy	Less than 1%
Cardiopathic conditions	1%
Arrested tuberculosis	Less than 1%
Diabetes	Less than 1%
Anemia	Less than 1%
Asthma and hay fever	2–4%
Hernia	Less than 1%
Epilepsy	Less than 1%
Mental retardation	1%
Other	1%

SEPARATE AND REGULAR CLASSES

Should separate classes be established for the exceptional students who are enrolled in school? There is some controversy among physical educators concerning the value of the separate class as opposed to the value of integrating the students into the regular physical education classes. However, there is agreement on certain circumstances in which a special class should be provided. When a student cannot participate to his advantage in the regular course because of a disability or because of low physical fitness or poor body mechanics, the school should provide a special class if it is able to do so. When a situation endangers the physical health of the student, he should be removed from that environment. If the regular class does not provide self-satisfaction or improvement of skills, attitude, and physical condition, a separate class may fit his needs better.

ADVANTAGE OF REGULAR CLASSES.   In certain situations the exceptional student can be accommodated satisfactorily in the regular physical education classes. When the planned activity can be participated in with safety, such as, for example, a student with a mild heart condition participating in table tennis instruction, then the integration of the student into the regular program is greatly to be desired. Sometimes, too, the student can be given a modified role in the game, as in permitting a crippled boy who cannot run bases to bat in a game of softball with someone delegated to run in his place. Such jobs as keeping score or timing can also be given to exceptional youngsters and are enjoyed by them if they derive a sense of participation from the experiences. However, the instructor should not make the mistake of substituting such jobs for the youngster's physical activity. Similarly, having the student of limited physical capacity or low physical fitness take charge of the equipment may make him feel more a part of the total situation, but such experience is limited in the contributions it can make and should not in any circumstance be considered a substitute for providing actual participation in physical activity.

Integrating exceptional students into the regular physical education classes has its advantage where the number of such students is few and the school cannot, because of financial or other restrictions, establish special classes. It has the advantage to the exceptional student of calling less attention to his difference than his segregation might. Those who favor this method of class planning point out that in this arrangement the student with the special problem is given additional opportunity to adjust to normal society. At the same time the normal students in the class can be guided to a better understanding and appreciation of those who, unlike themselves, cannot participate fully in life's activities.

It should be understood that these very desirable outcomes of the integrated class do not manifest themselves automatically; they may not even occur in the majority of situations. Such results are dependent upon a number of satisfactory conditions: the leadership of the instructor, the personality adjustment of the exceptional student, and the attitude of his peers.

STUDENT PROBLEMS.   Placing the exceptional student in the regular class can also work to a decided disadvantage for the student. His attempts to participate may only serve to emphasize his limitation and cause him to withdraw from class participation. Moreover, his own lack of acceptance of his condition may be reflected in his classmates with disastrous results to his self-esteem. Apart from these psychological implications, a physical condition may be aggravated by insufficient precautionary measures or poor instruction in the teaching of skills.

In view of the advantages and disadvantages to any individual student of either type of class situation, it would appear that a school should provide opportunities in both kinds of classes. The placement of a student in a separate class or integrated class would then be determined by how well the student is adjusted to his limitations, the degree of compensation for the deficiency, and the safety with which he can participate in the activities.

ADMINISTRATION PROBLEMS.   A number of problems confront school administrators and the physical education staff when they attempt to establish separate classes for exceptional students within the school system. The teaching of such classes requires, as a rule, more individualized instruction by a teacher who has some training in, and understanding of, the needs and abilities of the students involved. The class often requires additional space away from the regular class in physical education.

Then, too, scheduling conflicts may arise: it is frequently difficult to schedule the classes so that exceptional students can enroll in them at the hours they are offered. In small schools it is usually necessary to schedule so that all the exceptional students can be included in one class, since the instructor's time and the floor space are at a premium. In very small schools the number of exceptional students in the school system may be so limited as to make the assignment of a teacher to so small a class unjustifiable. A further restricting factor may be the already heavy teaching loads of the physical education teachers. Unfortunately, some administrators still feel that instructors of laboratory courses, of which physical education is one, should be expected to carry a considerably greater number of class hours than other teachers. A final difficulty may be presented by a prevailing attitude that the separate class may have an undesirable effect upon the exceptional student in that being segregated will increase his awareness of his difference.

SCHEDULING CLASSES FOR
THE ADAPTED PROGRAM

One effective method of scheduling the classes of adapted activities is to present them the same hour as the regular physical education classes. This has the desirable advantage of making it possible for the handicapped students to shift from the adapted class into the regular class when the activities being offered are such that they can participate with success. The separate adapted class will need a teacher who can take charge of the adapted activities during the time that the instructor is directing the activities in the regular class. It also requires that space be available for the special class, although, if the space is at a premium, the class can be accommodated on the gymnasium floor with the regular class. This, of course, calls for careful coordination and planning between the two instructors.

The school situation may be such that it is not practical to create a special class for the disabled under the supervision of a special teacher. This is the ideal, and many schools faced with ever increasing school populations and lack of finances cannot provide all the services that they would wish to. It is nevertheless possible to give the handicapped an excellent program of physical education within the regular class. This places great demands upon the ingenuity of the teacher and requires careful organization of the two programs which will run simultaneously under his direction, but these challenges can be met and with good results.

To the advantage of this dual program is the ease with which the handicapped are motivated. Most handicapped students want to take a more active part in the play activities of their peers and are eager to expand their limited skills. Given direction and encouragement, they can be relied upon to work to their capacity to achieve the desired goal. With these favorable circumstances, the physical educator can instruct the two programs at the same time with minimum hardships and maximum results.

The organization and supervision of the dual program may follow any one of several possible patterns. All the students, the handicapped and the nonhandicapped, may meet in the gymnasium for roll call and for instructions on the class procedures for that period. Those in the adapted class may then be excused to go to their activity area and begin their assigned activity, while the instructor starts the activity in which the regular class is participating for the period. When the activity is underway, he can look in on the special class to offer instruction and encouragement. Depending upon the specific circumstances, it may be more advantageous to the program for the instructor to meet with the handicapped students during a free period to explain the nature of the program being planned for them, and to brief them on a procedure for conducting the class largely on their own responsibility.

Many of the physical education activities suitable for the adapted program are classified as recreational games and include table tennis, shuffleboard, deck tennis, and similar activities. These games are fine co-recreational games, so both girls and boys may be included during the instructional period. This may help to alleviate some of the scheduling difficulties. It may also provide a partial solution to the problem of teaching two programs simultaneously in that the teachers of the boys' and of the girls' classes in regular physical education may be able to work out a system whereby one can assist in the co-recreational adapted program while the other instructs the regular class.

SCHEDULING CORRECTIVE AND DEVELOPMENTAL ACTIVITIES

As has been indicated, a large percentage of any regular physical education class will be likely to need special work in physical fitness and body mechanics. Consequently, a considerable portion of the total class time may profitably be devoted to exercises and activities for developing physical fitness and for improving and correcting body mechanics.

How much work is needed by individual students can be determined by body mechanics evaluations (Chapter 24) and physical fitness tests (Chapter 25). If the scores of the class fall in such a way as to make grouping easy, the students can be divided into groups, with each group working on the exercises it is most in need of. Another possibility for presenting exercises to the entire class is to establish stations around the gymnasium at which equipment is available for a certain type of exercise. Students rotate from station to station, doing the exercise at each station for a specified number of repetitions.

Students with extremely low physical fitness or very poor body mechnics will probably need work beyond that which is offered in the regular class. Such students may be placed in the special physical education class if such a class exists. If there is no special class or if the students' attendance there is not feasible, the teacher will need to work out a program of exercises for the students to follow on their own, with as much assistance and encouragement from the teacher as is possible.

EXEMPTION FROM PHYSICAL EDUCATION

What criteria should be used in determining which students may be exempted from physical education? As a general rule it may be stated that a student should be enrolled in physical education when he can participate in physical activity to his advantage. It would be difficult to imagine a situation in which a student with a physical deviation could not benefit from some type of physical education. Of course, some schools may not be set up to take care of all cases and will, therefore, not be able to provide a program for all. Consequently, some students will then need to be excused from the physical education classes.

MEDICAL EXAMINATION. A physical examination by a medical doctor to establish the activity tolerance level and the types of activities from which the individual can benefit is an absolute necessity. The identification of students who cannot participate in regular physical education because of a disability should be made as soon as possible in the school year in order to get the adapted program started, and to prevent an aggravation of any condition precipitated by participation in regular physical education.

How often should a medical examination be made? For the screening of students who need remedial care or should be placed in the adapted class but who are not aware of their conditions, medical examinations are recommended four times during the school career. The first of the examinations is recommended at the time of entrance to school; the second during the intermediate grades, the third at the beginning of adolescence; and the final one at the end of the schooling. These recommendations have been made by the National Committee on School Health Policies of the National Conference in School Health and have been strongly supported by the medical profession. Students who have physical defects or have suffered from serious illnesses require more frequent examinations at the discretion of their physicians.

Students who are not capable of meeting the physical demands of the regular physical education class should be referred by the teacher to a physician for examination. The physical education instructor should be ever alert for students who are unable to meet the requirements of physical performance because of low vitality, lack of strength, poor coordination, and lack of endurance. Tests for subnormal strength and coordination may be administered by the physical education teacher (see Chapter 25).

Other conditions should be referred to the physician for examination. Cases in which sub-strength or coordination cannot be accounted for should also be referred to the physician.

It is recommended that in most situations the family physician should perform the medical examination. When a desirable family physician relationship cannot be arranged, other sources may be necessary. Depending upon the availability of personnel in any particular locality, one of these sources can be used: health consultants in the state department of health and education who will help teachers and nurses in conducting a screening program; private physicians, either individually or cooperating with their local medical society, will assist in performing medical examinations for the school; county and municipal health departments will provide the assistance of their personnel to schools wishing to conduct a screening program.

TRANSFERS TO THE ADAPTED PROGRAM.   In any school population there will be a number of students who should be transferred to the adapted program because of an abnormal attitude toward physical education which prevents them from receiving the benefits of physical activity which they might derive otherwise. Common among such attitudes are fear of contact, hatred of physical activity, and aversion to dressing in the presence of others. Students with these undesirable attitudes can be screened by the teacher of the regular class largely through observation.

POLICY FOR EXCUSES.   The exemption of students from physical education classes can present unanticipated difficulties. The best way to solve the problem which will inevitably arise is to establish a clear and definite policy about the granting of excuses. Where the program of physical education consists of a specified group of activities for all students regardless of the physical deviations and attributes of the class members, some excuses will necessarily have to be given to students unable to participate satisfactorily in the class situation. The more varied the program and the greater the provisions for adapted activities, the fewer will be the number of necessary exemptions from physical education.

Requests for excuses from physical education will be forthcoming from students and parents even when a good adapted program exists, because of their failure to understand the nature of the adapted program and the values that can accrue from participation in such a program. Students in the upper grades of the secondary school and in college are particularly likely to use the medical excuse to avoid the physical education requirement, because they lack an understanding of the contributions which the program can make to their physical well-being and the relationship of good physical condition to successful performance in their chosen professions and the enjoyment of life's activities. Then, too, the family physician may not be fully aware of the nature of the adapted program being offered to students whose participation in physical activity must be restricted. Failing to fully understand the program, such doctors are frequently inclined to grant the medical excuses desired by their patients or the parents of the patients.

The policy which is established to govern the acceptance of excuses from physical education must be realistically based upon the type of program in adapted activities which is being offered, not upon an ideal program which the physical educator hopes can be established in the future. If the lack of facilities or personnel places certain limitations on the adapted program, these must be recognized and exemptions permitted to those students who cannot be adequately accommodated in the adapted program as it exists. It is, after all, better to serve a few adequately than to serve many inadequately — even dangerously. The school has a responsibility, however, to continue to expand its adapted physical education program until all may be served to their advantage.

THE USE OF FORM SHEETS FOR THE ADAPTED CLASS

The next step is to inform the handicapped students and their parents and physicians about the offerings of the adapted program. If exemption from physical education because of medical disabilities requires a medical recommendation, the first educational endeavor could be directed at the school or family physician from whom the exemption will be coming. One technique is a mimeographed form sheet (such as that shown in Figure 1) which is sent to the doctor to bring his attention to the nature of the adapted program and the activities which will be offered. The form sheet should be fairly brief but should provide space for detailed information regarding the patient's needs and the reason for medical exemption. This technique will encourage a physician who is acting chiefly on the desire for the excuse by the patient or his parents to reconsider the request for exemption.

There should also be room on the form sheet for the physician to indicate the duration of the excuse. If a time limit of, for example, one semester is placed on the form, this will encourage a reexamination of the patient to determine changes in his condition which may be of importance to the physical education teacher.

A list of the offered adapted activities may also be included on the form with directions to the doctor to check those in which his patient can or cannot participate. Activities which have been modified or can be adjusted to meet the requirements of the handicapped students should be described briefly. For example, weight-lifting may be modified by having the student seated rather than standing. Described to the doctor in this way, he may recommend this as an activity in which a boy with a broken leg may engage while he would not otherwise permit him to participate in regular weight-lifting.

If space can be allotted the physician for a brief description of the

---

ADAPTED PHYSICAL EDUCATION PROGRAM
_____ School

Date _____

To Dr. _____ Family Physician for _____

Our program of physical education includes a wide variety of activities for all students in the school. The activities are adapted to fit the needs of each individual student regardless of his physical attributes, and any pupil who is unable to participate in the regular program is provided with special activities modified to meet his needs and to contribute to his welfare.

Please indicate the type(s) of activities that your patient cannot participate in and state the reason. _____
_____
_____
_____

Please state the length of time for which the patient is restricted from participation in the above activities: _____ to _____; all year _____.
A list of the activities to be presented in the adapted physical education program this year is given below. Please check those in which your patient may participate.

bowling	shuffleboard	deck tennis
badminton	weightlifting	volleyball
table tennis	*calisthenics	softball
golf	bag punching	archery
tennis	dancing, social,	swimming (no diving)
running	folk and square	swimming (regular)
walking	squash	

Please state any modifications of the above activities which may be made to permit your patient to participate in them. _____
_____
_____

---

* Indicate the types of movement which are contraindicated.

FIGURE 1. Form sheet for family physician.

limitations of the activities for the patient, this is extremely helpful when planning a program to meet the individual needs of the enrolled students. As an example, the doctor might in this space make the notation that the student for whom he is filling out the form has a knee difficulty and should not be allowed to join in activities such as soccer or basketball which require sudden twisting and turning while running. Such limitations might extend to include certain precautions in the dressing room such as not taking a shower because of a severe skin condition.

Parents of handicapped students should also receive a form letter (Figure 2) explaining the adapted program, its objectives and the activities which are offered. The policy for exempting students should be explained and the parents urged to discuss the program with their physicians and with the physical education teacher. With their questions answered and their reservations eliminated, the parents can give wholehearted support to the adapted program.

_____ School

Date _____

Dear Parents:

The program of health and physical education at our school has a wide variety of activities to offer to all students. The activities are adapted to fit the special needs of each pupil regardless of his physical attributes. After receiving the recommendations of your family physician, it was found that your child could participate in the following activities which are being offered in physical education this year:

_____

_____

_____

By giving your child an opportunity to participate in these physical activities, we hope to achieve these objectives:
develop his physical fitness and health to optimum potential;
develop skills in the basic motor movements of sports and everyday living;
develop a variety of sport skills for use in worthy leisure time activity;
promote a desire for continuous physical improvement;
promote an understanding of his physical limitations and potentialities;
provide opportunities to play and participate socially with others.

We hope that our plans meet with your approval. If you wish to discuss the program further, please call me at _____.

Yours truly,

FIGURE 2.   Form letter to parents.

PERSONAL DATA SHEETS AND HEALTH
RECORDS FOR THE ADAPTED CLASS

Most schools now keep a cumulative health record for each student. These can be a very valuable aid to the adapted physical education teacher. They provide a history of the disability and the nature of the disability. Many schools keep the health records through all 12 grades. Although the records do not follow the student to college if he attends, they could be very valuable to the instructor of the college adapted program. Secondary teachers should perhaps make a practice of encouraging handicapped students to have their health records sent to the colleges in which they enroll.

Not all school health records include a description of the limitations of the student in physical education. The value of such information to the teacher of the adapted program is evident. If the school does not include this information, it should be encouraged to begin to do so, including also the physical education activities in which the student has participated.

The teacher of the adapted program will find it extremely helpful to keep his own files on the students enrolled in the program (see Figure 3). The record on each individual might include a brief description of the disability, physician's recommendations, special safety controls, a summary of the progress toward the desired objectives, and the special problems and needs of the student with which the teacher may be of help.

Files are confidential, and any discussion of them should be only on a professional basis with parents, physician, and the student involved.

RECORD OF STUDENT IN ADAPTED CLASS

Name _____ Class _____ Section ____ Date _____
Physician's recommendations _____
_____
_____

Limitations _____
_____

Recommendations for participation _____
_____

Physical fitness test results _____
_____

Past experience in physical education _____
_____

Special problems _____
_____

Specific objectives _____
_____
_____

FIGURE 3.

TEMPORARY TRANSFER OF ADAPTED STUDENT TO REGULAR
PHYSICAL EDUCATION CLASS

Name _____ Class _____ Section ____ Date _____
Limitations _____
_____

Recommendations _____
_____
_____

Date student will report to class _____
Date student will return to adapted class _____

FIGURE 4.

In situations in which the students in the adapted program are assigned to the regular class for activities being presented there in which they can participate, the teacher of the adapted class must supply certain essential information about the students to the teacher in charge of the regular class. This information should include the limitation on their participation and description of their personal needs. A sample form is shown in Figure 4.

ABSENCES FROM THE ADAPTED CLASS

The action which the physical education teacher takes regarding absences from class must be partially dependent upon the school's policy in the matter of absences from school. In general such policies are not concerned with the matter of making up the actual time lost but with making up the work which has been missed, so that the student can be better assured of fulfilling the objectives of the course. In regular physical education classes it is often the practice to require students to make up within a given period the class time he has missed. This means that the student will participate in more than the usual amount of physical activity until he has made up the work missed. Such practice for make-up will probably not be applicable in the adapted class. These students will, for the most part, be exerting physical effort up to their tolerance level in the scheduled activities, and to increase their expenditure of energy by requiring additional work equivalent to the hours of class time missed would most certainly be disadvantageous, if not actually detrimental, to their health. Consequently, some other method of making up the work must be devised which will help the student to achieve the objectives of the course without undue exertion on his part. To accomplish this, the student may be assigned to become familiar with the rules and regulations or to investigate the history of the sport or some similar assignment which is consistent with the overall objectives of the course.

Cases in which the students are absent from physical education classes but are not absent from school also plague the physical educator. Frequently, students or their parents believe they are well enough to attend classes but not well enough to participate in physical education. There are circumstances in which this is undoubtedly true, but in the great majority of cases it is not. If a student is well enough to be in school, he is well enough to participate in physical activity. On the other hand, if he doesn't feel well enough to attend physical education, it is questionable if he should be in school at all. Cases of slight fever and colds are examples of conditions when students shouldn't be in school much less in physical education.

An explanation of this to students and to parents will cut down the number of requests for excuses from physical education by students attending their other classes. Rigidly enforcing the concept that anyone too ill for physical education is too sick to be in school is, moreover, a good health measure because it helps to insure that an ill student gets the rest he needs and safeguards against the possible spreading of colds and other communicable diseases.

SPECIAL HEALTH AND SAFETY NEEDS OF THE HANDICAPPED

The adapted class presents certain problems in health and safety which are not found in the regular classes of physical education. Many students in the class lack endurance and strength, particularly in the early months of the class, and must be protected from overexertion. Students should be made aware of their tolerance levels and educated to exercise caution for their own protection. Although some of the enrolled students will shun physical activity because of the sheltered life they have led as handicapped children, others will be so enthused with the opportunities to participate in the activities which are being taught them that they will fail to regard the safety precautions. They will require supervision and direction until they become fully aware of the importance of taking the necessary precautionary measures. The poorly coordinated ones will not be adept at avoiding accidents, and they may be more prone to falling and stumbling and less adroit at catching and dodging thrown objects.

Certain students are highly susceptible to infection. Even a small cut or scratch can be potentially serious to a diabetic, for example. Other students may have other hygienic problems. For still others the problems will be related to dietary needs; the obese, the poorly coordinated, and the chronically fatigued may have problems essentially dietary in nature. All of these must be given consideration in planning the adapted program for a class of handicapped students.

The handicapped should be taught to assume responsibility for their own health and safety. The teacher must, of course, provide the best possible environment for learning the necessary protective measures. This will include not only good program planning and superior teaching methods but also safe, clean equipment and facilities.

There is always some hazard for exceptional students who engage in play with normal peers. They may not be able to move quickly enough to avoid collision, or they may not see a thrown ball until it is too late to dodge it. Then, too, in their desire to compete successfully they may overexert themselves or take unnecessary risks which result in accidents. Every precaution should be taken to reduce the possibilities of accidental injuries by removing all physical hazards, such as unessential playing equipment and unnecessary barriers and obstructions, from the playing area. Specific safety measures which should be observed for each kind of handicapping condition will be suggested in subsequent chapters.

In addition to these, however, the teacher should instill in the class respect for the playing courtesies of the game and a sportsmanlike regard for the abilities and limitations of others.

LIABILITY.   It is not only the moral responsibility but the legal responsibility of the adapted physical education teacher to exercise all precautions necessary to avoid accidents and injury, and to protect the welfare of the students involved. Statistics indicate that more accidental injuries occur in physical education classes than in any other area of school life. There are also more damage suits involving injury in physical education classes than in other classes or school activities. Although statistics are incomplete concerning the frequency of accidental injury in adapted programs, there is evidence to indicate that the percentage of injuries in this program are considerably less than in the regular physical education program. This is probably due to the greater precautions exercised by teacher and students alike.

Regardless of the fact that injuries in the adapted program are less likely to occur, the teacher must remember that he is liable for damage if negligence is shown to be the cause of injury. State laws governing negligence vary from state to state, but generally, negligence is said to occur when the teacher has not fulfilled his duty or when actions which were obviously wrong or were not those of a reasonably prudent person directly contributed to the injury.

UNIFORMS.   Requiring students to wear a special uniform for participation in physical education is now a fairly common practice. Although the clothing worn by the students need not be uniform in style and color, it should be the type which permits the greatest freedom of movement. Some problems may arise from requests by students with disfiguring skin conditions or deformities to be exempted from wearing the required type of costume. If these students feel more comfortable wearing long trousers or long-sleeved shirts, this should be permitted. However, the teacher could well point out to them that wearing different apparel doesn't really solve anything and may even direct more attention, rather than less, to them because they are dressed differently from the others. They should be reassured that it is likely others will learn to accept their conditions if given a little time.

SHOWERING.   Some students may also wish to avoid showering in the presence of others for reasons of disfigurement or deformity. If they cannot be convinced of the importance of trying to accept their condition and giving others a chance to do so, they should be excused from showering and dressing with the rest of the class. A separate dressing area should be allocated to their use, and an individual shower should be made available if at all possible. If showering facilities cannot be provided, the student in question may be excused from showering.

EQUIPMENT AND FACILITIES FOR ADAPTED, CORRECTIVE AND DEVELOPMENTAL ACTIVITIES

The types of equipment necessary for a special physical education program depend upon the scope and variety of offerings of the program. A program that will serve *all* students regardless of the nature of their needs will require some very special pieces of equipment not needed in a more limited program. A fairly good program can be developed, however, utilizing the equipment used in the regular classes, if there is considerable variety in regular class offerings and therefore variety in the available equipment. In addition, these pieces of special equipment are useful:

full-length mirrors	weighted spats	plinths
weights	horizontal ladder	scales
punching bag stands	stationary bicycle	shoulder wheel
benches without	rowing machine	muscle-testing
backs	balance beams	instruments
wall pulleys	knee exerciser	goniometer
stall bars	ankle exerciser	postural measuring
stall bar benches	iron boots	instruments

The area in which the adapted class is taught should be isolated from spectators and other classes for the most favorable environment. It is, of course, highly desirable that the handicapped develop a positive attitude regarding curious spectators, but it is probably best that new skills be learned in private and exhibited only when developed to a fair degree.

FIGURE 5. Students using an ankle exerciser and rowing machine in adapted physical education class. (Photo by Carl Fischer.)

If the adapted activities are taught in a separate room, the room should be well lighted and ventilated. Wall space may be utilized for charts and other visual aids and for a blackboard, which is such an essential piece of equipment for teaching these students. A filing cabinet may be placed in the room for easy access to the health records, reports, and recommendations on the adapted class students. Book shelves for a library of self-help instructional books may also be provided in the room.

Easy access to the adapted physical education room should be provided for those on crutches and in wheelchairs. Standard specifications for provisions in buildings for those with physical disabilities have been published by the American Standards Association, Inc., in a booklet entitled, "American Standard Specifications for Making Buildings and Facilities Accessible to, and Usable by, the Physically Handicapped." It may be secured from the Association by writing to 10 East 40th Street, New York, N. Y. 10016.

THE ORGANIZATION OF PHYSICAL EDUCATION IN SPECIALIZED INSTITUTIONS

The organization and administration of physical education in private and public institutions established specifically for handicapped students are in many respects similar to the school situation. In certain other institutions the methods of organizing and putting the physical education program into effect will differ significantly. The types of institutions which house the physically handicapped, the mentally defective, and the socially maladjusted, and the programs of physical education adapted to the needs of each, will be briefly presented here.

In all institutions, such as schools for the blind and the deaf, where an educational program similar to that in a regular school is carried on, the administration of the physical education program will not differ greatly. In schools of this kind the entire physical education program will be organized to fit the needs of the students enrolled in the school; that is, the entire program consists of activities adapted to meet the needs and physical attributes of the students. The same will hold true of educational programs in schools for the mentally retarded. The specific organization and methods of teaching in these school situations will be discussed in separate chapters. It should be pointed out here that certain students may have more than one kind of handicap; for example, the blind boy may also have diabetes. Certain adjustments or further adaption of the activities may be necessary to meet the additional limitations of such students.

The administration and organization of physical education in penal institutions and reformatory or training schools are determined by the organization of the institution itself. If an educational program is part of rehabilitation, physical education may be included in the curriculum following a pattern similar to that of regular schools. Generally, however, the physical education activities will be chiefly recreational. In these institutions recreation takes on added significance because recreational outlets are necessarily limited. For young delinquents, physical educational activities can be a valuable tool for social rehabilitation. Security is one of the chief problems of the program in penal institutions; the instructor in charge of physical education or recreation must exercise care that play equipment is not smuggled away for use as escape weapons or in revolt against authority.

In mental institutions the recreation or physical education period is a means of therapy. The program in these institutions is closely allied with the psychiatric treatment, and the doctors will recommend which patients can participate to their benefit in the activities. Scheduling is usually not a problem, for demands upon the patients' time are not great. Activity periods where many patients are brought together for play and instruction in recreational skills can be scheduled. At other times the activities may be brought into the ward where the patients are housed if circumstances permit.

Physical education activities for those in hospitals are under the guidance of medical personnel. In special children's hospitals where convalescence is over a considerable period of time, educational instruction is provided for the youngsters. However, the chief responsibility of these institutions is therapy, not education; in no way should the physical education program take precedence over or hinder the therapy. A definite line must be drawn between physical, or corrective, therapy and physical education. Therapy is concerned with the scientific application of prescribed physical movement of exercise for specific corrective purposes such as restoring normal alignment or function, while adapted physical education refers to the learning of sport and recreational skills and their concomitant learnings. It is a complement to therapy rather than a substitute. The physical education activities may be given in the wards and hospitals to those confined to bed. Ambulatory patients may gather in special areas for these activities. Physical education for those confined in homes for the aged has been sorely neglected. It is only recently that recreation for senior citizens has begun to play a significant role in making the lives of these people more full and enjoyable. Scientific evidence points to the need for oldsters to keep in physical condition through exercise. Certain physical education activities can be brought into the rooms of those confined and, for others, in areas designated for their use.

QUESTIONS

1. Discuss the need for estimating the number of handicapped children who may be expected in any given school as this relates to the planning of an adapted physical education program.

2. What are the values of a separate class for the handicapped in physical education? What are the disadvantages?

3. What are the pro's and con's of assigning handicapped students to such jobs as scorekeeping for their physical education?

4. What is the general policy of schools throughout the country concerning physical education for the handicapped?

5. At what educational level are the best adapted physical education programs found? Why do you think this is true?

6. Discuss some of the problems that confront school administrators in setting up an adapted physical education program. Which of these seem to you to be the chief obstacles to the establishment of an adapted program in a school?

7. Discuss ways in which scheduling problems could be overcome.

8. What value is the medical examination to the physical education teacher in planning an adapted and/or corrective program?

9. How often should school age children be given medical examinations?

10. Under what circumstances is it justifiable for one who is normal physically to participate in adapted physical education?

11. What factors should receive consideration in establishing a policy for granting excuses from physical education?

12. Discuss the methods that a physical education teacher may use to acquaint physicians with the nature and scope of the adapted program.

13. How can the cumulative health record be used to set up a program for the individual handicapped student?

14. What special health and safety precautions must be taken for the handicapped in physical education?

15. Add to the list of equipment for the special physical education room given in this chapter. Explain why you think the equipment should be in an adapted physical education room.

16. What constitutes negligence in physical education classes?

17. How may the organization and administration of physical education in institutions for the handicapped differ from that in the regular school?

SELECTED READINGS

AAHPER: *Current Administrative Problems in Health, Physical Education, and Recreation.* Washington, D.C., American Association for Health, Physical Education, and Recreation, 1960.

Bucher, Charles A.: *Administration of School Health and Physical Education Programs,* ed. 3. St. Louis, The C. V. Mosby Co., 1963.

Daniels, Arthur S.: *Adapted Physical Education,* ed. 2. New York, Harper & Brothers, 1964.

Havel, Richard C., and Seymour, Emery W.: *Administration of Health, Physical Education and Recreation for Schools.* New York, The Ronald Press Company, 1961.

Hughes, William L., *et al.: Administration of Physical Education for Schools and Colleges,* ed. 2. New York, The Ronald Press Company, 1962.

NEA Safety Education Commission: *Who Is Liable for Pupil Injuries?* Washington, D.C., National Education Association, 1950.

Stafford, George T., and Kelly, Ellen Davis: *Preventive and Corrective Physical Education,* ed. 4. New York, The Ronald Press Company, 1965.

Vannier, Maryhelen, and Fait, Hollis F.: *Teaching Physical Education in Secondary Schools,* ed. 2. Philadelphia, W. B. Saunders Co., 1964.

Williams, Jessie F., Brownell, Clifford L., and Vernier, Elmon L.: *Administration of Health Education and Physical Education,* ed. 6. Philadelphia, W. B. Saunders Co., 1964.

4
TEACHING ADAPTED
PHYSICAL EDUCATION

It is the function of the teacher to provide a good learning situation. Toward this end the effective teacher helps the student set up desired goals, selects the material to be learned in the light of the special attributes of each student, conducts the learning experience, and evaluates the results. As a consequence of having fostered a good learning situation in physical education, certain changes occur in the student. The most obvious change will undoubtedly be in an improvement of skills. This will be evident not only in the success with which he participates in games and physical education activities but also in general improvement in movement patterns. Another desirable change which will occur from good teaching, but which is likely to be less obvious to an untrained observer, is the student's increased understanding and appreciation of his personal limitations and attributes. This manifests itself in an improved attitude toward himself and toward others. For many handicapped individuals who suffer serious personality maladjustments, this is the first long step toward better adjustment and the development of more wholesome personality traits.

In order to provide the kind of learning situation which makes these desired results possible, the teacher needs both knowledge and training and certain special qualities of character and personality. Because of the specific problems which a physical or mental handicap creates for the individual who is so afflicted, a teacher of the handicapped must possess certain attributes in excess of those generally required of the teacher of normal individuals.

ATTRIBUTES OF THE ADAPTED
PHYSICAL EDUCATION TEACHER

Perhaps the single most important attribute the teacher of the exceptional students can possess is emotional maturity. Emotional maturity is the ability to solve problems and adjust to the circumstances without undue emotional involvement. The teacher of the handicapped must be a stablizing influence, must represent to the students the ultimate in successful adjustment. A teacher who is himself unable to resolve his own psychological problems is not likely to be able to assist his students in the solving of their problems. If his behavior is particularly immature, he may even contribute to the maladjustment of his students rather than help them make satisfactory adjustments to their handicaps.

Patience and a sense of humor are indispensable qualities in any good teacher. Those who work with the handicapped need to be endowed with a generous portion of each, for progress is more often than not very, very slow. When the results of long hours of work do manifest themselves, however, they are extremely rewarding to the student and to the teacher.

A good imagination is yet another desirable quality in the teacher of those who deviate from the norm, for it may be necessary for him to improvise equipment as well as techniques for performing skills. When facilities and equipment for the teaching of adapted activities are limited, the imaginative teacher adjusts and modifies the available facilities and equipment to fit the requirements of his program. He meets the challenge of an unusual handicap by devising suitable adaptations of the activities to meet the needs of the particular individual.

Organizational ability is essential in the good physical education teacher. Carefully planned class procedures and well-organized class activities are time and energy savers. They make achievement of the desired goal easier and more certain. Class instruction left entirely, or even partially, to chance results in wasted time and motion, in poor learning, and in poor teaching.

Strong leadership is more important in teaching adapted physical education than good equipment, a fine gymnasium, or any other single contributing factor. A good teacher of adapted physical education has great enthusiasm for teaching physical education to all, regardless of their capabilities in the performance of physical skills. He is convinced of the contributions he can make to the lives of the handicapped and has developed numerous methods and techniques to implement his program. He has acquired the gift of insight, he knows when a technique is applicable, and he is willing and able to adjust his methods to meet the specific needs of the moment.

QUALIFICATIONS OF THE ADAPTED
PHYSICAL EDUCATION TEACHER

As regards the qualifications which a teacher should have to instruct adapted activities, it should be said that the background subject areas are essentially the same as those for physical education. A thorough knowledge of sport and recreational game skills is very important, as is a sound understanding of the nature of the human body and its response to exercise. Training in methods of teaching and the psychology of learning are very necessary.

In addition to knowledge pertaining to physical education generally, the teacher should acquire some specific information about the causes, nature, and psychological implications of the various handicapping disabilities. It is necessary to understand the effects of exercise upon these conditions and how sports and games may be utilized to improve the social and emotional as well as the physical well-being of exceptional individuals. The teacher must also have a basic knowledge of first aid for the treatment of minor injuries and, most particularly, the first-aid practices that are applicable to certain handicaps such as the first-aid measures to be administered to an epileptic in a seizure or a diabetic in insulin shock.

OBJECTIVES OF THE ADAPTED
PROGRAM

The aim of the adapted physical education program is to help the student achieve optimum physical, mental, and social growth through a carefully planned program of selected activities. To accomplish it these objectives are set forth:

(1) develop optimum physical fitness;

(2) develop skills in the basic motor movements;

(3) develop a variety of sport skills for participation in sports as a worthy leisure-time activity;

(4) develop a desire for continous physical improvement;

(5) promote an understanding in the student of the nature of his handicap and its limitations while emphasizing the potentialities which may be developed;

(6) give the student a feeling of value and worth as an individual, regardless of his handicap.

Physical fitness is just as necessary and important to the handicapped boy or girl as it is to the normal child. Although the fitness level that is possible for the handicapped may be lower, body efficiency can be improved by a program of regulated activities within the tolerance level of the student. Strength, endurance, agility, power, speed, and recovery from exercise are all important factors of fitness. An optimum increase in these factors results in a more efficient body and is the outcome of a well regulated program of physical activities.

Exercise serves also as a prophylaxis of certain diseases. There is evidence to indicate that coronary diseases, diabetes, and duodenal ulcer are more frequent in those who are sedentary than in those who are active. A tension syndrome produced by an insufficient outlet for aroused emotions and anxieties provides a basis for certain orthopedic difficulties such as stiff neck, painful back and shoulders, and tension headaches. The handicapped individual who has not been guided into a program of vigorous physical activities in which he can participate with success may be more prone than others to these conditions.

Increasing the skills in basic motor movements such as running, changing direction, and falling correctly are tremendously important to the handicapped child. These skills are fundamental to everyday movement, and an improvement in them enables the handicapped individual to work and play more efficiently and with greater pleasure.

Improved basic motor skills also increase the ability to perform certain sport skills with greater success. As he becomes more skilled in the execution of motor skills in game situations, the handicapped student begins to feel less set apart from others; he approaches normalcy. Skills in a wide variety of sports and games also provide the student with increased recreational opportunities, which can, in turn, promote further physical development and social growth.

The handicapped, more often than not, are acutely conscious of their limitations. A well organized program of physical activities helps such students to recognize their potential for doing many things they have always thought were restricted for them. The psychological implications of this are tremendous: the student's entire appraisal of himself may change.

SPECIAL METHODS FOR TEACHING ADAPTED ACTIVITIES

Special methods of instruction are necessitated by the limitations imposed by the specific handicap; however, some methods of teaching can be applied to the adapted class in the regular school and in special schools and institutions. In this chapter the discussion will center around the basic methods, generally applicable in most situations; the special techniques required by each type of handicap are presented in the chapters dealing with these handicaps.

MOTIVATING THE HANDICAPPED STUDENT.   Highly motivated students learn more quickly and retain more of the learning than those who are not motivated. Some handicapped students are highly motivated by their own desires and goals and will present no problem to the teacher. They will be driven by their wish to acquire the same skills as the nonhandicapped, or by their desire to develop body physique or to increase the strength and proportions of certain areas of the body. Other students, however, have no such self-motivating goals. They will have given up the struggle to keep up with the normal world. They have no desire to improve themselves or to compensate for their disabilities. Perhaps, because of overindulgence and overprotection by well-intentioned adults and peer companions, there will exist an apathy toward the need for making any effort which requires physical exertion. This is not a condition peculiar to the handicapped. It is fairly prevalent in regular physical education classes but is probably not as deeply rooted in the normal child as in the handicapped. The teacher will need to help these students set up desirable objectives and arouse an enthusiasm for working to achieve them.

Motivation of the student requires insight, the ability to visualize the chain of events and causes which have produced a certain effect or behavior. To exercise this ability in the interest of properly motivating the individual student, the teacher must know and understand him well. He must know the student's abilities, interests, ambitions, and potential.

RECOGNIZING INDIVIDUAL DIFFERENCES.   Good motivating techniques cannot be developed without a recognition of individual differences. The difference from others created by the physical or mental disability of an individual is obvious. If he is not actually different in appearance, he moves in a different fashion because of the restrictions of his disability. It is fairly obvious, also, that this individual experiences problems in adjustment which also set him apart. There is a tendency to think of these apparent differences as constituting the only "individual differences" of a handicapped person. This is, of course, inaccurate, for he possesses assorted abilities, traits, and characteristics which make him the person he is. He differs from others in certain aspects of these qualities just as ordinary individuals differ from each other. The teacher should never be blinded to these less obvious personal differences, for in understanding the *total individual* lies the soundest basis for good educational practices and procedures.

UNDERSTANDING THE HANDICAPPED.   The more a teacher knows about his handicapped student, the better able he is to teach him. Medical knowledge about the student's condition is necessary and is usually fairly easy to obtain from health records or in consultation with medical personnel who have served the patient. There are, however, other facts which are invaluable to the physical educator in planning his program and which he may secure best in personal conversation with the student himself. Such facts have to do with the student's acceptance of his handicap, his attitude toward activity and toward showering and dressing with others, the type of activities he aspires to take part in, and his fears and his emotional disturbances.

For students beyond the elementary school age, a conference of an informal nature can be arranged with each student individually. For younger children an actual conference is not necessary to obtain the desired information. Indirect questions to the youngsters while they are under the instructor's supervison will reveal a good deal about their attitudes towards themselves and others. The observations of other teachers and conversations with the parents will supply additional information.

It is not always easy for the teacher to gather reliable and useful information from the conference. The student may be uncooperative or inattentive, or so eager to please that he will say whatever he thinks the teacher wishes to hear. The teacher should not become distressed over these "failures"; much more has probably been accomplished than surface evidence indicates. The important thing is for the student to know of the teacher's genuine interest in him and his welfare.

Actual observation of the student in the physical education class will reveal things about him which have not been brought out in the conference. A comparison of the statements made by the student about his limitations with actual observation and with the medical record will give a truer indication of the student's capacities and limitations than any one of these can give by itself. This is not to be interpreted to mean that the medical record is not reliable; just that it does not tell the whole story. The medical report is largely a factual record of the disability and does not purport to present the psychological implications.

In the conference the teacher may be able to pave the way for acceptance of the values of the adapted program and the creation of favorable attitudes toward physical activity. If the student can be convinced of the values of his wholehearted participation in the program, his aid can be enlisted in working out a tentative program of adapted activities determined by his needs and interests. The conference may also afford the teacher the opportunity to establish the controls necessary for protecting the condition from aggravation.

INFORMING THE HANDICAPPED OF HIS CONDITION.   Mature students will be interested in learning all they can about their condition: its cause, nature, possible treatment, the benefits of specific exercises. Such students might be given a library assignment to gather these facts as part of the orientation of the adapted physical education program. A word of caution should be interjected here: only emotionally mature students who will benefit from a better understanding of their conditions should be expected to seek a fuller knowledge of themselves. It should also be pointed out that such an assignment should have the approval of the students' parents, because some parents feel strongly that their handicapped offspring should be protected from the true facts of their conditions.

TEACHING METHODS

Teaching methods can be categorized into three general groups: verbalization, visualization, and kinesthesis. These are extremely broad groupings, but they are used here because they lend themselves uniquely to the discussion of adapted activities.

VERBALIZATION.   Verbalization refers to the use of the spoken word in the process of teaching. Describing a skill or explaining the strategy of a play vocally is an example of such a teaching method. Spoken questions and answers by the teacher and students are included in this category. Oral reports and class discussions are other examples of utilizing verbalization in classroom teaching, although their use is more limited in the teaching of physical education than in other types of classes.

Some concepts can only be put across to students by means of verbalizing them: their presentation cannot be clearly made in any other way. However, in physical education classes where a great deal of the teaching is demonstration, verbalization is most frequently employed to clarify a concept which could not be clearly identified without the use of a descriptive vocal explanation. Students observing a demonstration of the badminton stroke, for example, would likely fail to notice the wrist snap which plays such an important role in an effective stroke. However, when the teacher calls attention to the wrist action with the spoken word, the action is identified and impressed upon the minds of the observers.

VISUALIZATION.   Visualization is a method which employs the visual attention of the students. A number of diverse teaching techniques are included under this general heading: demonstrations, motion pictures, filmstrips, posters and pictures, diagrams, and the printed word.

Demonstration is the physical educator's most effective tool; students probably learn a new muscular skill easier and faster through demonstration than any other method. In a good demonstration, the skill is executed in perfect form one or more times, depending upon its complexity. The students then attempt to execute the skill by duplicating the movements they have observed. It is obviously essential for the physical education teacher to have mastered a wide variety of sport and game skills if he is to demonstrate them adequately for teaching purposes. When an instructor is obviously inadequate in the performance of a skill, he may call upon a competent student for a demonstration. If there is no one capable of demonstrating it, the teacher may have to resort to performing the skill to the best of his ability, pointing out to the class the errors in his techniques and the ways in which these might be corrected.

The use of *movies and filmstrips* is an effective method of showing the proper techniques of performing skills. They have a certain limitation for use in the adapted class, however, since they show how the skills are performed by normal individuals without the handicaps which these students must circumvent in their performances. If the teacher is prepared to describe the possible adaptations of the skills for the students watching the film, this could be a very effective teaching situation. Alert students with active minds and imaginations could be assigned to watch the films and plan their own individual adapted skills. These can then be discussed with the teacher and tried out under his supervision.

Showing films often constitutes a considerable problem because they must be shown in a darkened room. Then, too, setting the film up takes time so that if the film is lengthy, most or all the period is taken up with watching the film and discussing it at its conclusion. This means that the students are denied valuable active participation for that period. Consequently, films should be used judiciously in the adapted program.

If the adapted class is held in a separate classroom rather than within the gymnasium, there is the possibility that the room can be sufficiently darkened for the showing of movies or filmstrips. The showing could be kept brief enough to permit practice of the demonstrated skills immediately afterward in the same room. Given sufficient time, the films may be shown again after the practice session to emphasize the correct techniques.

Still pictures, posters, and diagrams may be used effectively to illustrate correct skill techniques. Pictures of nonhandicapped performers executing the skills are less desirable than ones in which an adapted technique is illustrated, but they are nevertheless extremely useful. Figure 6 shows a prospective weight lifter how to perform the lateral raise. Diagrams of plays on the blackboard are used to good advantage in the adapted physical education class, where students may be more unfamiliar with the strategy of games than normal students who have participated in sports more widely would be.

The use of *the printed word* is a technique that has been largely overlooked as an effective teaching tool in physical education. Textbooks, pamphlets, and other written materials can be particularly advantageous in the adapted class in a dual program situation. Students in the adapted

FIGURE 6. Lateral raise. (Fait *et al.*: A Manual of Physical Education Activities.)

class can use the written materials to answer questions which may arise when the teacher is busy with the regular class. Handicapped students who know little about a particular activity may be assigned to read about it before work in that activity begins, so they will be familiar with the terminology and the general objectives of the activity.

There are many textbooks available, some designed especially for a comprehensive activity course in physical education and others devoted entirely to the skills and strategy of a particular sport or recreational activity. Most of these are suitable for use by college and high school students. They are directed chiefly toward the nonhandicapped, but the student in the adapted class may still utilize much of the instruction. For example, in teaching weightlifting to a student who suffers a chronic dislocation of the shoulder, the instructor might direct the student to read about all the lifts except those which bring the arms higher than the shoulders, as a student with this diability can perform all the lifts except these.

Textbooks designed for service classes usually offer a brief history of the game and stress the care of equipment and the playing courtesies, all of which are essential if the student is to attain the fullest possible understanding and appreciation of the activity. While an effective and well organized teacher can manage to bring this additional information to his class, his job is made considerably easier by the use of a textbook. Moreover, by assigning the students to acquire this information from books, a little more time is gained for working with individual students.

Worksheets are helpful when the student is working by himself. An example of the kind of worksheet which may be used is given in Figure 7. A mimeographed form sheet such as this will aid the student in determining the cause of his skill faults and also show his progress.

KINESTHESIS.   The use of kinesthesis refers to the involvement of muscular activity in the teaching-learning situation. When a student attempts to perform a skill and must make an adjustment in his stance or grip because it doesn't feel right to him, he is making use of kinesthesis. Of course, in the case of beginners, the student will not know how the correct form feels. In fact the correct form may feel more awkward than the incorrect. This is often the case in assuming the grip of a golf club or tennis racket. It is only after the student begins to associate the desired result with the correct form that he will begin to "feel right" about his performance.

In a sense, the adjustment which the student makes when his muscular movements have not achieved satisfactory results is a phase of kinesthesis. Adjusting the serve in table tennis after the ball has fallen short of the net is a learning related to kinesthesis. Of course, the player's eyes tell him that his serve was no good, but the adjustment in the muscular movement made to perform the skill more accurately is kinesthetic in nature.

	PRACTICE GUIDE	
TECHNIQUES	COMMON ERRORS	MY ERRORS
Grip	Gripping too high up on the handle	
Serve	Failure to watch the bird while serving Failure to use the wrist in stroking Serving to the same spot repeatedly Moving the feet during the serve Holding the bird too close to the body; this causes the bird to go into the net Setting up the bird for the opponent which may be caused by holding the bird away from the body or by not using enough or too much wrist in the stroke	
Strokes in General	Standing too close to the bird while stroking Failure to use the wrist in the stroke Failure to place the shot away from the opponent Telegraphing shots or using strokes in a specific pattern	
Overhead Stroke	Allowing the bird to drop too low before stroking	
Forehand Stroke	Failure to hit the bird up when it has dropped lower than the net	
Backhand Stroke	Failure to abduct the wrist in the backswing and snap the wrist forward as the swing comes forward	
Net Shots	Hitting net shots too high	
Drives	Hitting up on the bird	
Court Positions	Failure to return to the proper position after stroking the bird Encroaching on partner's court area Backing up for deep shots instead of pivoting and running back	

FIGURE 7. Practice guide for badminton. (Fait *et al.*: A Manual of Physical Education Activities.)

Circumstances in which the student performs a skill and then attempts to correct his own errors are in reality self-teaching situations. The method is frequently called the "trial and error" method of learning, which is very descriptive of the process. It is an integral phase of the learning of any new activity and is particularly to be fostered among the students in the adapted class.

Still another phase of teaching which employs kinesthesis is that of actually leading the student's hand, arm, or part of the body involved in the activity through the performance of the skill. Such a teaching technique is helpful to students who have failed to grasp the fundamentals by visualization or verbalization. With students who have sensory deviations, as in the case of blindness, the technique is invaluable. It would be practically impossible, for example, to teach a blind boy to punch the light bag unless his hands were led through the movements by his instructor.

DEMONSTRATION, DIAGNOSIS, AND DIRECTION.   It has often been said that the teaching of physical education consists of three big D's: Demonstration, Diagnosis, and Direction. Their mastery is no less important to the teacher of adapted physical education than to those teaching in regular classes.

Various methods of *demonstration* have already been presented. To present to handicapped students the best method of performing a skill will require considerable insight and imagination on the part of the instructor. He must try to put himself in the place of the student with artificial limbs who wants to bowl or the blind student who desires to become a wrestler. At times it may be helpful to the teacher to attempt the skill simulating the handicap, as, for example, attempting the side stroke in swimming without using one of the legs so as to demonstrate more clearly for the student who has lost a leg. Not all handicaps can be simulated successfully: loss of both arms, for instance, seriously affects the balance of the body, and while the instructor can attempt to perform a skill without the use of his arms, he will not be confronted with the

FIGURE 8.   The instructor on the left is employing kinesthesis in teaching a swimming skill while the one on the right is using verbalization to help a youngster understand the skill. (Journal of Health, Physical Education and Recreation.)

same problem of balance as his armless student. Consequently, his demonstration will be limited in its value to the student and he must rely more completely upon analysis of the student's movements as he attempts the skill, making suggestions for a more accurate and satisfying execution of the skill.

We have just spoken of the need for *diagnosis* of the skill performance in the case of a handicapped student for whom a demonstration is not entirely satisfactory. Diagnosis goes beyond this, however; it is an integral factor in teaching skill improvement. Every good physical educator becomes an expert in diagnosing or analyzing learning difficulties and in giving clear explicit directions to the student to enable him to acquire a new pattern of movement.

It is not enough for the teacher to show a learner how to do the skill and to diagnose his learning difficulties, he must also direct the student in overcoming his difficulties. *Direction* is extremely important in the teaching of students with handicaps, for these students want intensely to succeed in performing the skill, and the more quickly any learning difficulties can be overcome the sooner the skill can be mastered.

The techniques that are utilized by the teacher are dependent upon the circumstances and the objectives which are sought. The beginning teacher must choose his techniques on the basis of what he knows about the needs of the handicapped and on his prediction of the success a particular technique will have in accomplishing the changes he hopes will be effected in the students. An analysis of the outcome of his teaching methods will enable him to see what improvements can be made to make his future teaching more effective. Of course, the class situation will not be exactly like the previous one, but on the basis of experience in a previous situation it is possible to predict with greater accuracy the success or failure of any one teaching method as it is applied in similar circumstances.

EVALUATION.   Testing is essential to determine how well the pupils have learned the skills and information being presented to them. This is a good motivational technique as well as a means of evaluation. Evaluation is a continuous process. Daily observation provides evidence of accomplishment, but specific tests must be given periodically to measure the amount and quality of progress achieved. The test results also help the teacher to evaluate the success of the methods used in teaching the class, for without such evaluation no substantial improvement is possible either in the program offerings or in the methods of teaching.

The written test is readily utilized in the adapted physical education class. Written tests, subjective or objective, can be used to evaluate information gained about rules and regulations, strategy, and techniques; they also serve as motivators. Some textbooks provide tests to be used with the book. Standardized tests for many sports appear in the *Journal of Health, Physical Education, and Recreation* and the *Research Quarterly* published by the American Association for Health, Physical Education, and Recreation. All of these may be used with success; however, some of the tests will need to be changed slightly to conform to the material as it is taught and applied to the adapted physical education activities.

Skill and fitness tests are frequently used in determining the level of motor efficiency of the regular physical education students. Fitness tests measure such factors as speed, strength, muscular endurance, cardio-respiratory endurance, flexibility, agility, power, and balance. A complete discussion of fitness testing of the handicapped is found in Chapter 25. Skill tests provide measurements in body mechanics, individual, dual or team sports, rhythmic activities, and aquatics. Standardized skill tests are available in the periodicals of the American Association for Health, Physical Education, and Recreation and textbooks in the area of tests and measurements. These tests are, of course, designed for use with normal students and must be modified to make them applicable.

Because of extreme individual differences, it has been difficult to devise norms for skill tests for the handicapped. In circumstances in which the handicap is such that it does not interfere with the performance of a specific test, a comparison of the results to those achieved by the regular class or to established norms is possible. Where this is not possible, a record of successive test scores by the pupil may be kept to indicate statistically the amount of progress he has achieved.

GRADING.   The established policy of the school regarding the reporting of physical education grades must, of course, determine the method of grading students in the adapted physical education class. Some schools require a letter grade while others prefer only a mark indicating passing or failing of the course. A few schools substitute a progress report by the teacher for marking in adapted physical education. Although this may be somewhat more time consuming, it is the best method of reporting the progress, or lack of it, made by the student. Parents are usually greatly pleased to receive a comprehensive report of this kind.

If a letter grade or mark indicating passing or failing must be given in the adapted class, it must in all fairness be based upon the degree to which the student has achieved the objectives set up for him. This should be clearly understood by all who may see the grades so there will be no misinterpretation of the grade received by any pupil.

QUESTIONS

1. What attributes should the teacher of adapted physical education possess? What skills and training does he need that may not be required of a teacher in a regular physical education class?

2. Compare the objectives of the adapted physical education program with those which are commonly given for regular physical education.

3. What are the factors involved which may make motivation of the handicapped in physical eduation either relatively easy or very difficult?

4. What factors must be taken into consideration in the motivation of any student in physical education?

5. What is the value of the conference in an adapted physical education program? At what educational levels is it most appropriate?

6. Discuss the values of the use of textbooks and written materials in the teaching of adapted physical education.

7. In what ways may the demonstration technique be inadequate in teaching the handicapped in physical education?

8. What is meant by kinesthesis? In what situations would this method be indispensible to the physical education teacher?

9. Explain what is meant by diagnosing performance in muscular activity. Of what value is this to the performer?

10. What are the values of testing and evaluation in the adapted physical education program?

11. Discuss the possible different methods of grading in adapted physical education. What are the strengths and weaknesses of each method?

SELECTED READINGS

Cowell, Charles C., and Schwehn, Hilda M.: *Modern Principles and Methods in Secondary School Physical Education,* ed. 2. Boston, Allyn and Bacon, Inc., 1964.

Davis, Elwood C., and Wallis, Earl I.: *Toward Better Teaching in Physical Education.* Englewood Cliffs, N. J., Prentice-Hall, Inc., 1961.

Fait, Hollis F.: *Physical Education for the Elementary School Child.* Philadelphia, W. B. Saunders Co., 1964.

Knapp, Clyde G., and Hagman, E. Patricia: *Teaching Methods in Physical Education.* New York, McGraw-Hill Book Co., Inc., 1953.

Kozman, Hilda, Cassidy, Rosalind, and Jackson, C. O.: *Methods in Physical Education,* ed. 2. Philadelphia, W. B. Saunders Co., 1955.

Vannier, Maryhelen, and Fait, Hollis F.: *Teaching Physical Education in Secondary Schools,* ed. 2. Philadelphia, W. B. Saunders Co., 1964.

5
VISUAL HANDICAPS

Physical education for the sightless has a long and interesting history. In the 1830's three schools for blind children were founded in the United States, providing the first educational opportunities for such children. One of these schools, Perkins Institute in Boston, had as its director a medical doctor who was an enthusiastic advocate of the benefits of physical exercise. He organized a program of vigorous physical activity for the blind students in his school which included playing outdoors, swimming in the ocean, and work on gymnastic apparatus. His program was far in advance of the physical education in the public schools of his day.

Gradually, other schools for the blind were established. Some of these made provisions for physical training classes in which gymnastics constituted the chief activity. Military training, which received emphasis in the public schools following the Civil War, displaced gymnastic training in schools for the blind. The consequence was that marching and military exercise or formal gymnastics have formed the core of physical education for blind students in many schools until very recent times. In other schools, the play movement which swept the country in the early part of this century encouraged administrators to begin athletic programs in wrestling and track and field. Intramural teams in these sports became prevalent, and soon varsity teams entered into interschool competition.

THE NATURE AND CAUSES OF VISUAL HANDICAPS

Approximately one child out of every four or five has some significant deviation from the accepted norm of good vision. A large majority of these have such slight deviations that they are not extremely detrimental to the child or are remediable either medically or by wearing prescribed lenses. For these children no special educational provisions need be made. However, a small remaining proportion of preschool and school-age children, about 1 out of every 1500, has such severe deviation from normal vision that it cannot profit from the educational opportunities offered in the normal school situation.[1]

The degree to which the child is handicapped is determined largely by how greatly his vision deviates from normal. Although for purposes of classification those with visual acuity of 20/200[2] or less with glasses are considered *blind*, most of those so classified have some useful sight. They may be able to perceive light, form, or movement and are, consequently, considered to be *partially seeing*. The partially seeing have usually been enrolled in schools for the blind along with the totally blind because their visual handicaps require special educational methods and equipment. However, the enrollment of partially seeing students in regular school systems, with some special arrangements made for their needs, is an increasingly common practice. Sometimes this has taken the form of special classes with a teacher trained in methods of instructing the partially seeing and with equipment designed especially for their needs. In other situations they are accommodated in the regular classroom. The basic philosophy behind this is that any unnecessary segregation works to the disadvantage of the education of the whole child. In most circumstances it is also less expensive to provide education for these children within the existing facilities of the regular school.

The age at which the individual became blind has as much bearing on his educational needs as the degree to which his sight is affected. Blindness at birth is more handicapping than blindness which occurs later in life, because it prevents the individual from establishing visual concepts of any kind. Blindness at birth is not common, however. The most common causes of blindness are diseases, accidents, and heredity. Conditions of a hereditary nature which produce blindness are cataract, atrophy of the optic nerve, and retinitis pigmentosa. Accidental injuries on farms and in industry produce numerous incidents of blindness among adults, while playing with sharp instruments and hazardous toys causes many vision accidents among children.

Infectious diseases cause many cases of vision loss. The secondary infection of a contagious disease which has attacked the body, such as smallpox, scarlet fever, or typhoid fever, may cause eye difficulties, or they may be caused by infectious diseases which affect the eyes primarily. Among the infectious diseases which affect the eyes and frequently

[1]Harry J. Baker: *Introduction to Exceptional Children*, ed. 3. New York, The Macmillan Co., 1959, pp. 312–320.
[2]These figures mean that the individual is able to see at 20 feet what those with normal vision see at 200 feet.

cause loss of sight are trachoma and ophthalmia. Trachoma is a chronic inflammation of the conjunctiva believed to be conveyed mechanically to the eye through the use of common washcloths, towels, and handkerchiefs or by the fingers. Ophthalmia is an inflammation of the conjunctiva occurring most often during the first two weeks of a baby's life. It is the result of infection by any one of several pathogenic organisms contracted by the baby during birth, or from the presence of contaminated objects near the eyes.

Gonorrhea, once a common cause of prenatal blindness, has been brought under effective control by state legislation requiring doctors delivering babies to use silver nitrate or other effective medicinals in the eyes of newborn babies. Another cause of blindness, occurring in premature infants, is also being successfully controlled. This is a condition known as retrolental fibroplasia, which was discovered to be related to the administration of oxygen to premature babies.

NEEDS AND ADJUSTMENTS OF THE BLIND

Blind children have the same needs for physical activity as other children, but the fact that they are unable to see does in numerous instances restrict their play activities to such an extent that they are noticeably retarded in their physical development. Fear of injury instilled in them by protective parents reduces their natural interest in big-muscle movements such as running, climbing, and jumping which are an inherent part of the normal child's play and contribute to his muscular growth and the development of coordination. As a result, physical vitality and resistance to certain diseases are low. Posture may be poor both because of the lack of strength in the postural muscles and because of the lack of visual examples of good posture to emulate.

Because the blind child's urges to move and play are restricted, he often develops certain mannerisms known as *blindisms*. These are physical movements through which he seeks to fulfill the need for muscular movement without moving about through space. Rocking back and forth, twitching of the head, and jerking of the limbs are characteristic blindisms. It is desirable to overcome these mannerisms, since they set the blind child apart from his seeing peers. Moreover, in working to eliminate the blindisms a greater sense of security in moving about in space will be developed.

Those who are blind are likely to have personality problems as well as physical incapacities. Because of their fears of activity, the blind tend to pursue solitary and sedentary occupations. This limits their social contacts, which may in turn feed a feeling of inferiority. Frustrations experienced in attempting normal activity or normal social relations contribute to maladjustment. Fantasies and day dreaming are common among the blind who have made unsatisfactory adjustments to their circumstances. The age at which the blinded individual lost his sight has considerable effect upon his social adjustment. Children who have been without sight since birth have more difficulty in social adjustment than those who had achieved some degree of social maturity before losing their sight. However, the latter may experience anxieties and fears about their future, resulting in extreme cases of despondency and depression.

The age at which blindness occurs also influences the movement patterns. These are also governed by the degree to which the person can see. Those who have gained assurance from previous experiences or from their ability to see slightly will move about with less awkwardness and with more confidence than others whose fears are heightened by lack of such assurance.

The blind tend to develop their other senses to a higher degree than normal people to compensate for their lack of sight. Some believe the blind to have a "sixth sense" because they have developed such an awareness of their environment that they appear to perceive things which their normal associates cannot perceive. There is no evidence to support the concept that the blind have an unnatural or mystical gift which enables them to perform activities which would seem possible only for the seeing. The adroitness with which a blind person walks down the crowded sidewalk avoiding other walkers and obstacles, negotiates the curb, and crosses with the light seems almost superhuman to the fully visioned, who cannot conceive of doing this themselves without the use of eyes. Behind the skill of the blind walker are a highly developed kinesthetic sense, a keenly developed sense of hearing, and experience in the interpretation of the various stimuli to his other sense. His "sixth sense" is actually the acute development of the other senses.

PLANNING THE ADAPTED PROGRAM IN THE REGULAR SCHOOL

About one-tenth of the partially sighted attend regular classes. This number can be expected to increase substantially in coming years as the philosophy of accepting handicapped children into the regular school system becomes more widely accepted and as increased funds are made available to purchase the special equipment needed to teach such youngsters. Consequently, the physical education teacher should anticipate that his classes will include some children with partial vision.

At times these students may be placed in the adapted class while at other times they can be readily included in the activities of the regular class. As with most handicapped children, these partially visioned youngsters will want to participate as nearly as possible on an equal basis with their classmates. Giving them this opportunity is one of the greatest contributions the physical education class can make to their well-being.

TEACHING PROCEDURES.   Let us consider some teaching procedures which may be used to make students with visual handicaps an active part of the games and physical activities of the physical education class. Before these methods can be used, of course, the teacher must ascertain the degree to which the students can perceive and how well they have developed compensatory skills. With this knowledge about the students, the teacher can make simple modifications in the activities to accommodate the youngsters in the games of the class. An example should suggest many more similar possibilities to the physical education teacher. Assuming that a student with partial vision is able to distinguish a white covering over the bases but cannot see well enough to bat a pitched ball, someone may be appointed to bat for him and he will do his own base running. The worn path between the bases will also help to guide him around the bases because it will feel different to his feet than the grass.

It is a sensible procedure to have the partially seeing students equally divided between the teams. In this way no team will feel at a disadvantage, and the normal team members will tend to think of these students as teammates who can help them win if they all work together. In this matter, as in all classroom situations, the teacher will set the tone with which the problem is solved. If he is overly protective and solicitous of the handicapped students in the class, such will be the general attitude displayed by the class. Acceptance of the students for what they are with an appreciation of the talents and abilities they display will be the response of the class if this is the attitude demonstrated by the instructor.

The student who wears glasses for corrected vision presents a safety problem in vigorous participation in sports. If he cannot remove the glasses during play, he should wear either the special type of rugged glasses made to withstand rough treatment or he should wear glass guards. In lieu of either of these measures, if they are impractical for one reason or another, the student may be removed from the more strenuous types of activities and placed in the adapted program. It may be necessary to give the glasses protection and support in some instances by placing adhesive tape over the stems of the glasses at the temples.

Another problem with which the teacher must be concerned is a condition of retinal detachment. Partially seeing individuals who suffer from myopia sometimes have this condition, in which there is a partial detachment of the retina from the choroid. It will be necessary to safeguard such individuals from situations which might produce a blow to the head, as such a jar may cause further detachment which can result in total blindness. Contact sports and diving are contraindicated for them.

PLANNING THE PROGRAM IN THE SPECIAL SCHOOL

The discussion which follows concerns the teaching of physical education in a special school for the blind; however, the presentation has many recommendations which can be used by the physical educator in the regular school system to provide a better program for the partially seeing students who are enrolled in his classes.

PLAY AREAS.   The play area, indoors and out, should be a large, uncluttered space. As a safety precaution the play area should be free of nonessential equipment and unnecessary obstructions. For outdoor playing fields hedges and shade trees are considered desirable boundaries rather than walls or fences, which present a certain element of danger. Boundaries for games can be indicated by varying the composition of the court as, for example, having the in-bounds area composed of concrete and the out-of-bounds area of sand or grass. Players will then be able to tell by foot sensitivity when they have stepped out of bounds.

Boundaries in the indoor playing area should be painted in white for the benefit of those students able to distinguish white. The gymnasium should be well lighted to present the best possible seeing conditions for those who are able to perceive light. A contrast in playing surfaces in the gymnasium can be achieved with wood and concrete.

To guide blind children in running activities and to give them greater security, hanging ropes and rings which are grasped in the hands may be suspended from wires strung across the gymnasium well above the heads of the participants. For outside running events wires can be placed along the path of the runner to guide him. The runners will need some type of warning at the finish line; this may be a knotted cord hanging from a suspended crossbar which will brush against the runner as he passes the finish line, or some sort of auditory signal such as a whistle may be sounded.

EQUIPMENT.   Playground equipment for younger children may be the same type found on any playground, including swings, jungle gyms, and teeter-totters; however, greater care must be exercised in locating them to avoid possible injury to the nonseeing participants. Swings should be constructed with no more than two swings on the stand; a third swing in the center is difficult to reach without danger when the other two swings are occupied. The use of guard rails or ground markers is a necessary safety precaution to prevent youngsters from bumping into equipment or being hit by flying swings.

It is recommended that balls to be used by the blind be larger in size and softer than regulation balls and that they be painted yellow or white to make them more easily seen by those with some vision. Bells or rattles inside the balls help to indicate the location to the blind.

The blind should be thoroughly introduced to an unfamiliar playing area before they are allowed to play. They should know the size and shape of the area and the nature of the boundaries before they engage in activity in the area. To orient the students the teacher should walk them around the area, describing the essential details. A few simple games or contests might be played to help the students gain familiarity with the playing area before engaging in strenuous play.

Only such playing equipment as is actually in use should be permitted in the playing area to insure maximum safety. Blind children can memorize the location of the permanent fixtures but cannot avoid superfluous equipment which has been left in their way. The youngsters can also memorize the place in the storage closets where each item of equipment is kept and are capable of securing these and returning them at the end of the play period.

CLASS ORGANIZATION.   Class organization may be determined by the schedule of other classes and activities for the students in the school; that is, the physical education class may have to be organized on the basis of the students who are available at the hours when physical education is offered. If the schedule permits, the best method of class organization is on the basis of general strength and coordination rather than chronological age. If the students are all of about general physical ability, the class activities can be more easily planned to meet the specific needs of the group. However, with a little ingenuity a wide range of ages and abilities can be planned for.

PROPER APPROACH.   The introduction of new skills requires a kinesthetic approach. The teacher and perhaps a few of the students who have learned the skill may demonstrate it while the sightless examine the parts of the body involved with their hands. At times it may be helpful to the student for the teacher to place the student's hands and feet and other parts of the body into the desired positions. Lengthy verbal explanations should be avoided. However, clear concise descriptions which accompany the kinesthetic approach may be used with great effectiveness. In planning his teaching methods, a sighted instructor may gain greater insight into the problems which the skill will present to his sightless students if he closes his eyes while performing the skill.

A whistle is an essential piece of equipment for the instructor of visually handicapped students, and it may be blown to identify for the students the location of the teacher, to signal for attention, or another purpose. A meaningful set of signals may be worked out with the students. A megaphone is useful to the teacher in making his voice heard to the players. The players will need to be given a great many details of the progress of the game which would be naturally observed by players with normal vision. For example, if a kick ball game is in progress, the players will need to be told which players are on which bases; who will kick next; the placement of players on the field; when an out or a score is made. Here again, if the teacher will try to put himself in the position of the blind player and try to think of the game information that he would want to know as the game progresses, this will guide him in selecting the most useful information to give the players.

Nearly all the varieties of activities offered to normal children in the physical education curriculum can be presented to blind children. Some require more adaptation than others, but blind children enjoy and need

FIGURE 9. The teacher wears a blind-fold while performing a skill to gain insight into the problems which the skill may present to a blind performer. (Photo by Carl Fischer.)

participation in the same games, sports, and physical activites as other children. In addition, the activities can help them overcome some of the problems, physical and emotional, which are the direct result of the visual handicaps.

FREE PLAY.   Although children should be encouraged to use the playground equipment on their own during the leisure hours, they should be given explicit instruction in the use of the play equipment for their own safety and for that of others. All children should be taught the skills involved in the use of the apparatus and the safety measures which must be observed. This is most especially true of children with visual handicaps.

The teacher may find some hesitancy on the part of some blind children to play on the equipment. This is most likely to be true of those who have led extremely sheltered lives. The teacher must begin with the children at their level of motor skill development and their level of self-confidence and strengthen both by encouraging participation at the tempo they will accept. In very young children and very timid ones, it may be necessary to inspire a desire for carefree play on the equipment.

Chair seats on swings and teeter-totters require less balancing skill and promote confidence and security. In introducing these pieces of equipment, the teacher should tell the children something about how they look and how they are used while the children explore them with their hands. Each child may be assisted in sitting on the equipment and trying it with the help of the teacher. A reassuring grasp on the shoulders or arm promotes confidence during the first trip. When a certain amount of confidence has been developed, mounting and dismounting and safety precautions can be taught to the children.

The safe and enjoyable use of the slide requires careful instruction by the teacher. The children must be taught to wait their turn at the bottom of the ladder and not to climb the steps until the one who is having his turn claps his hands to let everyone know that he is going down the slide. When he reaches the bottom, he must inform the one who is waiting at the top that the slide is clear. The one who is waiting at the top signals by clapping to the one who is waiting to climb up.

To encourage a reluctant child the teacher may first have to help him sit on the slide near the end and help him as he slides down. This may be done several times at increasing heights. The child should be shown how he may slow down the speed of the slide by forcing his feet against the sides.

Jungle gyms and parallel ladders are dangerous if improperly used by either sighted or nonsighted children. Children often have sufficient confidence to get on the bars but do not have sufficient skills and strength to perform with safety. A low single bar can be utilized to develop sufficient arm and hand strength and to develop skill in hanging or swinging the body through space. Or a child may be started out very low on the jungle gym where the danger of falling would be minimal. On the parallel ladders a thick board may be placed between the rungs of the two upright ladders of a very high ladder. This lessens the distance of the drop and the board can also be used as a jouncing board to spring up and down on, which is an excellent exercise in itself.

PRIMARY GRADE ACTIVITIES.   In the primary grades physical education activities and games are often utilized as tools in the learning of reading, number concepts, and other areas of study. There are many methods of doing this, and each primary school teacher has worked out numerous ways of her own which might be employed in teaching the blind. Many activities suggest themselves, and the suggestions made below are given only as a foundation from which other ideas will spring.

For teaching number concepts, the turns taken in certain activities may be counted, such as the number of times a ball is bounced or the steps taken on a balance beam. In developing reading readiness the background of meaningful experience is expanded, and toward this end numerous physical activities may be utilized. Exploration of the surrounding areas, following paths and sidewalks, going up and down hills, and climbing trees are a few possibilities.

Many of the singing games and mimetic games of the primary grade level need no adaptation for the blind. A game such as London Bridge or mimetic activity such as a measuring worm race does not need any modification. Other games may need only slight modifications to offset the disadvantage of being unable to see the other players. In the game Red Light and Green Light, which is recommended for blind children because it encourages them to run freely and swiftly, the teacher should name those who are moving on the call of "red light," since the children will not be able to tell which runners should be brought back.

GAMES.[3]   There are many games suitable for elementary, junior high, and senior high school students which need no modification, such as Bull in the Ring and Crows and Cranes. Many dual competitive games such as arm wrestling or Indian leg wrestling can be presented without modification. In tag games and other games in which the players need to make their location known to the one who is "It," the players may make vocal sounds. When partially or totally visioned players are participating in the game, these students may be assigned to join hands with a blind player and play as a couple. Certain games with balls such as dodge ball and wall ball are easily modified by slight rule changes which prevent seeing players from having undue advantage and which provide for the calling out by players so that blind opponents can locate them by the sound of their voice.

Some games lend themselves more easily than others to adaptation for playing by blind and partially seeing students. As a guide for the selection of those games which can be readily used without much modification, Charles E. Buell suggests these eight characteristics:[4]

1. Blindfolding one or two players.
2. Sounds whereby the sightless know what is happening.
3. Different duties for the blind and partially seeing.
4. Running to a goal easily found by the totally blind.
5. Limited playing area such as gymnasium or tennis court.
6. Direct contact as in wrestling.
7. Line or chain formations.
8. The possibility of players pairing up in couples.

DANCE AND RHYTHMIC ACTIVITIES.   One of the most essential and satisfying skills that the blind can achieve is the movement of the body through space. Exploration of the complete range of movement of each part of the body and the body as a whole must precede the actual teaching of skills. Simple dance and rhythmic activities provide excellent media for such exploration. Every movement has tempo, size, and space or distance. The discovery of the infinite variety of possible body motions is encouraged by responses to the musical accompaniment. For this purpose, rhythmic activities such as walking, sliding, leaping, and running at slow, medium, and fast tempos may be used. Various other body movements may be used with these motions, or they may be performed in a standing, lying, or sitting position to musical accompaniment.

Because the blind rely so much on sound to receive their impressions, they are particularly receptive to the tempo not only of music but also

[3]For descriptions of basic skill games see Chapter 16.
[4]Charles E. Buell: *Sports for the Blind.* Ann Arbor, Mich., Edwards Bros., Inc., 1947, p. 106.

of the human activities which surround them. The knowledge thus gained of rhythm patterns is a valuable asset in learning to dance. All types of dance may be taught to the blind: musical games, folk dances, modern dance, and social dancing. The musical games such as Farmer in the Dell are limited to young children. Social dancing, which can be an important skill for the blind because it enables them to participate socially with seeing people, may be taught beginning at the sixth or seventh grade. All other types of dance can be taught at almost any age level as soon as children have learned to move freely, with confidence and skill, through space.

SPORTS.   Team sports most frequently played by the blind and partially seeing are football, softball, and volley newcomb. Basketball can be played by the partially seeing, but the blind cannot usually participate with success.[5]

Individual sports such as wrestling, swimming, gymnastics, and tumbling need very little modification. Blind children will usually learn more slowly because the teaching process is necessarily slower.

In training for running events in track, the totally blind can run with a partially seeing partner and be guided by his footsteps. Overhead wires with drop cords which slide along the wire that the runner can grasp in his hand will aid him in keeping a steady course. Guide wires about hip high along one side of the track which the student can slide his hand along as he runs is good for the training period. Later, as confidence and skills develop, another wire is placed on the other side so that the runner runs between and is guided by them without placing his hands on the wires. This permits greater speed in running and, if he swerves off the course, the wires brush against him and remind him to adjust his position.

Bowling is a very popular individual sport in blind schools, and a large majority of the schools have bowling facilities. Blind bowlers orient themselves by feeling the sides of the alley. Golf is another individual sport much favored by blind players. The only adaptation is the necessity of playing with a sighted person who locates the ball.[6]

INTERSCHOLASTIC ATHLETICS.   There is some difference of opinion whether the blind should participate in interscholastic athletics. There is no substantial evidence to indicate that either the values or evils which appear in the competitive sports programs for normal youngsters are greater or less great for blind players. Because of the wide acceptance of interscholastic sports for boys in the regular schools, it would seem desirable to provide the same opportunities for blind students. The controversial questions of participation for blind girls and junior high

[5]For descriptions and adaptations see Chapter 20.
[6]For descriptions and other adaptations see Chapter 18.

school age boys would need to be settled on the same principles by which regular schools resolve these issues.

What activites should be included in the interscholastic program? An answer to this is partly dependent upon the offerings in the physical education and intramural programs, for it is considered good policy for the interscholastic program to be an outgrowth of the other two. Another factor which will determine the sports to be offered is the availability of competition. Since there will be few blind schools near enough to make travel feasible, competition may present a difficult problem. Competition in some sports can be arranged with regular schools, and this does, of course, supply a fine opportunity for players and student bodies to build a mutual respect and regard for each other.

Wrestling is perhaps the sport most commonly utilized in the interscholastic sports program because if offers the least disadvantage to the blind. Wrestling has been highly developed in schools for the blind but remains a relatively minor sport in public schools. This makes possible competition with large schools and college freshman teams. Blind wrestlers without much experience may be at a disadvantage when starting the match from a standing position. Starting from a referee's position overcomes this disadvantage. The crowd may be asked to remain as quiet as possible so that the blind boy may use his auditory acuity to locate his opponent. However, experienced blind wrestlers have learned to compensate and will not be at a disadvantage under regular rules and crowd situations.

Track and field constitutes another popular activity for interscholastic sports competition. In competition with other blind schools the events usually included are dashes; standing high jump; standing broad jump; hop, step, and jump; 16-foot rope climb; and tug of war. Competition with regular schools in certain events has been found satisfactory. The dashes and shot put are the usual events. However, sometimes the regular school can be persuaded to participate in all of the events listed above.

Gymnastics also lends itself well to interscholastic competition, but gymnastic teams have not been developed on the secondary level in either regular schools or schools for the blind. Football and basketball can also be included in the interscholastic athletic program, although basketball is restricted to the partially seeing. Swimming offers an unusually fine interscholastic activity. Blind swimmers can participate in all of the various strokes and dives used in competition and can compete successfully against sighted as well as other blind swimmers.

QUESTIONS

1. What unit of measurement is used to determine visual acuity?
2. How does the age at which one becomes blind affect his educational needs?
3. What are the most common causes of blindness?
4. What is meant by the "sixth sense" developed by the blind?

5. When should the partially sighted student who is attending regular school be placed in a special adapted physical education class?

6. Discuss some of the possibilities of adapting activities to allow the partially sighted to participate in regular physical education.

7. What precautions must a physical education teacher take in working with students who have a partial retinal detachment?

8. Make a list of special equipment and adapted facilities which would be helpful in teaching physical education to blind and partially seeing students.

9. Which of the teaching methods discussed in an early chapter are most applicable in teaching the blind?

10. Discuss some of the safety precautions which are necessary for blind children using playground equipment.

11. Using the criteria suggested by Buell, show how several games might be adapted for play by the blind.

12. What are the possibilities and limitations of interscholastic sports for the blind?

SELECTED READINGS

Buell, Charles E.: *Sports for the Blind.* Ann Arbor, Mich., Edwards Bros., Inc., 1947.

Cutsforth, Thomas D.: *The Blind in School and Society; A Psychological Study.* New York, American Foundation for the Blind, 1951.

Frampton, Merle E., and Gall, Elena D. (ed.): *Special Education for the Exceptionals:* Vol. II— *The Physically Handicapped and Special Health Problems.* Boston, Porter Sargent, Publisher, 1955.

Goodenough, Florence L.: *Exceptional Children.* New York, Appleton-Century-Crofts, Inc., 1956.

Hathaway, Winifred, and Lowenfeld, Berthold: *Teaching the Visually Handicapped; Forty-ninth Yearbook of the National Society for Study of Education—The Education of Exceptional Children.* Chicago, University of Chicago Press, 1950.

Lowenfeld, Berthold: *Our Blind Children.* Springfield, Ill., Charles C Thomas, Publisher, 1956.

Zahl, Paul A.: *Blindness.* Princeton, N.J., Princeton University Press, 1950.

6

AUDITORY HANDICAPS

Auditory handicaps of varying degrees of severity constitute as a group one of the most common disabilities affecting children and adults. Statistics show that 25 out of every 1000 adults experience some hearing impairment while 8 out of every 1000 children to the age of 20 have an auditory handicap. These hearing handicaps range from slight deviation from normal hearing to total loss of sound perception.[1]

Too often in the past a hearing loss has been considered to be handicapping in much the same way as the loss of sight and to affect the victim in much the same way psychologically. Such thinking was to be expected in view of the fact that both handicaps arise from a complete or partial loss of one of the senses. However, this tendency to regard the two conditions as similar has retarded a true consideration of the psychological implications of hearing loss. In recent years, the problems of those with hearing disabilities have been approached with new insight into the effects they may have upon the lives of those whose hearing is partially or totally destroyed. It is extremely important for those who are teaching children with auditory handicaps to understand not only the kinds of hearing difficulties and their causes but also to comprehend the depth of the personality problems which may accompany hearing loss.

[1]Harry J. Baker: *Introduction to Exceptional Children*, ed. 3. New York, The Macmillan Co., 1959, p. 365.

THE NATURE AND CAUSES OF
HEARING DISABILITIES

Those with hearing disabilities are divided into two categories: the hard of hearing and the deaf. The *hard of hearing* are identified as those who, with or without hearing aids, can hear enough speech to learn how to speak. In contrast to these are the *deaf,* who cannot hear speech well enough to learn to speak except by a specialized training procedure, or, in the case of the handicap being acquired after speech has been learned, those who cannot hear well enough to comprehend the spoken word.

Deafness may result from structural causes or it may be psychogenic or functional in nature.

STRUCTURAL CAUSES.   Hearing disabilities which are structural in origin are of two fundamental kinds: conduction deafness and nerve, or perceptive, deafness.

Conduction deafness is caused by a physical obstruction to the conduction of the sound waves to the inner ear, such as impacted wax or a middle ear infection. Although the nature of the obstruction may be severe and the hearing seriously impaired, deafness is almost never total. The condition can be treated medically with relatively good chances for arresting or improving it, particularly in its early stages. A hearing aid is very useful in improving a hearing loss due to conduction difficulties.

Perceptive deafness is usually a more serious condition and less likely to be improved by medical treatment. Moreover, a hearing aid is usually of little value. The loss of sensory cells or nerve fibers, which receive and transmit the sound stimuli, cause perceptive deafness. The loss of hearing may range from mild to total disability. Some degree of perceptive deafness is common among the aging. A certain amount of high-tone nerve deafness appears to be part of the natural process of aging in many people, just as many of advanced years suffer hardening of the arteries and deterioration of eyesight. This condition is in fact so prevalent that the commonest cause of nerve deafness is attributed to senility.

In children and young adults the most frequent cause of nerve deafness is *congenital,* the nerve having been injured or destroyed before or during birth. The term congenital indicates that the child was born deaf or inherited the tendency for the hearing to deteriorate at an early age. However, researchers into the causes of deafness in children have discovered that a number of cases heretofore classified as hereditary were actually associated with certain contagious diseases which the mother contracted during the early months of pregnancy. German measles, mumps, and influenza have all been indicated as causes of deafness in infants whose mothers were afflicted during early pregnancy.

Cases of nerve deafness which have a noncongenital origin are classified as *acquired* deafness. Among the common causes are brain infections such as meningitis, brain fever, and sleeping sickness and communicable diseases such as scarlet fever, measles, influenza, and others.

Prolonged noise of high frequency (loudness) can produce temporary or permanent hearing loss. A loss of short duration is frequently auditory fatigue, and hearing is usually restored to normal within a day. But if the noise is loud enough and continues over a long enough period of time, cells in the organ of Corti are injured and this results in permanent hearing loss. People differ greatly in sensitivity to noise, so that it is difficult to say when a noise becomes dangerous, but as a general rule the ears should not be exposed to noise over 130 decibels[2] more than momentarily.

FUNCTIONAL CAUSES. The organic causes of hearing loss are numerous and for many years were thought to be the only causes of deafness. In relatively recent times it has been recognized that not all hearing difficulties have structural causes: some are definitely functional in nature; that is, originating in the mind. This kind of deafness is called *psychogenic*, or *functional,* and is apparently more frequent than is generally suspected. The frequency of incidence and the causes are not definitely known. The causes are related, as in other psychological cases, to deep-rooted personality problems from which these individuals have sought escape or refuge in nonhearing.

Some hearing problems cannot be classified as strictly organic or psychogenic in origin but are probably due partly to both.

NEEDS AND ADJUSTMENTS OF THE DEAF

The most obvious adjustment to their handicap which the deaf must make is to the loss of the normal means of communication. A new way of receiving messages must be found if the deafness is acquired after speech has been learned, usually lip reading. If the loss of hearing is congenital or acquired before speech has been learned, a means of conveying as well as receiving communications must be learned. Deaf persons who could not speak were once taught hand manipulation as the sole means of communication, but deaf children are now being taught to speak by the technique of properly utilizing the mouth and vocal cords in the production of sounds. They also receive lip-reading instruction and some hand manipulation.

While the deaf can compensate satisfactorily for their loss of the usual conversational method of communication with others, they experience other losses which are less easily adjusted to. One of these is being deprived of the warnings which exist in sound. The honking of the auto horn or the raised voice which warns of impending danger cannot reach the deaf. Until they have learned to adjust to this and compensate

[2]For purposes of comparison, a loud shout at one foot distance is measured at 110 decibels while ordinary conversation is about 60 decibels.

for the loss satisfactorily, they experience more than usual anxieties and fears.

The deaf hear nothing of the sounds of life and activity which fall continually upon the normal ear and form a background of noises which those who hear are generally not even conscious of. Many recently deafened people have been reported as describing the loss of this auditory background as "living in a dead world." This extraordinary loss has a deep psychological impact upon the victim, and to it is attributed the severe depression experienced by most people who lose their hearing after years of living in a world of sound.

The noises and sounds which constitute the auditory background of daily life produce, in those who hear, muscular tensions which are largely involuntary and unobserved. One who is recently deafened characteristically substitutes body movement for the missing sensations of movement and sound which formerly surrounded him. These continuous purposeless movements must be understood by the teacher so that he may plan more worthwhile motor movements as substitutions.

Without the orientation of the auditory background and the symbols and warnings which are customarily provided by sound perception, the deaf are prone to frustrations and anxieties. This is more particularly true in cases where hearing is impaired in adolescence or adulthood. The longer a person has had full powers of hearing, the more difficult is his adjustment to a severe hearing loss. The loss of background sounds contributes also to inaccuracy in the recognition of space and motion, and, as a consequence, the movements of the deaf are often vague and distorted.

Isolated in his "dead world," the individual with a severe auditory handicap often becomes withdrawn and inactive. The attempt to communicate with others may be so unsuccessful even for those with mild handicaps that they withdraw from social contacts. Children with hearing losses often find they are unable to participate with success in games and sport activities which demand communications and direction and so avoid playing with others. A failure to participate in normal childhood play has been shown to have far-reaching consequences. Not only may such children be deprived of the social maturation which results from the common interchange of play, but also their physical growth and development may be retarded.

PLANNING THE ADAPTED PROGRAM
IN THE REGULAR SCHOOL

It is estimated that approximately 4 to 5 per cent of the school population actually experience some hearing loss.[3] The child with a slight auditory

[3]Harry J. Baker: *op cit.*, pp. 343–344, 365–366.

deficiency will not be readily noticed in the classroom; or, if noticed because of his behavior, his actions may not be attributed to hearing loss. The child may be inattentive, fail to answer questions, require frequent repetition of directions. He may watch those who are speaking very closely in order to grasp something of the meaning of the speech from the movements of the mouth or gestures of the body, or he may incline his head when spoken to so his ear is directed toward the speaker. Evidence of such mannerisms or behavior patterns may be more quickly revealed in the physical education class than in the regular class, for in the vastness of the gymnasium or playing field the student is even less likely to hear directions and explanations, particularly when these are given in game situations and he is some distance away or has his head turned away from the instructor. Consequently, the teacher should be alert to the possibility that a child who fails to grasp his directions or fails to respond well may have a hearing loss and should take steps to see that the child is adequately tested.

A considerable number of those children who fall in the hard-of-hearing category will be enrolled in the regular school classes, and the physical education teacher may expect to have such children in his classes. Generally speaking, such children can be successfully included in the regular physical education class. However, if the child's impairment has kept him from normal participation in play activities so that he has marked physical needs or personality problems, the teacher should consider his case more carefully to determine if he could profit more from enrollment in the adapted class. Children who have experienced recent hearing loss and are still in a period of adjustment may well profit from individualized instruction in the adapted program, as may those with subnormal strength and coordination.

Many hard-of-hearing students will wear hearing aids which will be removed during physical education classes. Without this assistance to his auditory perception, the student will again be handicapped in the amount of verbal direction he can comprehend. The teacher must anticipate this and be prepared to help the student make the necessary adjustment.

For calling roll or giving preliminary instruction to the class before the class activity begins, the teacher should place the students with auditory handicaps where they will be in the best position to watch his face. During actual play, when the teacher wishes to make comments, he may move close to those students who cannot hear well before speaking. Or the student may be granted "roving" privileges so that he may move without permission to a location where he is better able to hear the speaker.

Other students in the class are usually very cooperative in helping those who cannot hear to make the right responses in game situations once they understand their difficulty. As long as they are unaware that a certain student responds the way he does because of a handicap and not because he's an "oddball," they often ignore or ridicule him. Consequently, the physical education instructor must set the pattern for the class. His kindness and patience in directing and explaining the class activities to the deaf student will be imitated by the others. Soon the teacher will find that when a deaf student has muffed a play by being out of position, a couple of his teammates will quietly step over to him and show him what was wrong.

Students with impaired hearing may demonstrate a lack of cooperation in class activities and undesirable behavior in competitive play. Such tendencies are related largely to their failure to have understood the directions or rules of the game. In the lower grades where the play is less dependent upon vocal directions and rulings, the handicapped child is usually a considerably more successful participant than in later years when games become more dependent upon the comprehension of spoken words. Displays of anger and aggressiveness and other unsportsmanlike conduct increase as the child feels more and more inadequate in the increasingly complex games offered in the physical education program at advanced grade levels. Clear explanations directed at the student and careful demonstrations of the skill to be performed should do much to alleviate the misunderstandings which prompted the undesirable behavior.

Students with hearing losses need to be taught more factual information about a game than a normal child whose ears as well as his eyes have given him insight into the activity. The vocabulary of the game as well as the rules and playing strategy must be conveyed with greater care and exactness than is necessary for the student who can hear. Well described and illustrated written materials may be used to good advantage for this purpose with students who read.

Visual aids have greater significance as a teaching technique in the instruction of the hard of hearing and deaf than in perhaps any other situation. Their use can substitute for considerable amounts of verbal instruction. Both movie films and slides can be used to good advantage, although slides will frequently require more explanation than moving pictures. However, the required explanation can be shown on the screen in written form if the students are old enough to be good readers. The films chosen should show performances of the skills in such a way that they are largely self-explanatory. Frequently, re-runs of the demonstration will help to make it more clear to those who are trying to learn the correct techniques from the picture.

A blackboard is an indispensable aid in the physical education class which contains students with auditory handicaps. The blackboard can be used to introduce the playing court of a new game with its service and boundary lines and to demonstrate the strategy of many different games.

PLANNING THE PROGRAM IN THE
SPECIAL SCHOOL

Children who have had extreme hearing impairments or have been totally deaf since birth or early infancy are usually enrolled in special residential schools for the deaf. Schools directed entirely toward the education of the deaf are located in nearly every state, and many of them provide special daily instruction to children who have less severe handicaps but can profit from the speech training, language instruction, and lip reading offered to the students in residence. The physical education teacher employed by these special schools will, then, find students in his classes who have considerable sound perception in addition to those who have very little hearing, or none.

These students are best instructed in relatively small groups of perhaps seven to ten. The instructor should place himself so that his face can be well seen by all the students in the group. A circular or straight-line formation is undesirable because not all the students will be able to face the instructor. Some type of staggered line formation is good; and, when the teacher has worked out the most advantageous arrangement for each class, he would do well to teach this placement to the students so that upon signal they will go immediately into this formation to receive any verbal instructions or to watch a demonstration.

Some type of signal will need to be arranged to assemble the class. Many students even with very limited hearing are able to hear very low tones, so that some type of percussion instrument producing low tones

FIGURE 10. The teacher kneels so the children can better see her face to comprehend her spoken instruction. (Photo by Carl Fischer.)

might be sounded as a signal. Those who cannot hear it will take their cue from watching the others. The switching on and off of lights is another signal that can be used to attract the attention of the students.

During this instruction the teacher should be situated in the best possible light and preferably with his face on approximately the same level as the students. This may necessitate sitting or squatting when speaking to young children who are considerably shorter than the teacher. A good view of the teacher's face is extremely important to these students, who must rely almost entirely on lip reading to grasp the verbal instruction. The teacher should speak at a moderate rate and without exaggeration in mouthing the sounds. Teachers unfamiliar with the deaf often think they are simplifying the lip reading by exaggerating their speech. The students, unaccustomed to the distortions, will actually be confused.

Deaf children are reluctant to leave the old games in which they are comfortable and confident to learn new games and activities. Small children enjoy solitary play on playground apparatus such as swings and bars and usually prefer this to the seeming hazards of group play. But deaf children of every age need the socialization and physical exercise provided by group games and competitive play. With careful and patient instruction they can learn new activities and experiences with the same pleasures as any other children.

THE PROGRAM FOR STUDENTS WITH AUDITORY HANDICAPS

There are few restrictions on the activities which may be offered to students with auditory handicaps in the regular or adapted physical education class in the usual school or in the physical education program of the special school. The limitations imposed on these students by their disability are of a social rather than physical nature. To help these students in their adjustment to their handicap and in their relationship with others takes precedence in planning the program to meet their greatest need.

Students who have sustained damage to the semicircular canal of the ear will have poor balance and experience dizziness. Certain limitations in activities are necessary for the safety of these students: activities which require climbing on high equipment or demand acute balancing are prohibitive. Students who have had fenestration operations (a surgical opening of a window to the inner ear to restore hearing), require certain precautionary measures also. During cold windy weather they must wear ear plugs, and they must guard against sudden movements of the head which will produce dizziness. Swimming is prohibited.

GAMES AND SPORTS.   All the individual and team sports may be learned by the deaf and hard of hearing. Many special schools are fielding basketball, baseball, and football teams which compete successfully against teams of hearing players. Deaf students enjoy competitive play and play to win, but more important than the winning or losing are the social contacts provided by the game and the acceptance of their worth by opponents with good hearing.

There are, of course, some hazards to the safety of those with auditory handicaps in competitive play because they are unable to hear signals and other warning sounds. As a precautionary measure, certain visual signals such as the waving of colored flags should be arranged. The instructor should be sure that each participant understands the meaning of each signal before play begins. If the opponents are also nonhearing, the signals should be agreed upon and understood by both teams. If the opponents can hear, they should be alerted to the need for the visual signals and for their cooperation in preventing accidents to players without hearing.

Fencing, archery, bowling, tennis, golf, and badminton are other sports with demonstrated appeal both for students in deaf schools and in regular schools. Activities such as archery and bowling which can be participated in without others have great value as leisure-time activities for those who cannot hear, for whom many avenues of recreation are closed because of their handicap. Because listening to records, radio, concerts, and similar recreational pursuits which require normal hearing are lost to them, many deaf people do not have adequate recreational outlets and their leisure hours are boring and depressing as a consequence. They should be taught some individual sports which they can participate in during leisure time; however, these should not be emphasized to the detriment of team play, which encourages the give and take of social intercourse so extremely vital to these students.

SWIMMING.   Water play and swimming are enjoyed by those with hearing impairments equally as much as by other active people. Although some may experience balancing difficulties in the water, nearly all can make satisfactory progress in learning the swimming skills. A modified stroke which permits the head to remain above water will be necessary for those who must not get water in the ears or who become disoriented when their heads are submerged.

RHYTHMIC ACTIVITIES AND DANCE.   Children of all ages with auditory handicaps take pleasure in rhythmic movement, even though their hearing of the rhythm in music in totally or partially restricted. For successful performance in musical games and dancing, the students must be taught the pattern of movement, with emphasis upon the length of time each phase of the movement is held before it is changed. To students with hearing this is evident in listening to the musical accompaniment, but for those who cannot hear adequately the teacher must accentuate the rhythm with hand movements so that the student can perceive visually what he cannot perceive by hearing. Some students will, of course, hear some of the music, and even those who do not hear melody experience musical vibrations. For this reason a percussion instrument is helpful in establishing rhythms.

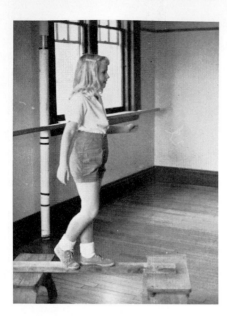

FIGURE 11. An improvised balance beam provides important balancing exercise. (Photo by Carl Fischer.)

Students should be taught simple tap or folk dances first. The basic steps may be presented in demonstration with the back to the students so they will not become confused as to which foot is being used, as is often the case when the teacher faces the class. Dances and musical games which are performed in circles or squares and involve complex formations are best taught in a straight-line formation and in short parts which are later put together in the required formation.

BODY MECHANICS AND PHYSICAL FITNESS.   Those with auditory handicaps may be underdeveloped physically, owing to their withdrawal from vigorous play activities; they may also be poorly coordinated and purposeless in their movements because of their lack of sound orientation. The physical education program at all levels should include a variety of activities for well-rounded physical development as well as specific exercises which develop cardiorespiratory endurance, coordination, flexibility, and muscular tonus.

Balancing stunts and activities should be included for those students who have difficulty maintaining good balance because of damage to the semicircular canal. Through practice the kinesthetic sense can be developed and the eyes trained to aid in maintaining body balance, to compensate for the loss of semicircular canal control. Young children will enjoy such stunts as walking a line and performing the stork stand (standing on one foot). For older children, work on the pogo stick or on a low balance beam are effective in improving balance. Training in all sport activities encourages the development of better balance in those who lack it.

QUESTIONS

1. Explain the difference between structural and functional causes of deafness.
2. What is meant by conduction deafness? Nerve deafness?
3. What are the causes of deafness?
4. Describe what is meant by background noises? Of what significance are they in the study of the deaf?
5. What procedures may the teacher use in regular physical education classes to help the hard of hearing?
6. What significance do visual aids and textbooks on sport skills have in teaching the deaf in physical education?
7. Discuss the different formations and groupings which may be used to present verbal instructions to the deaf or hard of hearing during physical education class.
8. Which activities may be contraindicated for some of the deaf students? Why?
9. What place do music and dance have in the physical education program for the deaf? How may they be presented?
10. How may balancing activities be utilized in the improvement of balance in those deaf students who have semicircular canal damage?

SELECTED READINGS

Dale, Dion M. C.: *Applied Audiology for Children.* Springfield, Ill., Charles C Thomas, Publisher, 1962.

Ewing, Alexander W. G.: *Educational Guidance and the Deaf Child.* Manchester, England, Manchester University Press, 1957.

Ewing, Alexander W. G. (ed.): *The Modern Educational Treatment of Deafness.* Manchester, England, Manchester University Press, 1960.

Fielder, Miriam F.: *Deaf Children in a Hearing World.* New York, The Ronald Press Company, 1952.

Frampton, Merle E., and Gall, Elena D. (ed.): *Special Education for the Exceptional;* Vol. II— *The Physically Handicapped and Special Health Problems.* Boston, Porter Sargent, Publisher, 1955.

Heck, Arch O.: *The Education of Exceptional Children,* ed. 2. New York, McGraw-Hill Book Co., Inc., 1953.

Hunt, Valerie V.: *Recreation for the Handicapped.* New York, Prentice-Hall, Inc., 1955.

7
CEREBRAL PALSY

Historically, cerebral palsy is at least as old as recorded history. There are references in Biblical scriptures and in early Egyptian art that would indicate that cerebral palsy was prevalent in very ancient times. Medical attention to the condition was insignificant until the middle of the 19th century, when an English physician, W. J. Little, became interested in it and identified some of its causes.

The problem of cerebral palsy has not been generally understood by the public. In early times it was believed to be the infliction of punishment on the victim or his parents or the curse of the devil upon the child. In more recent times, as the mystical point of view changed, the outward manifestations of the condition were often misinterpreted as signs of feeblemindedness; the grimacing of the face, the drooling, and the inability to speak were accepted as evidence of the child's mental impairment. Widespread information about the absence of mental deficiency among those with cerebral palsy has dispelled the association of feeblemindedness. There is, in fact, a tendency to believe that no mental impairment exists. This is not the actual case, however, since in some conditions of cerebral palsy a large portion of the brain is damaged and the victim has a mental deficiency in addition to his neurological impairment.

In spite of the lack of understanding of cerebral palsy, a growing public concern has been expressed for the needs of its victims. Such groups as the National Society for Crippled Children and Adults, the

United Cerebral Palsy Association, and the Association for the Aid of Crippled Children have helped to develop public support for the improvement of treatment and education. Medical care and treatment, although still not adequate, is continually expanding. The divisions of special education for exceptional children in the state departments of education are endeavoring to provide greater educational opportunities for youngsters afflicted with cerebral palsy. Among the various current developments for bettering their lot, physical education is a recent, but significant, newcomer.

THE NATURE AND CAUSES OF
CEREBRAL PALSY

Cerebral palsy is a condition affecting the motor control centers because of lesions in various parts of the brain arising from injury, infection, or faulty development. The condition is not an orthopedic disability but a neurological impairment and often produces different kinds of learning disabilities than does an orthopedic handicap. Movement is impaired and awkward and frequently accompanied by postural difficulties. Speech is, in many cases, noticeably affected, and the hearing and other sensory perceptions may be of below normal acuity. The physical manifestations of cerebral palsy may vary from a total inability to control muscular movement, in some victims, to only a very slight lack of muscular coordination, in others.

CAUSES. Cerebral palsy may occur before or during birth or at any time in later life. The vast majority, approximately 90 per cent, of all cases have prenatal or natal causes. The major causes contributing to cerebral palsy before birth are: maldevelopment of the brain, anoxia (lack of oxygen), cerebral hemorrhage, and blood incompatibility (Rh factor). Severe metabolic disturbance in the mother or infection contracted by the mother during early pregnancy are other important causes. Causes related to the period of birth are chiefly anoxia and cerebral hemorrhage. Postnatal causes of cerebral palsy account for only a small percentage and most often arise from acute infectious diseases, such as measles, mumps, whooping cough, and encephalitis, and from accidents resulting in severe head injuries.

FREQUENCY. It has been estimated that in the general population about 1 in every 1000 children will be afflicted with cerebral palsy. Of these, about 10 per cent will be so mildly handicapped that they can attend the public schools. Another 80 per cent may receive their education in special schools and hospitals, but the remaining 10 per cent are so severely handicapped that they cannot be helped or educated and are given custodial care in private and public institutions. Of all those with cerebral palsy, approximately 50 per cent have motor disability only; the others are handicapped by mental and/or sensory impairment as well as motor disability.[1]

CHARACTERISTICS.   The syndrome of cerebral palsy owing to brain injury occurring in later life differs from that occurring before the first three years of life, during which time the brain is developing at a very rapid rate. Growth of the total brain may be disturbed by a lesion in the brain during this early period of fast growth, whereas an injury or lesion in a fully developed brain of an older individual will be localized. This difference is significant in planning physical education programs: the child who has never functioned normally needs to learn basic skills which he has never developed, but the older person must re-learn skills that have been lost. The problem of education is much greater in the former group, and it is to this group that the term cerebral palsy is generally applied rather than to those who have suffered brain injury later in life.

Cerebral palsy is classified as *mild, moderate,* or *severe* based upon the neuromuscular involvement and the effect upon the mentality and the sensory organs. Cerebral palsy is also classified as to the syndrome.

CLASSIFICATIONS OF NEUROMUSCULAR DISABILITY

The types of neuromuscular disability found in those with cerebral palsy are usually classified as spasticity, athetosis, ataxia, rigidity, and tremor. These categories are subject to many subclassifications. Also, there are often mixed types of cerebral palsy. The physical education teacher will need to know only the general classifications and their implications for physical education. The diagnosis and muscular limitations and needs should be provided the teacher by the doctor.

SPASTICITY.   Most cases of cerebral palsy suffer from spasticity. This is a condition in which muscular movement in the area involved is restricted due to contracture of the muscles. The movement is jerky and uncertain. In his attempt to move a specific joint the spastic may move other joints in the same limb involuntarily because of the uncertain pull of the spastic muscles. Sometimes the movement is very slow; at other times it is explosive. The spastic responds to the slightest stimulation; a noise, sudden movement, or slight touch will evoke a muscular response. In the muscular movement of a normal person, when the muscles contract to move a joint, the antagonistic muscles relax. However, when a muscle is stretched quickly, it has a tendency to contract reflexly. This reflex contraction is known as the *stretch reflex* and is kept under control by various motor centers of the brain. In spastic paralysis many of the connections between the motor centers and muscles are lost, and the stretch reflex is

---

[1]Harry J. Baker, *Introduction to Exceptional Children,* ed. 3. New York, The Macmillan Co., 1959, pp. 145–146.

disturbed both in timing and in strength. When spastics are relaxed, the stretch reflex is not active and the abnormality is not as great.

Spasticity is most common in the antigravity muscles of the body and hence the maintenance of good posture is extremely difficult. Walking gait is disturbed if leg muscles are affected, since overcontraction of certain muscles will cause the legs to adduct and the hips to rotate inward. The heels may also draw up, so that the person walks on the outer part of the ball of the foot and on the toes. This results in the characteristic "scissors gait" of the spastic. If the arms are involved, they are usually drawn up to the body with the elbows bent and wrists and fingers flexed. Balance is usually not disturbed, but contracture in the spastic's lower limbs provide poor support and hence poor body balance.

Mental impairment is more frequently associated with spasticity than with any other type of cerebral palsy.

ATHETOSIS. Athetosis is another common form of cerebral palsy. The individual so affected, unlike the spastic, has no difficulty in moving; rather, his difficulty is in moving too much. He is unable to produce the movement that he wants. Often the movement starts before he wants it to, and he has very little control over its speed. Sometimes the movement accomplished against tension is slow and at other times it is fast. A voluntary movement of one part of the body produces extraneous movement elsewhere in the body. This action is called *overflow*. Some overflow is normal and common to nearly everyone, as evidenced in the extraneous rhythmic movements of the body of the drummer in the band or the facial contortions of an athlete as he puts forth maximum effort. In normal individuals such movements are kept under control by a specific area of the brain which in the athetoid is affected so that control is no longer possible. There is less overflow, however, when he is relaxed and calm; nervousness and tension increase the overflow.

Because of the absence of control, the body position of the athetoid is constantly changing. There is frequently an overextension and spreading of the fingers, and the toes turn up and the foot rotates inward. The arms are often drawn back with the palms held downward. The head is thrown back with the mouth open. A peculiar expression or grimace is usually evident. There is less possibility that the athetoid is mentally deficient than that the spastic is.

ATAXIA. Ataxia is a less common form of cerebral palsy than spasticity and athetosis. It is usually acquired rather than congenital. In this form the sense of balance or equilibrium is disturbed. The victim of ataxia has a poor sense of kinesthesis. When he reaches for something, he may over or under reach. In walking he may lift his feet too high. In severe cases, the walking gait is staggering and stumbling is frequent. The speech is drawling and slow. Muscle tone is poor. In severe cases, the eyeball moves in a rapid involuntary movement.

RIGIDITY. In the condition of rigidity, both the contracting muscles and the antagonistic muscles are affected. The stretch reflex is lacking. Hypertension of the muscles creates stiffness or rigidity. There is less motion in the person suffering from rigidity than in other types of cerebral palsy. However, often movement in one limb incites another to move involuntarily. Mental deficiency is frequently associated with rigidity.

TREMOR.   Tremor results in involuntary alternate movement of the flexor and extensor muscles, which produce a rhythmic motion. The speed is constant and timing regular, but both are accentuated in activity. In some types the rhythmic contractions occur only upon attempting movement. In another type the rhythmic movement is present all the time. The muscles of one who suffers from tremor have much more strength than do those of victims of other types of cerebral palsy, and he is consequently able to perform slow heavy work more successfully than less strenuous but finer muscle movements.

Unlike other types of cerebral palsy, there is no habitual posture characteristic of tremor. Muscular relaxation is of some help in slowing down the tremor in some cases; in others it is of no help.

TOPOGRAPHICAL CLASSIFICATION.   In the various types of cerebral palsy not all parts of the body are affected to the same degree. Another method of classifying the conditions of cerebral palsy is based upon the extremities involved:

Monoplegia is a condition in which only one limb is involved.

Paraplegia involves only the legs.

Diplegia is an involvement primarily of both legs, with the arms affected to slight degree.

Hemiplegia involves the limbs on one side of the body; the arm is usually more affected than the leg.

Triplegia involves three extremities.

Quadriplegia is an involvement of all four limbs.

Monoplegia, paraplegia, diplegia, hemiplegia, and triplegia are more often spastic, while quadriplegia is more frequently athetoid. Spastic hemiplegia is the most common involvement.

NEEDS AND ADJUSTMENTS OF THE
INDIVIDUAL WITH CEREBRAL PALSY

Unless he is only slightly handicapped in appearance and motor performance, the individual with cerebral palsy faces many difficult adjustments. Because cosmetic appearance so often influences acceptance or rejection by others, those with severe muscular impairment find themselves greatly handicapped in establishing normal social relationships. The facial grimaces, drooling, and queer jerking movements of the body often arouse ridicule or repulsion, although some may react with excessive sympathy. The acceptance the individual is seeking is not offered him and he is likely to become withdrawn. He is consequently denied the experiences in play and work with others that are so vital to satisfactory social development.

Lacking motor development and coordination, the youngster with cerebral palsy is unable to keep up with the play activities of his normal peers when he is accepted in the group. His lack of success in motor performance may contribute to already existing anxieties and frustrations resulting from his inability to communicate easily and to succeed in other endeavors. His problems may be further complicated by other handicaps, mental and sensory. Defeatism and excessive fears are common to these persons.

The opinion that some of the lack of emotional control and instability of those with cerebral palsy is a result of damage to specific areas of the brain appears to be somewhat substantiated by professional observations of certain pronounced behaviorism in certain types of cerebral palsy. Spastics, for example, often exhibit withdrawal traits. Daydreaming is common. They do not usually express their emotions strongly; they are slow to anger and not overly responsive to love. Athetoids, on the other hand, are generally extroverted. They express their emotions easily and show affection readily. They are also less easily discouraged by their failures. Ataxics show no extreme emotional characteristics as do the other two types. Whatever structural damage may contribute to the lack of adjustment, there is considerable reason to believe that the restricted experiences in successful association with others play the major role in the poor adjustment and in the development of undesirable personality traits in cerebral palsied individuals.

THE NATURE OF PHYSICAL EDUCATION FOR THE CHILD WITH CEREBRAL PALSY

When presented under medical supervision, physical education for cerebral palsy patients is an educational activity closely related to physical therapy. It is not, however, either a duplication or a substitute for the physical therapy program. It is, rather, a complement, a valuable adjunct. The physical education program supplements physical therapy by providing opportunities in play for the utilization of the motor movements which have been established.

In hospitals and special schools, the physical education for those with cerebral palsy consists of developing the basic sport skills. The muscular education is chiefly a medical problem and is handled by a medical team consisting of the doctor and the physical therapist and possibly others. Some understanding of the therapeutic techniques utilized in the muscular education is important to the physical educator because, although he is not directly involved in this phase of the training, this knowledge will enable him to plan a better program of supplementary activities.

There are a number of techniques used by physical therapists in the muscular education of cerebral palsy patients, but the most widely used method is one pioneered by Phelps. The technique of passive motion in which the therapist leads the limb through the desired movement is utilized in initiating muscular movement. Gradually the patient attempts to help make the movement; after a time, the patient is required to move on his own and, finally, to move against resistance.

For spastics the movement must be slow in the beginning to avoid stimulating the stretch reflex. Gradually the speed of movement is increased. The spastic needs exercises to strengthen the antagonistic muscles of the spastic muscles, since they are relatively weak. The athetoid must learn to perform motor movements while generally relaxed. He is taught muscular relaxation before he attempts to learn any muscular skills. The athetoid may have some muscles which need to be increased in strength. The ataxic is taught movement while watching himself in a mirror. This watching of the movements compensates for his lack of kinesthesis. The therapist will apply resistance to all muscles, since they all need increased strength.

In developing motion in the cerebral flaccid muscle (muscle that cannot be moved voluntarily), a method is used called *association technique*. In this technique, contraction is brought about in the flaccid muscle by the movement of another muscle. For example, there is involuntary flexion of the ankle when the knee and hip are flexed, so to induce motion in flaccid muscles of the ankle the hip and knee are moved.

PLANNING THE PROGRAM

Physical education for children with cerebral palsy in the regular school will differ in the extent of adaptation from that which is necessary in the special schools and hospitals. Children attending the regular school usually have only slight disabilities and can therefore participate successfully in most phases of the program. Children who have received maximum rehabilitation in muscular movement in the hospital or special school and are considered emotionally well-adjusted to their handicaps may be released to attend the regular school. The physical education activities will need to be adapted to the limitations of these more severely handicapped youngsters. The suggestions made in Chapter 8 for an adapted program for crippled children are applicable for these students.

EMPHASIS. The same values that accrue to the normal child from participation in a good physical education program are needed by and can be gained through physical education by the cerebral palsied child. However, a somewhat different emphasis is given the objectives of the program in the special schools and hospitals than in the regular school. The most important contribution physical education can make to the lives of children who are so severely handicapped that they must be hospitalized or enrolled in special schools is to bring fun and laughter into their daily routine.

FIGURE 12. Simple activities can be used by the physical educator to further develop the basic movements learned under the direction of the physical therapist. (The National Foundation, New York, N.Y. 10017.)

The acquisition of enough motor skills to take pleasure in play with others makes a tremendous difference in their lives, and this objective takes precedence over all others in teaching physical education in the special school or hospital.

The movements taught by the physical therapist which are basic to sport skills are the ability to grasp and release with the hands, extend and flex the arms, bend and straighten at the waist, and walk. If the cerebral palsied has these basic movements developed to some degree, he can successfully participate in many active games, sports, and dances if the initial experiences in these activities are correctly chosen and introduced. Games and activities that are to be introduced by the physical educator should have the approval of the medical personnel concerned. Games should be modified so that success is immediate.

NEED FOR ACTIVE PLAY. Frequently, in planning recreational and physical education activities, only passive games are considered suitable. Cerebral palsied children need vigorous play and, given an opportunity, can participate in a number of active sports. Games requiring extreme amounts of movement can be adapted so that the child is afforded a workout up to his tolerance level.

GENERAL TYPES OF ACTIVITIES. Activities that require slower responses are better than those which require a fast response. A game of catching and throwing a ball is slower if the ball is bounced rather than thrown. A large ball is easier to catch than a small one, for it doesn't require the fine finger-and-hand control that catching a small ball requires. The ball should be soft so that if it is missed it does not injure the catcher.

Moving objects are more difficult to control. Kicking a stationary ball is easier than kicking a moving ball. Hitting a ball hung from a cord is easier than hitting a thrown ball. Consequently, games built around putting stationary objects into motion are more successful than those which necessitate stopping a moving object. Rolling a ball at pins is an example of such a game.

Activities which require free gross body movements are more satisfactory than ones requiring finely coordinated movements. Individuals with cerebral palsy respond better to activities that require only simple repetitive movements than to those that call for many different movements. For example, in dancing the cerebral palsied will probably be more successful in waltzing than in square dancing, because the former requires fewer different movements. However, if the pattern of the square dance can be modified to keep the movements simple, participation can be successful.

However, different types of individuals will respond differently to activity. Frequently, the athetoid will demonstrate better movement than the spastic in the large muscle groups required in running and dancing. On the other hand, he may have more difficulty in performing activities requiring accuracy and fine movements than the spastic.

An emphasis upon playing rather than upon perfection of the skill creates an environment which encourages freer and easier movements. This is highly desired because the extraneous abnormal movements will be less pronounced. Inhibited emotions increase motor difficulty. Play activities tend to act as a release for pent-up emotions. Such a release is possible, however, only if the players are not overly concerned with the performance of the skills.

Individuals with cerebral palsy perform best when they have frequent rest periods. The rest period should be taken even though the patients are performing well, rather than waiting until the performance decreases in efficiency. Games and activities that require taking turns work well in providing periods of rest throughout the period of performance.

Movements that are continuously repeated are easier for the spastic. However, in the case of the athetoid best performance is achieved if he rests and relaxes between movements. The ataxic will not perform well in skills requiring balance and kinesthesis. He is able to move his body successfully but has difficulty responding to objects around him, as in the instances of picking up or catching or kicking objects in a game situation. Because of his poor kinesthesis he often moves too far or not far enough in executing the required movement. Success will be more likely if such youngsters can remain stationary. Kicking the ball while running will be very difficult, but if the ataxic can stop and then make the kick the chances of performing the skill successfully are immeasurably better.

FREE PLAY.   Free play is just as necessary for the child with cerebral palsy as for the normal boy or girl. There is a tendency to plan all activities and to provide supervision for him. The child should have opportunities to use his own imagination and inventiveness for creative play alone as well as with other children. The instruction that he receives in supervised physical education should help him achieve skills which he can use in free play.

MUSIC AND RHYTHM.   Music and rhythm have been utilized in both therapy and physical education programs. Music therapists have observed that music is very relaxing to some, while in others it produces greater tenseness and lack of coordination. For those whose coordination is not diminished by the musical accompaniment, rhythmic games may be included in the programs. Singing games may be used successfully in groups having reasonable control of the muscles concerning with speech. The more severe cases can be limited to such simple measures as clapping and stamping the feet to simple tunes. Modern dance is an area that has not been fully explored as a physical education activity and as therapy, but it holds fruitful promise.

SWIMMING.   Swimming should be given a major place in the physical education curriculum because in the water children with cerebral palsy are able to make movements which are otherwise impossible. Special techniques for teaching swimming skills to these students are presented in Chapter 21.

THE PROGRAM FOR STUDENTS WITH CEREBRAL PALSY

Cerebral palsied children who will be enrolled in regular schools will usually have mild muscular disabilities and can participate relatively freely in sports and recreational activities. However, there are many situations when they will not be able to participate in the regular physical education class work. The ability to participate will depend upon the degree of affliction. There are some types of activities that are easier for them to perform, and there are certain situations when motor movement is easier. Strong stimulations are confusing and loud noises, extreme temperatures, and strong emotional situations are to be avoided. Highly competitive games are contraindicated. These children should not be exposed, as a rule, to participation in tournaments and games where winning is highly emphasized.

Children with spasticity, ataxia, and rigidity are inactive and tend to be overweight. Consequently, the physical education for them should provide for the expenditure of energy which is stored in the body as excess fat. As with all overweight individuals these overweight children will need to be highly motivated for participation in physical activity.

Before a program is initiated for the student with cerebral palsy, his personal limitations and abilities should be clearly understood. A list of activities in which he can participate should be approved by his doctor. If the student is receiving physical therapy treatment, the sport and recreational skills that will be included in the program should complement the exercises given by the therapist.

Activities selected for the cerebral palsied will be determined by the kind and severity of the disability, the amount of muscular education that has taken place, and the interest level of the child. Any physical education for severe cases is limited until the basic movement patterns of grasp-and-release and extend-and-return arm have been established. Suggested activities for the development of basic sports skills by those who have developed these basic movements are:

1. Simple throwing and catching activity. A volleyball attached to a rope is suspended from the ceiling above the child. He throws it and attempts to catch it on the return swing.

2. Rolling and catching exercise. Two students sit on the floor a few feet apart and roll a large ball back and forth.

3. Throwing and catching activity. Two students sit a few feet apart, tossing a heavy rubber balloon between them. (The balloon is slower than a ball and permits more time for performing the catch.)

4. Bouncing and catching exercise. Each student sits in a chair and bounces and catches a large ball.

5. Throwing for accuracy exercise. Students sit in a circle around a target of concentric circles. They throw a beanbag at the target.

6. Mimicking games. The students mimic animals by assuming various arm positions suggestive of the animals, such as holding the arm down from the head to resemble the elephant's trunk.

7. Interpretative movements. Various emotions are expressed by movements of the arms, such as waving them gaily or letting them droop sadly.

8. Acting out a story. The students make movements with the arms to act out a favorite story.

For less severely afflicted elementary school age children, the physical education program may be similar to the regular elementary program. Activities and basic skill games[2] which are applicable with a minimum of adaptation are:

> Walking while balancing a beanbag on the head
> Kicking a soccer ball for accuracy
> Dribbling a soccer ball with the feet
> Walking a low balance beam
> Call ball

[2]For descriptions and adaptations of basic skill games see Chapter 16.

Red Light	Three deep
Magic Carpet	Pussy Wants a Corner
Eagle and Sparrows	Ringmaster
Fire on the Mountain	Farmer and the Chickens
Crows and Cranes	Hot Potatoes

Older students with limited disabilities may participate in these activities:

Archery	Bowling on the green
Horseshoes	Calisthenics
Interpretative dance	Running games
Croquet	

RELAXATION.   Muscular relaxation is a very important aspect of teaching physical education activities to those with cerebral palsy. There is a tendency for these students to become very tense when striving to perform well. For the athetoid, particularly, motor movement is more successful if done in a relaxed state. Developing an attitude toward accomplishing the motor skills which encourages relaxation while doing the skills is basic to successful teaching of physical education activities to these students. Excessive pressure by the teacher or the student himself to perform the correct way creates tension which in turn produces uncontrolled movements. Consequently, an attitude which frees the performer from overconcern is highly desirable.

Techniques of teaching muscular relaxation that may be helpful in working with athetoids are found in Chapter 24.

QUESTIONS

1. What is cerebral palsy? Discuss its most common causes.
2. What is the chief factor causing the difference in symptoms produced by cerebral palsy which occurs in the first three years of life and that which occurs later in life?
3. Describe the nature of these disabilities: spasticity, athetosis, ataxia, rigidity, and tremor.
4. What are the topographical classifications of cerebral palsy?
5. Discuss the statement that the lack of emotional control and instability of the cerebral palsy patient may be due partly to the damage to certain areas of the brain which control emotional maturation.
6. Explain the difference between the physical therapist, recreational therapist, and physical educator.
7. Describe Phelps's technique in teaching movement to the cerebral palsied.
8. What is the "association technique"?
9. Make a list of things the physical educator must take into consideration when adapting games and activities for students with cerebral palsy.
10. In what way may music be used in physical education for students with cerebral palsy?
11. What is the chief factor that tends to make the spastic overweight? Is the same true for children suffering from ataxia and rigidity?
12. What place does swimming have in the physical education program for those with cerebral palsy?
13. Describe a technique of teaching muscular relaxation.

SELECTED READINGS

American Psychological Association: *Psychological Problems of Cerebral Palsy,* A symposium sponsored by the Division of School Psychologists, American Psychological Association, and the National Society for Crippled Children and Adults. Chicago, National Society for Crippled Children and Adults, Inc., 1952.

Cardwell, Viola E.: *Cerebral Palsy; Advances in Understanding and Care.* New York, Association for the Aid of Crippled Children, 1956.

Courville, Cyril B.: *Cerebral Palsy: A Brief Introduction to its History, Etiology, and Pathology.* Los Angeles, San Lucas Press, 1954.

Crothers, Bronson, and Paine, Richmond S.: *National History of Cerebral Palsy.* Cambridge, Mass., Harvard University Press, 1959.

Cruickshank, William, and Raus, George: *Cerebral Palsy, Its Individual and Community Problems.* Syracuse, N.Y., Syracuse University Press, 1955.

Denhoff, Eric, and Robinault, Isabel P.: *Cerebral Palsy and Related Disorders.* New York, McGraw-Hill Book Co., Inc., 1960.

Frampton, Merle E., and Gall, Elena D. (ed.): *Special Education for the Exceptional:* Vol. III — *Mental and Emotional Deviates and Special Problems.* Boston, Porter Sargent, Publishers, 1956.

Lewis, Richard S., et al.: *The Other Child, the Brain-injured Child: A Book for Parents and Laymen,* ed. 2. New York, Grune & Stratton, Inc., 1960.

Towbin, Abraham: *The Pathology of Cerebral Palsy.* Springfield, Ill., Charles C Thomas, Publisher, 1960.

8
ORTHOPEDIC HANDICAPS

Any kind of physical disability, whether it is a cardiac condition, paralyzed limb, or an infectious disease, is crippling in its effect upon the victim. Consequently, the word *cripple* is widely used in describing those whose normal participation in life is restricted by a physical disability. There is no general agreement, however, among users of the word as to the types of disabilities which are properly included under its label. Some use the word to describe all physical handicaps; it is in this inclusive sense that the word is used in the legal profession. Others limit the crippled to those who cannot walk or cannot walk without the aid of braces, crutches, or cane. In still other instances, the disabled who can move about satisfactorily in the normal environment, although he uses an appliance, is not regarded as crippled. Because of this lack of uniformity in the definition of cripple, a more delimiting term, orthopedic handicap, will be employed in this chapter.

Orthopedic is derived from the Greek words meaning "to straighten the child," and in modern usage is applied both to a specific type of disability and to the branch of medicine concerned with its prevention and treatment. An orthopedic handicap is one which will not allow the patient to perform properly the motor and locomotor functions of his body and limbs. Such disabilities may be concerned with the functions of the bones, joints, tendons, and the peripheral blood vessels and nerves.

The public attitude toward individuals handicapped by crippling disabilities has changed immensely since the Middle Ages, when the only hope of acceptance in his society of one so handicapped was to become a court jester. Today the individual with an orthopedic handicap has opportunities for treatment, rehabilitation, gainful employment, and social acceptance far beyond the dreams of even the most imaginative court jester. While much remains to be done, especially in equalizing the opportunities, those with orthopedic disabilities have suffered less from a lack of public understanding of their needs and problems than have most other kinds of handicapped people. This is due partly to the fact that the disability is itself more obvious to the observer and is of such a nature as to elicit sympathy rather than fear, suspicion, or repulsion. The extensive work of the veterans' hospitals in the rehabilitation of wounded soldiers and the medical and educational endeavors of the special schools and hospitals for crippled children have contributed greatly to public understanding of the nature of these disabilities and the problems which face those who are thus disabled.

Care for crippled children was extremely limited until the 19th century, when the work of several prominent orthopedic surgeons in England, on the Continent, and in the United States began to direct attention to the prevention and remedial treatment for the crippling conditions. Interest in the plight of crippled children remained almost entirely medical until the closing years of the century, when the increasing number of crippled children aroused interest in adequate educational provisions for them. Special schools for crippled children were established, as were special classes within the public schools. Currently, most of the states provide special classes, and all provide for home instruction for those unable to attend the public schools. A number of hospitals for crippled children exist throughout the country, and these provide educational instruction as well as medical and therapeutic treatment. In all these situations, children with cerebral palsy and cardiac difficulties are included in addition to those with orthopedically incapacitating conditions. Conditions other than orthopedic in nature are treated in other chapters of this book; the concern of this chapter will be with the physical education opportunities for children whose participation in physical activity is restricted by orthopedic handicaps.

THE NATURE OF ORTHOPEDIC HANDICAPS

CAUSES. Most cases of orthopedic incapacitation are caused by *infection, trauma, congenital conditions*, and *osteochondrosis*. Infectious causes are chiefly poliomyelitis, osteomyelitis, and tuberculosis of the bone. Traumatic causes are most frequently amputation and peripheral nerve injury. Congenital conditions include those abnormalities and deformities present at birth, such as club feet, scoliosis, spina bifida, and dislocated hips and arms. Osteochondrosis is a disease of one or more of the growth or ossification centers in children which begins as a degeneration followed by recalcification. The most common involvement is the head of the femur. This condition is known as Perthes' disease.

Although some orthopedic handicaps will require no appliances, most will necessitate the use of wheelchairs, braces, crutches, or prosthetic devices. Those using wheelchairs will have no useful locomotion, although they may be able to stand for a few moments or even take a step or two. Braces and crutches provide support and stability enabling the user to control his movements and so to move about in a limited fashion. Prostheses permit the greatest possible range of normal movement. Modern amputations are performed to permit the best possible stump for the fitting of the prosthesis so that, particularly in amputations below the knee, nearly normal locomotion can be restored.

FREQUENCY.   Because of the lack of uniformity in defining the conditions of crippling and orthopedic handicaps, statistics of incidence are neither very meaningful nor very accurate. The number can be doubled or cut in half by the inclusion or exclusion of certain conditions. It is consequently not possible to determine how many cases of orthopedically handicapped youngsters, as here defined, there are currently or how many of these may be expected to be found in the regular school, the special school, or the hospital.

NEEDS AND ADJUSTMENTS OF THE ORTHOPEDICALLY HANDICAPPED

When a normally active human being finds his usual movements restricted by disease or accident, he faces the necessity of changing many of the patterns of his daily life. The degree to which he is able to make these changes determines to a large extent how satisfactory his adjustment will be. The age at which and the suddenness with which the incapacitating disability strikes appear to have considerable effect upon the adjustment which the individual makes. Very intense emotional reactions usually follow a sudden loss of limb by amputation, but these usually subside as the patient discovers that he is still capable of many of the activities of his former life. He is likely to make a satisfactory adjustment as he acquires compensatory motor skills. A child with a limb missing from birth or early infancy may have a deep-seated but less easily detected emotional disturbance as the result of the continual frustration he experiences in attempting to do the things which normal children do. On the other hand, he may have made an entirely adequate adjustment as the result of having acquired such satisfactory compensatory skills that he and those with whom he associates do not think of his being different. If the child has not made this kind of adjustment, he needs help in overcoming his fears and frustrations so that better adjustment will be possible.

The incapacitation produced by an infectious disease like poliomyelitis is usually much less sudden than that resulting from amputation. Nevertheless, a strong emotional reaction is usually evidenced during the early stages of the disease, which increases as the disease progresses and the crippling becomes more evident. It is likely to continue even after the disease has been terminated if the limitation to normal locomotion remains. The most common emotional reactions are withdrawal, hostility, and aggressiveness.

The age of the patient presents certain other problems in adjusting to the disability. Children and adolescents are particularly susceptible to the reaction of others to the cosmetic appearance of their disabilities. They may worry unduly about how they look and become overly sensitive to the responses of others to their appearance. The anxieties thus aroused are not easily relieved.

Orthopedic crippling occurring early in life frequently limits the child's opportunities for play and other social contacts and greatly restricts the development of satisfactory social growth. Courage, resourcefulness, and initiative fostered in the vigorous exchanges of childhood play activities are commonly deficient in physically disabled children who do not engage in normal play.

These desirable characteristics are also frequently lacking in orthopedically handicapped adults, stemming from their inability to participate in the normal patterns of living. In addition, many of them have inferiority feelings or have excessive anxieties usually related to their inability to support themselves economically. On the whole, a change of any kind is more difficult as age advances, owing to the force of daily habits. Consequently, unless the adult is given a good deal of help, satisfactory adjustment is very difficult.

The lack of active play in the lives of these youngsters and adults has detrimental physiological, as well as psychological, results. General body fitness is lacking. Coordination is poor. There is increased susceptibility to injury and hypokinetic diseases.

To achieve satisfactory adjustment, the orthopedically handicapped person must compensate for his lack of success in physical performance or he must seek satisfying substitutions. Some people compensate by achieving superiority in intellectual endeavors, in the development of musical, artistic, or literary talents, or in the creativity of crafts. Some measure of compensation can be achieved by nearly everyone, but compensation is not enough—satisfactory substitutions for the loss of motor skills must also be found.

Physical education can make one of its most significant contributions to the welfare of the handicapped in the teaching of substitute motor skills which will enable them to take pleasure in active participation in games and sports. This is, of course, only part of the role of physical education for the orthopedically handicapped. Play provides the incentive for the improvement in motor skills, and as locomotion increases the patient's morale receives a needed lift. When more complex game skills are achieved or former skills are reacquired, the patient's self-esteem reestablishes itself and he looks forward with greater confidence and reassurance to achieving satisfactory substitutions for his lost skills.

As participation becomes more active, physical fitness is increased and body mechanics are improved. The patient becomes more skilled in the use of previously unused portions of the body and in the use of his appliance, if one is required. Because he can play better and longer, owing to the improved conditioning and better playing skills, he enjoys himself more and others enjoy playing with him. In such an atmosphere of social acceptance, the first steps may be taken toward a more satisfactory adjustment.

PLANNING THE PROGRAM

The physical educator employed in a special school or hospital for crippled children which provides physical education as well as therapeutic exercises must clearly understand the division between the physical therapy and physical education. His program in this situation must be limited to those big-muscle activites used for leisure-time play and to promote body conditioning, but not specifically concerned with correction of the handicap for the purpose of increased motor function. The activities should not, of course, detract in any way from the physical therapy; they can and should complement the therapeutic exercises. Consequently, the program should be carefully planned in consultation with the medical authorities so that muscles will not be used incorrectly, thus negating the therapeutic treatment.

THE HOSPITAL OR SPECIAL SCHOOL. During the hospital stay or active treatment stage, the physical education teacher must consider the medical problems that are related to specific types of disabilities. Weakened muscles must not be strained by overwork; the muscles of the set antagonistic to the weaker ones must be protected from overdevelopment, which would produce muscular imbalance; the hip joints in Perthes' disease must bear no weight; a joint that is tubercular must be protected from all movement. In most cases of crippling diseases, after the disease is arrested and muscular re-education is nearly complete, the physical education activities need be limited only by the structural limitations of the student.

One of the important objectives of the physical education program for adults in hospitals and children in special schools and hospitals is to provide play opportunities which encourage the patients to try the motor skills which they are acquiring or re-learning under the care of the physical therapist. Consequently, the program must be carefully planned to provide good progression of skills and experiences. When the very simple skills are satisfactorily mastered, more complex ones can be introduced, and finally very complex skills can be taught. The variety of skills required by the games should be as wide as possible. Included among the earliest skills presented should be throwing and catching, because these are fundamental to so many games. Because missing the ball presents an obstacle difficult for nonambulatory patients to overcome, a ball attached to a string or elastic is useful in retrieving a missed ball. Among the other fundamental skills which are taught must be included the technique of falling correctly; this is an essential safety precaution for these patients.

The patients should be prepared for the amount of practice which may be necessary to accomplish a skill. If they understand this, they will not become discouraged when they compare their present rate of skill acquisition with their former rate before they were afflicted. Words of encouragement and praise should be spoken often by the instructor.

Everyone can gain a satisfactory degree of proficiency in one or two or possibly more sports. Achieving skill in at least one activity beyond the fundamental motor skills would seem to be essential to adults, because it is a means of keeping in good physical condition and because it opens the door to socializing with others who also enjoy that particular activity. Such socializing, we have seen, can help to fulfill certain psychological needs of the individual.

Those who have lost the use of a single arm, if it is not the dominant arm, can play most games and sports without significant modifications except in the technique of catching. If the use of the dominant hand is lost, the patient can learn to use his other hand. Performing the skill with this hand will at first seem extremely awkward, but practice will overcome this. The development of arm dexterity should be initiated with simple throwing activities such as throwing beanbags or darts at a target. Devices are available which fit into the arm prothesis to hold sport equipment such as gloves. Patients having difficulty learning to catch with one hand may wish to try such a device.

Those who have lost or are without the use of both arms may successfully participate in soccer and track and in other activities adapted to require the use of feet but not of hands and arms. Patients confined to wheelchairs with involvement of both lower limbs can participate in wheelchair square dancing and basketball and engage in a number of interesting games adapted to their particular limitations. Amputees able to wear prostheses for both missing lower limbs are able to play the games adapted for those on crutches.

An involvement of one lower limb does not hinder participation to any great extent, particularly if the patient has learned to use a prosthesis. The greatest restriction is in running games. Those using crutches will need to be instructed in the technique of propping them against the body to give it support so the arms can be freed for use, as in archery, for example.

Certain devices can be used to help the patients in the performance of the skills. Poles of wood or metal can be erected in playing areas to which players who require support while using their hands can be strapped. Tables with recessed areas which permit the disabled to stand by supporting himself against the table are available but are better suited to indoor than to outdoor play. Those who cannot stand but can sit unsupported in a straight chair can perform many activities while so seated.

The playing area for games and sports is usually reduced in size, playing equipment is lighter, and frequently the handles of rackets and mallets are extended to increase the range of the reach. Team games are modified in various ways: the area that each player must cover is reduced, the assignment of duties is made on the basis of the players' abilities, or two people with different abilities share an assignment.

THE REGULAR SCHOOL.   A student returning to school after hospitalization with an orthopedic disability may display no apparent aftereffect, while others may exhibit a mild or even severe crippling condition. Although there may be no visible debility, the physical education teacher should not immediately include the student in the regular physical education class. Possible muscular weakness or lack of endurance may not be observable. The teacher should not attempt to include the student in the activites until he has received medical recommendations as to the amount of activity in which the student should engage and the kinds of activities which will prove most beneficial, as well as those which should be restricted. With this knowledge the teacher will be able to plan the kind of program which will help the student increase his general level of fitness so that he will be better able to meet the daily physical demands on his strength, endurance, and coordination.

The returning student who has a moderate or severe disability may need considerable help in achieving maximum physical efficiency. Upon receipt of the medical report, the teacher should work out a carefully planned, graduated program of exercises and activities to meet the special needs of the student. It is advisable to secure medical approval of the planned program. The student who has considerable residual paralysis or a limb amputation is also likely to need a great deal of help in making a satisfactory adjustment to his handicap. Because of his possible concern about his appearance and his inabilities to perform motor skills, he may experience more anxieties about physical education class than about other phases of his school life. The teacher can help to alleviate his fears by helping him to find a solution which is satisfying to him about dressing and showering in the presence of others, and by preparing him to meet the challenges of his restriction with good humor rather than with fear of embarrassment or ridicule.

The specific activities of the adapted program for the orthopedically handicapped will be determined by the nature and extent of the handicap and the general debility. The early phases of the program for the returning student will be largely exercises and games, approved by the doctor, which will increase physical fitness and body mechanics (see Chapters 24 and 25 for program suggestions). Leg amputees returning to class may profit from additional work in improving the walking technique, since this may not have been fully mastered before their return to school. The leg amputee often has an improper gait resulting from his bearing the weight of the body upon his good leg while he raises the hip and shoulder of the opposite side to swing the artificial leg forward. More stability and improved appearance of the walking gait can be achieved by keeping the hips and shoulders level and moving the leg forward as normally as possible, with the length of the stride and the walking rhythm matched to that of the normal leg. Practice of the desired walking form in front of a mirror is helpful in overcoming the improper technique.

As the physical condition and motor performance improve, modified games, dances, and team sports can be introduced into the adapted program. When the situation warrants it, the handicapped student should be included in the activities of the regular class.

THE PROGRAM FOR STUDENTS WITH ORTHOPEDIC HANDICAPS

The orthopedically handicapped will be able to participate in a wide selection of games and sports if suitable adaptations are made so that the restrictions imposed by the handicap are minimized. The resourceful teacher will be able to devise many ways of modifying activities to enable the handicapped to participate in individual, dual, and team sports. Some suggestions for adapting these sports are found in Chapters 18, 19, and 20. Other activities which are easily adapted for play by the orthopedically handicapped are given below. The activities are suitable for use by the physical education teacher in his work with orthopedically handicapped youngsters in the normal school situation, as well as by the teacher in charge of the physical education program for children in the special school or for adults and youngsters in hospitals.

ADAPTED ACTIVITIES FOR THOSE WITH LOWER LIMB INVOLVEMENT. These are for players with or without crutches.[1]

1. Fly and bait casting and spinning: These activities may be performed while seated in a chair or while standing propped by the crutches.

2. Tether ball: The player may be braced by his crutches in a standing position or he may be seated in a chair. The rope may need to be adjusted in length.

3. Croquet: A long handle should be attached to the mallet if the player cannot bend over. A block of wood may also be attached to one crutch, to propel the ball in place of a mallet.

[1]Adapted activities for those confined to wheelchairs are described in Chapter 10.

4. Horseshoes: The distance between stakes is reduced. The player is braced on his crutches so as to free his throwing hand.

5. Ring toss: The player braces himself as for horseshoes. Those using crutches will usually find ring toss easier than horseshoes.

6. Light bag punching: Those using crutches will need to brace themselves to free both hands. If this is not possible, they may work with one hand.

7. Rings, bars, parallel ladder, and ropes: If the arms are normal in function and development, the individual can perform on these apparatuses with minimum adaptations.

8. Square dancing: Dances should be chosen which have uncomplicated patterns. The following substitutions are suggested as ways in which the regular movements may be modified for those who must use crutches:

Honor your partner. Bow heads.

Swing your partner. Hold out one hand while balanced on crutches to partner who dances around. If both are on crutches, touch bottom parts of one crutch of each partner forming a pivot which both partners go around.

Alemand left. Walk around to the left.

Right and left grande. Walk around first to the left and then to the right.

Promenade. Noncrippled partner places hand on partner's shoulder. If both are on crutches, they move their crutches in unison as they walk.

Do si do. Noncrippled partner may do most of the movement if it is difficult for the other partner to perform. If both are on crutches and movement is difficult, the swing may be substituted.

Balance. One crutch is placed forward. If the handicapped has sufficient strength and skill to raise himself and balance on the crutches, as some do, this movement may be substituted for the balance.

ADAPTED ACTIVITIES FOR THOSE WITH UPPER LIMB INVOLVEMENT. Those with one arm are able to participate in most activities as soon as they have learned to perform skills with one hand which are normally performed with two hands. They may participate in racquet games, softball; soccer; volleyball; the running, jumping, and throwing events of track and field; and kicking a soccer or football for distance or accuracy. If both arms have been lost, participation is limited to those activities which utilize the feet, such as soccer and jumping and kicking events.

1. Volleyball: It is possible to play volleyball by using parts of the body to play the ball; the head and knee are the most effective for this.

2. Soccer handball: This game, developed at the University of Connecticut for those with no use of their arms, is readily played by those

with upper limb involvement in both arms. It is played in a handball court. The ball is kicked against the wall. The serve, to be good, must be kicked against the front wall and must return behind the service line. The ball is allowed to bounce once. It may hit any wall or combination of walls and remain in play. The ball may be played with any part of the body.

ACTIVITIES FOR YOUNG CHILDREN.   Some activities for young children can be adapted from the basic skill games described in Chapter 16. For example, games like circle ball, wonder ball, or target toss can be played while seated in a chair by children with leg involvements. Those with some degree of functional leg movement can play Driving Pig to Market, softball bowling, circle ball, and similar games in which leg agility is not essential. These children can also participate in singing games such as Here We Go over the Mountain, Rig-a-Jig, and Way down Yonder in the Paw-Paw Patch by substituting walking for the skipping. Nearly all games except ball games requiring catching can be easily performed by children with a single arm involvement. Activities which can be played without the necessity of using the hands such as Farmer in the Dell and Pussy Wants a Corner are good for those without the use of both arms. Many of the basic skill games can be readily adapted for play by children in wheelchairs by increasing the size of the formation to provide space for maneuvering the chair. Games for this purpose should not have complicated patterns.

SWIMMING.   Like the child with cerebral palsy, the child with an orthopedic handicap enjoys increased movement in the water not possible otherwise. Even children with Perthes' disease, who are denied participation in so many activities, can enjoy the pleasures of swimming. While they are not encouraged to stand erect in the water, they can do so without much risk because the buoyancy of the water reduces the pressure of body weight on the head of the femur. For others, the water buoyancy makes control of the body easier by minimizing the effects of weak muscles and the lack of balance and stability which hinder or restrict movement out of the water. Appliances which must always be worn otherwise can usually be removed for swimming.

For the best possible environment, the water temperature should be higher than normal to reduce tension and to prevent chilling. Nonskid material should be used around the pool area to prevent accidental falls. Ramps leading to the pool should be provided for wheelchair patients and those on crutches. Easily grasped supports should be provided on the deck and in the pool for those who have difficulty standing, handrails may be installed on the deck, and ropes or poles may be provided in the pool itself. Additional information about teaching swimming to the orthopedically handicapped is presented in Chapter 21.

QUESTIONS

1. Trace briefly public attitude toward the handicapped from ancient to modern times.
2. Define the word orthopedic.
3. List the chief causes of orthopedic incapacitation by infection and trauma.
4. List some of the deformities that may be congenital.
5. What is osteochondrosis?
6. Why is the age at which the incapacitation occurs important to emotional adjustment? What contributions can physical education make toward a more satisfactory adjustment?
7. In what ways does the physical educator work with the physical therapist?
8. What safety precautions must be taken with patients suffering from Perthes' disease?
9. What are some of the basic sport skills that should be taught first to the orthopedically handicapped?
10. What precautions need to be taken in physical education for a student who is returning to school after recovery from poliomyelitis?
11. Plan the adaptation of an activity or game not mentioned in the text for a student with a leg or arm disability.

SELECTED READINGS

Aegerter, Ernest, and Kirkpatrick, John A., Jr.: *Orthopedic Diseases*, ed. 2. Philadelphia, W. B. Saunders Co., 1963.

Daniels, Arthur S.: *Adapted Physical Education*, ed. 2. New York, Harper & Brothers, 1965.

Frost, Alma: *Handbook for Paraplegics and Quadriplegics*. Tarrytown, N. Y., R. Frost, Inc., 1951.

Garrett, James F. (ed.): *Physiological Aspects of Physical Disability*. Washington, D.C., U.S. Government Printing Office, 1952.

Heck, Arch O.: *The Education of Exceptional Children*, ed. 2. New York, McGraw-Hill Book Co., Inc., 1953.

Slocum, Donald B.: *An Atlas of Amputations*. St. Louis, The C. V. Mosby Co., 1949.

Stern, Edith M., and Castendyck, Elsa: *The Handicapped Child*. New York, A. A. Wyn, Inc., 1950.

Stone, Eleanor B., and Deyton, John W.: *Corrective Therapy for the Handicapped Child*. New York, Prentice-Hall, Inc., 1951.

9
CARDIOPATHIC CONDITIONS

Long before man understood the physiological function of the heart, he was concerned with its influence upon the body. The ancients at various times considered the heart the source of love, courage, and kindness; and the association of the heart with these virtues still fills our present-day language with such descriptive phrases as stout-hearted, queen of my heart, sweetheart, and kind-hearted. Actual knowledge of the heart dates from the early 17th century, when William Harvey, an English medical doctor, through animal experimentation and observation of his patients, determined its true function. He recorded his findings in a book, which is today acknowledged as the first accurate description of the heart's function.

With the discovery of the x-ray, a fairly generally held belief that excessive exercise was injurious to the heart appeared to be substantiated. Through the use of x-rays it was determined that pathological hearts were frequently enlarged hearts; it was also determined that athletes had larger hearts than nonathletes. From this evidence the conclusion was made that strenuous exercise worked to the disadvantage of the heart. It was many years before this theory was completely invalidated by physiologists investigating the effects of exercise upon the heart. They discovered that the heart subjected to strenuous exercise over a period of years probably did become larger, but this increase in size resulted from increased strength of the heart muscle rather than from a pathological condition.[1]

Recently, some investigators have found that athletic histories are common among those who experience coronary heart disease early in life. However, the increased incidence of heart disease is found also among those of mesomorphic body build. It has consequently been postulated that body build may be the predisposing factor in the increase of heart disease among athletes, since the majority of athletes are mesomorphic.[2]

Other recent studies have found a relationship between a lack of muscular activity and heart disease. It has been shown that those engaging in sedentary occupations are more prone to heart disease than those whose jobs require muscular activity. Although evidence is not complete, most experts are inclined to agree that a certain amount of exercise throughout one's life is to the advantage of the heart.[3]

Increased participation by junior high schools in varsity athletics during the 1940's gave rise to considerable concern about possible damage which might be inflicted on the immature heart by the strenuous activity of competitive play. Many physical educators and medical personnel voiced the opinion that excessive strenuous activity could affect the young heart detrimentally. However, the preponderance of evidence accumulated in recent years indicates that, if the heart of the young participant is not predisposed to cardiac disturbance, strenuous activity cannot injure it.[4]

THE NATURE AND CAUSES OF HEART DISEASE

The number of deaths due to heart disease is increasing. Over 50 per cent of all deaths in the United States are caused by heart disorders. This high percentage is attributed chiefly to the increase in the number of people who reach the age when heart trouble is most likely to occur. Heart disorders are the primary cause of death of all those over the age of 25.

Most heart disorders which occur in those under the age of 25 are of a congenital nature or are caused by rheumatic fever. It has been estimated that there are about 500,000 children in this country suffering from rheumatic fever. Approximately 18,000 to 20,000 new cases are added each year. Of these, approximately two-thirds show some sign

[1]Felix Deutsch, *et al.*: *Heart and Athletics.* St. Louis, The C. V. Mosby Co., 1927, pp. 17–18.

[2]Menard M. Gertler and Paul D. White: *Coronary Heart Disease in Young Adults.* Cambridge, Mass., Harvard University Press, 1954, pp. 58–59.

[3]Joseph B. Wolffe: "Prevention of Disease Through Exercise and Health Education," in *Health and Fitness in the Modern World.* Chicago, The Athletic Institute, 1961, pp. 75–81.

[4]Hollis F. Fait: *An Analytical Study of Competitive Athletics Upon Junior High School Boys.* Doctoral dissertation, University of Iowa, 1951, pp. 50–74.

of cardiac damage.[5] About half of these young heart victims will be able to attend school; the other half will suffer heart damage severe enough to require home instruction.

Heart disorders are of two classifications—organic and functional. In an *organic* disorder a definite lesion exists in the heart or other parts of the cardiovascular-renal system. No lesion is present in a *functional* heart disorder, but there is some disturbance in function. The symptoms are: irregular or accentuated heart beat, weakness after physical effort, shortness of breath, dizziness, fatigue, and considerable concern and anxiety. Some authorities believe the disturbance is chiefly psychogenic in origin, arising, for example, from an imagined heart condition. Treatment along psychiatric lines is indicated in this situation.

THE KINDS OF HEART DISEASE

Medical research has discovered at least 20 different kinds of organic heart diseases. Of these the most commonly occurring and consequently the most important health problems are: rheumatic heart disease, hypertensive heart disease, and coronary heart disease.

RHEUMATIC HEART DISEASE.   Rheumatic heart disease begins most often in children between the ages of 6 and 12 as the result of rheumatic fever. Early signs of the disease, which may occur singly or in combination, are pain in joints and muscles, twitching of muscles, frequent nosebleeds, pallor, poor appetite, and failure to gain weight. Evidence of these symptoms does not necessarily mean that a child has rheumatic fever; a period of medical observation and special tests may be necessary to determine the presence of rheumatic fever.

Rheumatic heart disease is the result of an attack of rheumatic fever, but the exact cause of it is not known. Two factors appear to be involved in its development: allergy and a particular kind of streptococcus infection. Rheumatic fever develops only in certain people who have suffered infection of the throat, respiratory tract, or middle ear caused by hemolytic (blood-destroying) streptococcus organisms and who have developed an allergic and inflammatory reaction to the infection. The rheumatic reaction usually occurs a few weeks after the initial attack of the infection but may not be evident until some time later. Rheumatic fever is not communicable, and there is no danger of contracting it by exposure to one who has it.

Rheumatic fever does not always cause heart disease, and the heart is the only organ which may be seriously affected. During the course of the disease the valves of the heart may become inflamed, and subsequent

---

[5]American Heart Association: *Heart Disease in Children.* New York, American Heart Association, 1956, p. 1.

scarring of the valves and surrounding tissue may result. The valves most frequently affected are the mitral and aortic. The scars may prevent their proper function. When the valves cannot close correctly, a back flow of blood is permitted; this is called regurgitation. If the valves do not open correctly to allow the blood to flow easily, the condition is called stenosis.

Immunity from rheumatic fever does not develop from an attack; on the contrary, the disease tends to recur. Repeated attacks are more likely to damage the heart. Recurring attacks usually cease by the age of 15 or 16 years. For as long as the disease is active and for a period of convalescence it is important to spare the heart unnecessary work. A child with the disease must remain in bed. It is the usual medical recommendation that those suffering from rheumatic fever stay in bed weeks or even months after the inflammation dies down. However, research work carried on during World War II would seem to indicate that exercise might be started at an earlier date to the benefit of the patient.

HYPERTENSIVE HEART DISEASE.   Hypertension, or high blood pressure, and changes in the arteries are often associated with heart disease affecting both young adults and adults. When the blood pressure is consistently high, the heart is forced to work harder. Arteriosclerosis (hardening of the artery walls) frequently accompanies hypertension, further increasing the work of the heart. When the heart begins to show the effects of this strain, hypertensive heart disease develops.

The causes of arteriosclerosis are not clearly understood. Some authorities feel that an upset in cholesterol (fat) metabolism is a contributing factor; others attribute the disease to hereditary factors. Still others are inclined to blame a mode of living in which excessive anxiety, worry, and fear and insufficient amounts of rest and relaxation, as well as too much eating and smoking, are common. Such factors are known to increase the work of the heart, thereby placing an added burden on it. Some hardening of the arteries does occur as one grows older as part of the natural process of aging. In males, arteries begin to harden about 10 to 15 years before the process begins in women. The reason for this is not known.

CORONARY HEART DISEASE.   Coronary heart disease is most prevalent in middle and old age. The most serious accident which may occur in coronary heart disease is occlusion (closure) of a coronary artery or a rupture of one of the blood vessels which hemorrhages into the muscle tissue of the heart.

Severe pain the chest accompanies a heart accident or attack. Weakness, pallor, and sweating are also present. This condition is known as angina pectoris and is due to lack of oxygen to the heart (anoxia of the myocardium). Excitement, fear, and effort make the condition worse. Bed rest of from two to four weeks is usually advised for a moderately damaged heart before convalescent exercises are begun. A longer bed rest is needed if there has been more extensive damage to the heart.

OTHER HEART DISEASES. Other causes of heart disease, not as frequent as rheumatic fever, coronary accidents, and hypertensions, are:

Overactive thyroid. An overactive thyroid can damage the heart because of increased metabolic activities that may place an excessive burden upon the heart.

Anemia. Severe anemia may injure the heart by placing an undue burden upon it to supply oxygen and by causing a deficiency of oxygen to the heart muscles as well.

Congenital heart disease. This refers to a condition existing at birth which interferes with proper heart function. An example of such a condition is that which occurs in so-called "blue babies." Here, a defect in the septum (center wall) allows the venous blood to seep into the arterial blood.

Infection. Heart disease may be brought about by infection of the inner lining of the heart. This infection is called *endocarditis.* If the outer covering of the heart, or pericardium, is infected, it is called *pericarditis.* Another condition, called *myocarditis,* is an inflammation of the heart muscle, or myocardium.

Childhood diseases. The heart can be affected by several of the childhood diseases, notably diphtheria. Tuberculosis and syphilis are other diseases causing heart disease.

SYMPTOMS OF HEART DISEASE

A normal heart makes certain characteristic sounds. These can be heard when the ear or stethoscope is placed in a specific area over a person's chest. There are definite variations in these sounds which accompany certain pathological conditions of the heart. These sounds are known as *murmurs.* Some murmurs are caused by a structural deviation such as valvular incompetence (leaky valves). Frequently, however, adolescents have functional heart murmurs not caused by a structural deviation. Such a murmur has little significance and should not become the focus of worry and concern. It will very likely disappear as the youngster grows older. Restriction of activity is not necessary.

The important danger signals of heart disease are related to the failure of the heart to perform properly. The following symptoms may indicate heart disease: pain in the chest; shortness of breath; edema (swelling) in the feet, ankles, or abdomen; dizziness; fatigue; indigestion; and double vision. People who experience a disturbance in heart rhythm (skipping a beat) often become greatly concerned, but there is usually no reason for concern as a very large percentage of these cases show no presence of heart disease. Chest pain may result from many different causes. A sharp pain accompanying deep breath inhalation is very seldom due to heart disease. The pain that accompanies heart disease is of a stifling, crushing nature. Dizziness, fatigue, indigestion, double vision, and shortness of breath also frequently come from other causes than heart disease. No one should assume he has heart disease because he has any, or even all, of the symptoms until he has had a thorough medical examination; in many instances the symptoms are not related to heart diseases.

FIRST AID FOR HEART CASES

Cardiac crises occur most frequently in older people. However, they do happen in school-age children. The steps in the first aid treatment which should be familiar to the teacher are:

1. Let the person assume the most comfortable position — this will usually be a sitting position.
2. Loosen tight clothing.
3. Give him plenty of air but avoid drafts.
4. Call the doctor immediately. Reassure the patient. The teacher's manner will affect the entire class as well as the patient, so he should strive to remain calm and unemotional.

CLASSIFICATION OF PATIENTS WITH CARDIAC CONDITIONS

The physical limitations of patients with cardiac conditions vary depending upon the degree and amount of malfunction of the heart. Patients with heart diseases are classified according to their functional capacity by the New York Heart Association, Inc., and Heart Fund as follows:

Class I: Patients with cardiac disease but without resulting limitation of physical activity. Ordinary physical activity does not cause undue fatigue, palpitation, dyspnea, or anginal pain.

Class II: Patients with cardiac disease resulting in slight limitation of physical activity. They are comfortable at rest. Ordinary physical activity results in fatigue, palpitation, dyspnea, or anginal pain.

Class III: Patients with cardiac disease resulting in marked limitation of physical activity. They are comfortable at rest. Less than ordinary activity causes fatigue, palpitation, dyspnea, or anginal pain.

Class IV: Patients with cardiac disease resulting in inability to carry on any physical activity without discomfort. Symptoms of cardiac insufficiency or of the anginal syndrome are present even at rest. If any physical activity is undertaken, discomfort is increased.

No Heart Disease: Predisposing Etiologic Factor: These are patients in whom no cardiac disease is discovered, but whose course should be followed by periodic examinations because of the presence or history of an etiologic factor that might cause heart disease.

Undiagnosed Manifestations. Patients with symptoms or signs referable to the heart but in whom a diagnosis of cardiac disease is uncertain are classified tentatively as undiagnosed manifestations.

NEEDS AND ADJUSTMENTS OF THE
CARDIAC PATIENT

The knowledge of the presence of a heart disease is usually charged with emotion for the patient, his family, and friends. If the disease is an outgrowth of a heart attack, the shock and fear which are created by the initial attack produce extreme anxiety. Heart disease resulting from causes other than a coronary is less sudden but often just as emotional in nature. Even though the symptoms are very mild, the patient may become very frightened because of the association he makes between heart disease and death.

The heart victim's first need, aside from medical care, is reassurance about the state of his health. This reassurance must extend to his family and close friends so that a relaxed and pleasant social environment conducive to recovery can be established. A program to promote the good mental health of the patient must continue beyond the convalescent period, for the patient will need help in adjusting to the limitations imposed upon many of his former activities and pleasures. If he has not previously been a close observer of the general good health practices such as eating a well-balanced diet and getting plenty of rest and sleep, he will probably need to be convinced of the necessity of their observance. Because of the close relationship of good health practices to physical education, the physical educator who works with cardiac patients in the hospital or in the classroom can create opportunities to stress the importance of the good health rules.

Youngsters who have had heart disabilities since early childhood do not usually have the same emotional problems as those who are suddenly afflicted. They are, however, likely to find their normal urges frustrated. Because active play with other children is restricted, the young cardiac may be socially immature. If his feeling of being left out of things is very great, he may become withdrawn and harbor feelings of resentment or inferiority. High-school-age youngsters often give evidence of severe frustrations arising from their inability to participate fully in the active games and social activities of their age group. Particularly emotionally distressing to some boys is the thwarting of athletic ambitions. Such a youngster may react with an attitude that since he is going to die anyway there is no need to practice care. On the other hand, he may withdraw entirely from social contacts. While this is not as dangerous physically, it can be very damaging psychologically.

Such children need to be counseled into a better course of adjustment, one which recognizes the restrictions as essential but points up the effective and enjoyable life which is possible within the limitations. Direct counseling is usually in the province of other school personnel, but the physical education teacher can do a great deal to reinforce the importance of exercising the necessary controls. If the cardiac patient is part of an adapted class, he will soon become aware that others must also live with certain restrictions. The adapted activities which he learns to play will not only help him to observe the necessary controls in regard to physical exertion, they will also give him the skills to fill his leisure hours with recreational activities which he can participate in with his own age group.

According to eminent authorities, most heart disturbances can be ameliorated by a program of exercises of gradually increasing difficulty. This does not mean, of course, that the organic disturbance is corrected. When there is an insufficient amount of muscular activity, the heart may show signs of strain due not so much to the disease as to the poor condition of the muscles of the heart. The crux of the problem lies in inducing the right amount of heart activity, well within the tolerance level, through body movement.

Muscular activity is valuable not only in maintaining the fitness of the heart, but also in promoting total body fitness. A certain amount of muscular activity is necessary to maintain strength and endurance of the skeletal muscle system. Moreover, exercise is an important factor in digestion and the elimination of wastes, as well as a factor in the feeling of well-being.

Many cardiac children can take part in many of the regular physical education activities. Whenever they can be permitted to do so, they should take part in the regular class. No limitations or restrictions need be imposed unless they have been advised by the doctor.

PLANNING THE PROGRAM

In planning the program for those with cardiac conditions the tolerance level for exercise for each patient must be established. If the patients have been classified according to functional capacity, as presented on page 103, the physical educator may make suggestions for each patient based upon his knowledge of the necessary limitations. The program must, of course, have the approval of the doctor before it is offered to the patient.

In determining activities for an individual case, it must be kept in mind that the strenuousness of an activity is not determined solely by its type but by how vigorously and how long it is performed. Some individuals may play table tennis at such a rapid pace that the activity might be classified as moderate whereas other patients may play much more slowly and deliberately so that the activity would be only mild in nature.

Age, personality, drives, and attitudes all determine the strenuousness with which a person performs an activity. Some may be more tense and work harder under the pressure of the learning situation with a teacher, while in free play they are much more relaxed. There are also those players, particularly among children, who in free play without the guidance of the instructor will not set a wise course in their play. There is a general tendency for children to overwork in muscular activity while adults are generally too sedentary. All such factors must be given consideration in planning the program.

Competitive play with its emphasis on winning is contraindicated for most heart patients. The emotions involved may speed the action of the heart so that the over-all work of the activity is beyond the tolerance level for the patient. Moreover, when there is an overemphasis on winning there is always a possibility that the participant may ignore safety precautions which he would otherwise heed.

THE PROGRAM FOR THE CARDIAC PATIENT

The student's tolerance level should be discussed with him, and he should have a clear understanding of his capacity and the amount of activity that constitutes an adequate work-load. A guide to help the participant keep within his tolerance level is that as long as he can perform the activity without breathing through the mouth or without forced breathing through the nose he is not overexerting. Activity should stop at once if any cardiac distress or shortness of breath is evidenced.

Heavy lifts that require holding the breath are contraindicated because this causes a rise in blood pressure and hence more work on the heart. However, some students may engage in weight training if they breathe normally and take the necessary precautions to conserve their energy. The procedures are discussed fully in Chapter 22.

Short periods of activity are usually best. Rest periods should be provided about halfway through an activity and should equal in length the time devoted to activity.

Some special consideration will need to be given to the influence weather conditions and certain features of the facilities may have on the planned program. In extremely hot weather or on damp rainy days, special precautions may be required for the cardiacs. If activity is to take place on rough or hilly playing areas, the expenditure of energy is likely to be greater, and consideration of this fact should be made in regard to the cardiac patient.

The following activities are suggested for each class of heart patients; they are intended as a guide for the physical education teacher from which he can develop a program for the approval of the medical doctor.

Class I (Mild): Most activities may be offered, including swimming. The participation should not extend over long periods of time. Long-distance running should be avoided, and participation in varsity athletic competition as well as other highly competitive play in which there is great emphasis upon winning is contraindicated.

Badminton and handball may be played as doubles to reduce the strenuousness of the activity, and tennis may be played with the court width cut in half and the elimination of the drop shot to modify the demands on physical exertion. Other activities which may be employed without modification are:

Softball

Paddle ball

Tumbling

Swimming

Tetherball

FIGURE 13. The strenuousness of throwing and catching can be modified by being seated or by lying down to play. (A, National Recreation Association; B, The National Foundation.)

Class II (Moderate): These activities are moderately active; players should be warned against making the game strenuous by becoming highly competitive or overactive while playing:

Bowling	Waltzing
Croquet	Folk dancing
Bowling on the green	Table tennis
Archery	Bag punching
Horseshoes	Hiking
Shuffleboard	Fly/bait casting and spinning
Volleyball	Horseback riding
Interpretative dances	Rope spinning

Class III (Moderately severe): Activities suggested for this group of patients are:

Walking
Shuffleboard
Rifle shooting
Fly and bait casting and spinning
Postural exercises (see Chapter 24)
Exercises for increasing muscle tonus (see Chapter 25)

Class IV (severe): Bed rest is frequently prescribed, although sometimes the patients are permitted to exercise while lying in bed. The activities described for convalescent patients confined to bed would be appropriate for these cardiac patients (see Chapter 10).

For very young children, many of the basic skill games described in Chapter 16 are applicable, depending upon the functional classification of the child. Singing games may be used but, if the child is joining in the singing, he should not attempt to perform at the same time as this may be too strenuous. The teacher or the others in the class may sing while he performs. Games that do not require sustained periods of running, such as red light and call ball, are very good for children with moderate functional capacity, as they enable the player to rest for short periods between action. Games such as wonder ball and circle ball, which utilize body activities other than running, are fine exercises. The work-load for heart patients may be further minimized by having the children seated to pass the ball around or the children may lie down in line and a balloon may be substituted for the ball. Another popular activity is modified volleyball. For this game a badminton net is stretched across the playing area three or four feet above the floor; the students sit on each side of the net and volley a balloon back and forth as in volleyball.

QUESTIONS

1. Discuss the relationship between heart disease and strenuous exercise.
2. Explain the difference between functional and organic heart disease.
3. List the symptoms of rheumatic fever.
4. What is a rheumatic heart?

5. Which causes of heart disease are the most significant to the physical education teacher in the school? Why?

6. Discuss the causes of hypertension heart disease.

7. What is a coronary occlusion?

8. What is a heart murmur?

9. Discuss the first aid treatment in a cardiac crisis.

10. What opportunities may the physical educator have to help a cardiac patient to establish good health habits?

11. What can the physical education teacher do to help alleviate some of the emotional problems of students with cardiopathic conditions?

12. What muscular activity is necessary for the patient who has heart disease?

13. Why must the physical educator be concerned with individual attitude when he is considering how strenuous any activity will be for an individual?

14. What rule-of-thumb guide may be used to determine when an individual with heart disease has reached his tolerance level in muscular activity?

15. What other activities can you suggest for each class of heart patients?

SELECTED READINGS

Bramwell, Crighton: *A Clinical Introduction to Heart Disease.* London, Oxford University Press, 1959.

Frampton, Merle E., and Gall, Elena D. (ed.): *Special Education for the Exceptional:* Vol. II — *The Physically Handicapped and Special Health Problems.* Boston, Porter Sargent, Publishers, 1955.

Kessler, Henry H.: *The Principles and Practices of Rehabilitation.* Philadelphia, Lea & Febiger, 1950.

Gertler, Menard M., and White, Paul D.: *Coronary Heart Disease in Young Adults.* Cambridge, Mass., Harvard University Press, 1954.

Moses, Campbell: *Atherosclerosis.* Philadelphia, Lea & Febiger, 1963.

Wilson, May G.: *Advances in Rheumatic Fever,* New York, Harper & Row, Inc., 1962.

Wolffe, Joseph B.: "Prevention of Disease Through Exercise and Health Education," in *Health and Fitness in the Modern World.* Chicago, The Athletic Institute, 1961.

10
CONVALESCENCE

Since the early days of World War II there has been a great change in medical opinion regarding activity for patients convalescing from illness or injury. Even though physicians in some branches of medicine, particularly orthopedics and cardiology, had been advocating for some time a planned convalescent period that included exercises to increase function and strength, it was generally considered that the safest thing for a convalescing patient was bed rest. Then, as wounded soldiers began to fill the hospital beds, research was instigated to find methods of shortening the convalescent period so that the beds might be freed and the men returned to active duty more quickly. The research proved conclusively that a period of rehabilitation after the acute stage of the disability had passed was of great benefit to the patient and reduced the period of convalescence significantly. The rehabilitation program for armed service personnel included therapeutic treatment of the affected part and prescribed exercises for developing general body strength.

The success of the military rehabilitation program influenced the acceptance of the superiority of an active convalescence over bed rest for most types of patients. Many civilian hospitals inaugurated broader therapeutic programs and provided opportunities for the patients to be more active physically. In veterans' hospitals, following the termination of the war, the Athletic Service Program was established to augment the rehabilitation program with games and sports adapted to the needs of the patients. As a consequence of this program, the physical educator joined the team of medical specialists, therapists, and counselors who work together to promote the rehabilitation of the whole man.

Various names are used to describe the physical education services provided the convalescents in the hospital: *physical reconditioning, exercise therapy*, and *adapted physical education*. Regardless of the name applied, the programs have a like objective in that all strive to achieve physical rehabilitation through a medically approved program of adapted physical education activities. However, adapted physical education, by its accepted definition, goes beyond this stated objective. Adapted physical education is concerned with total body fitness rather than specific improvement; moreover, it fosters the social growth and psychological adjustment inherent in play situations.

School physical education programs also benefited from the wartime research which established the importance of activity in the recovery of the convalescent. Previously, only students returning to school from hospitalization for neurologic, orthopedic, or cardiac difficulties were placed in adapted physical education. Others, who were convalescing from communicable diseases, respiratory infections, and like illnesses, or from appendectomies and other operations, were excused from participation in physical education. However, with the new emphasis upon the importance of physical activity in the convalescent period, such students began to be placed in the adapted physical education program, where they received the benefits of a carefully planned and medically approved program of adapted activities until such time as they were able to return to the regular class.

THE NATURE OF CONVALESCENCE

Convalescence is a period of recovery from illness. It can be said to begin when the acute stage of the disability has passed and to end when the patient is physically, mentally, and emotionally ready to take up his life where he left it when he was hospitalized. The nature of the convalescence depends largely upon the nature of the illness or injury, and the types of convalescence are consequently divided into five general areas, depending upon the nature of the initial illness. The five areas are: surgery, infectious disease, constitutional disease, accidental trauma, and obstetrics.

The convalescent period is characterized by general body weakness and low vitality which stem not so much from the illness or injury itself as from the forced inactivity during the acute stage. In extended bed rest, deterioration of the body functions is evident most conspicuously in the muscles. Considerable loss of muscular strength, endurance, and power occurs and there is some muscle atrophy. The patient's heart and blood vessels become less efficient in maintaining good circulation which decreases cardiorespiratory endurance. Lack of good circulation and constant pressure on areas of the back of a patient confined to his back causes bed sores. Bones decalcify from lack of muscular activity, and in very long periods of bed rest bone deterioration may be so great that strenuous muscular contraction can cause a bone to break. Appetite is affected by bed rest. Although less energy foods are required, the patient may become so finicky concerning his eating that it becomes difficult for him to get sufficient amounts of the nutrients needed by the body. Defecation is difficult for those without sufficient activity. Postoperative patients confined to complete bed rest are frequently bothered with distressing gas pains and difficulty in urination. Moreover, evidence indicates that postoperative patients confined to complete bed rest are more susceptible to pneumonia and thrombophlebitis.

The rehabilitation program of exercises can offset these undesirable consequences of extended confinement to bed. Participation in the adapted exercises and games helps to maintain good circulation and to prevent the deterioration of muscular strength, endurance, and coordination. Susceptibility to disease is decreased. Appetites are less likely to be dulled because the patient in hungrier and more interested in his food. Difficulties in elimination are reduced because of the beneficial effects of the exercise.

NEEDS AND ADJUSTMENTS OF THE CONVALESCENT PATIENT

The patient's hospitalization is in itself emotionally charged; if his convalescence is prolonged, the psychological import of the confinement may be a considerable factor in his recovery. Consequently, the adjustment that the patient makes to his being confined to the hospital is extremely important.

The onset of illness that requires hospitalization is usually sudden. The patient finds himself swiftly transformed from a normally active member of the community to one of the unwell, confined to a bed in the hospital. The suddenness of the transition is emotionally disturbing. Uncertainty of prognosis or lack of information about his condition may produce further anxieties and fears. Being restricted to bed and assisted with many of his personal needs tends to encourage the patient to think that he is a very sick person. If the patient can be relieved of these emotional tensions and disturbances, he is more likely to recover quickly and to find his hospital stay less frustrating and depressing.

Medical personnel have recognized the importance of helping the patient to make a satisfactory adjustment. Consequently, they encourage the patient to take part in activities which occupy his hands and mind and help to release his physical and emotional tensions. The patient is permitted to perform as many of the simple tasks of his own care as possible.

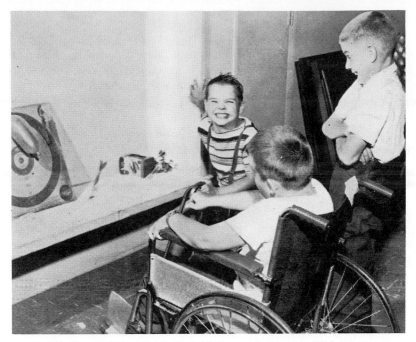

FIGURE 14.   Games fill the long hours for children confined to the hospital. (The National
Society for Crippled Children and Adults.)

Participation in physical activity gives the patient reassurance that he will recover and will return to normal life. The physical education program can greatly expand the patient's opportunities for physical activity and the physiological and psychological benefits of activity by presenting a varied and interesting program of activities and games.

Surgical patients frequently have an erroneous conception of the disturbances to their muscles by surgery and often believe that the slightest movement of the muscles will be disastrous. Muscular activity often gives the morale of such patients a positive boost by demonstrating to them that things are not so bad after all.

The use of physical education in hospitals is designed to make life as meaningful as possible for the patient as well as to speed his recovery. In long-term hospitalization a physical education program helps to tie hospital life to the patient's way of living before hospitalization. This in itself has value for him.

Children have a very difficult time adjusting to hospital routine. The younger the child, the more difficult it is for him to adjust. Games provide pleasant diversion. Because they are familiar to the child from home and school experiences, the games serve as a bridge between home and hospital which helps to ease the difficulties of adjusting to the strange surroundings.

PLANNING THE HOSPITAL PROGRAM

The hospital physical education program will vary according to the type of hospital and where the emphasis is placed in physical education. In general hospitals, where staying time is relatively short, the emphasis may be upon conditioning while, for example, in a tuberculosis sanitarium, where confinement is relatively long, the emphasis may be educational and recreational — developing or rechanneling sport interests into activities which patients may safely enjoy to their benefit while in the hospital and after they leave the hospital.

All muscular activity planned for the convalescent must have the approval of the physician. Special exercises may be prescribed. Exercises that are chiefly corrective in nature are given by the physical therapist, while activities for general body conditioning are in the area of physical education and are given by the physical educator.

Patients can be classified by the physician into groups based on their tolerance level for physical activity. Stafford[1] suggests the following grouping:

Class 1: Patients soon to be discharged.

Class 2: Prolonged ambulatory cases, but with few restrictions on physical activity.

Class 3: Patients released from bed but with specific restrictions on physical activity.

Class 4: Patients confined to bed but able to take certain light exercises.

Class 5: Patients who can tolerate no activity.

Exercise is contraindicated for only a very few. These include those with tuberculosis of the bone, acute cardiac patients, rheumatic fever patients, and those who are in shock, under sedation, and with high temperatures. Exercises are not given to patients with acute respiratory infection where activity will cause overwork of the lungs. When an area of the body is immobilized, as in a fractured leg which is in a cast or a lung affected by tuberculosis that is being rested by pneumothorax, movement is not permitted that area in the exercises.

The programs of exercises for all other classes of patients will be determined by the rehabilitation team. The medical personnel will make recommendations based upon their knowledge of the patients' physiological and psychological needs, and together the team will plan the most beneficial program for each patient. A special room or gymnasium in the hospital is highly desirable for ambulatory patients. Suggested equipment for this room is:

mats	weights
scales	exercise pull-up

[1]George T. Stafford: *Exercises During Convalescence.* New York, A. S. Barnes & Co., 1947, p. 24.

manometer	shoulder wheels
mirrors	stall bars
horizontal ladder	finger ladders
high bar	stationary bicycles

A hospital cart equipped with exercise equipment is rolled to the bedside of confined patients. Equipment available on the cart should include:

elastic exercisers	targets
weights	darts with suction cups and target
dumbbells	rubber sponges or grip exercisers
beanbag and balls	weight spats

THE PROGRAM DURING CONVALESCENCE

In choosing the activities for a patient, the tolerance level for any specific area must be taken into consideration. Parts that are not affected may receive more strenuous exercise than the others. Activity for injured areas of the body may be contraindicated or highly restricted. For example, a patient with abdominal surgery may exercise muscles in wrists, fingers, and arms relatively strenuously while exercises for the abdominal area may be limited to nothing more than contraction of the stomach muscles. Suggested exercises for bed-ridden patients follow.

The intensity of the exercise is roughly estimated and is to be used only as a guide. *Mild* refers to an intensity that is recommended on the first and second day of rehabilitation. *Moderate* refers to exercises that can generally be used after the third or fourth day. *Strenuous* activities are relative to the other two. They are to be used to prepare the patient for getting up from bed.

The combination of the abbreviations and the number indicates the area involvement and the degree of exercise for each specific activity.

Key

C — chest	Ab — abdomen	0 — none
Ar — arm	Ub — upper back	1 — mild
N — neck	Lb — lower back	2 — moderate
L — legs		3 — strenuous

EXERCISES LYING SUPINE IN BED.

1. With knees bent and supported with a pillow, contract muscles of buttocks and pull stomach down slightly. Hold a few seconds and release.

Ab−1, C−0, Ar−0, N−0, L−0, Ub−0, Lb−1

2. Curl toes strenuously, hold and relax. Then superextend toes, hold and relax.

Ab−0, C−0, Ar−0, N−0, L−1, Ub−0, Lb−0

3. As above but also extend foot when curling toes and flex foot when hyperextending toes.

Ab−0, C−0, Ar−0, N−0, L−1, Ub−0, Lb−0

4. Spread legs, slide feet upward, and bring soles of feet together.

Ab−2, C−0, Ar−0, N−0, L−2, Ub−0, Lb−0

5. With pillows under knees, straighten both legs.

Ab−2, C−0, Ar−0, N−0, L−2, Ub−0, Lb−0

6. Keeping knees stiff, raise one leg, lower, and raise the other. (Lower back involved but back muscles are not contracted.)

Ab−2, C−1, Ar−0, N−0, L−2, Ub−0, Lb−0

7. Raise one knee to chest, lower, and raise the other. (Lower back involved but back muscles are not contracted.)

Ab−3, C−1, Ar−0, N−0, L−3, Ub−0, Lb−0

8. With knees bent and feet on bed, raise up, grasp knees with hands and help pull up. (Upper back and lower back involved but back muscles are not contracted.)

Ab−3, C−3, Ar−3, N−1, L−3, Ub−3, Lb−3

9. With arms extended to the sides, rotate arms in a circle.

Ab−0, C−2, Ar−2, N−1, L−0, Ub−2, Lb−0

10. Lift and rotate neck while shoulders rest on bed.

Ab−1, C−1, Ar−0, N−2, L−0, Ub−1, Lb−0

11. Extend arms to the sides, open and close fingers rapidly.

Ab−0, C−0, Ar−2, N−0, L−0, Ub−0, Lb−0

12. Perform arm exercises with elastic exerciser.

Ab−0, C−0, Ar−3, N−0, L−0, Ub−3, Lb−0

13. With legs straight, press heels down against bed.

Ab−0, C−0, Ar−0, N−0, L−3, Ub−1, Lb−3

14. Grip exercise by gripping rubber sponges.

Ab−0, C−0, Ar−2, N−0, Ub−0, Lb−0

15. Muscle tightening.

Areas involved depend on muscles exercised−1 or 2

EXERCISES SITTING UP IN BED. All the upper postural muscles of the body are involved in these exercises, so they are not indicated by symbols.

1. With legs over the side of the bed, raise one leg, lower, and raise the other.

Ab−1, C−0, Ar−0, N−0, L−2, Ub−0, Lb−0

2. As above; raise both legs.

Ab−2, C−0, Ar−0, N−0, L−3, Ub−0, Lb−0

3. With legs over the side of the bed, bend at hips and place chest on thighs. Raise to original position.

Ab−2, C−2, Ar−0, N−1, L−0, Ub−3, Lb−2

4. With legs over the side of the bed, arm to the side, chin on chest, swing arms to the side and back over head. Raise head; return to original position.

Ab—0, C—2, Ar—3, N—1, L—0, Ub—2, Lb—0

Where more resistance is desired, the physical educator may put pressure on the patient's limbs in some exercises to increase work loads.

GAMES PLAYED IN THE BED.

1. Indoor bowling. Pins are placed about 15 to 20 feet from the bed. A softball is used as the bowling ball. Bed patients in prone position, with heads toward the pins, bowl by swinging their arms over the side of the bed to release the ball. In supine position with their heads raised, they bowl by swinging the arm to the side of the bed.

2. Indoor archery. A small bow is used. The bow is shot as a crossbow while lying on the back or side. Arrows should be tipped with suction cups unless a satisfactory backdrop can be placed behind the target.

3. Yoyo tossing. The yoyo is dropped and played over the edge of bed.

GAMES AND ACTIVITIES FOR YOUNG CHILDREN IN BED.

1. Simon Says. Motions appropriate to condition of patient are used.

2. Beanbag tossing. Concentric circles are drawn on the floor with chalk, or a paper target is placed on the floor. The bag is tossed at the target.

3. Story games. The children make appropriate movements to act out the story as it is read.

4. Mimicking games. An animal such as a flying bird is imitated by moving the arms up and down. A wood chopper is mimicked by raising the arms over the head while lying in bed and bringing them down in a chopping motion.

5. Games with a ball. Various throwing and catching activities can be devised for play in bed. A large soft ball should be used because it is easier to catch and will not injure anyone who is accidentally hit by the ball.

GAMES PLAYED IN WHEELCHAIRS.

1. Table tennis. The table should be stabilized to the floor to provide support for pulling the wheelchairs around the table. If the table legs are placed in the center of the table, this will permit the chair to go beneath the table. The table may be further adapted by placing a shield 4 feet long and 12 inches high along the edges of the table in the net area to prevent balls from bouncing off the table in this difficult-to-reach area.

2. Bowling and bowling on the green. The patient swings the bowling ball to the side of the wheelchair; otherwise, the game requires no other modification.

3. Archery. The wheelchair is placed on a diagonal toward the target. This position allows greater space for the bow.

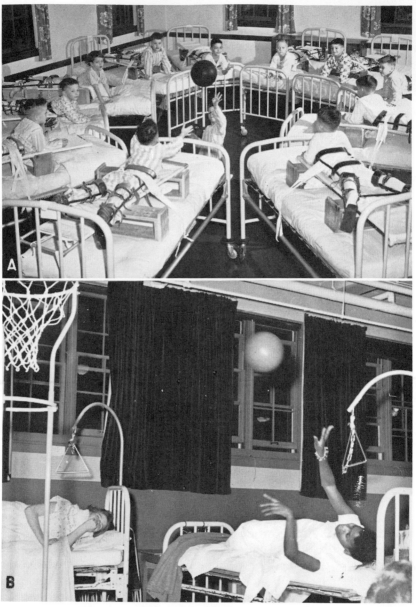

FIGURE 15. A, children in the Newington Home and Hospital for Crippled Children suffering from Perthes' disease have fun in a game of catch. B, a portable hoop is brought to the bedside of a hospital patient so that she may shoot "baskets" for exercise and fun. (Journal of Health, Physical Education and Recreation.)

4. Croquet. The court is enlarged to permit the passing of the chairs. Longer handles are affixed to the mallets.

5. Shuffleboard. No modification is necessary except that the delivery is made to the side while seated in the chair.

6. Square dancing. The formations will need to be large enough to accommodate the chairs and the patterns modified to keep them as simple as possible to perform in the chairs. Those without the use of their arms may be pushed through the dance patterns by helpers.

7. Basketball. The game is played according to the standard rules with just a few modifications, which are described in Chapter 22.

8. Hockey. The game is played indoors, using a flat puck and ice-hockey sticks.

THE PROGRAM AFTER RETURNING TO SCHOOL

Grade school and high school students returning to classes after illness or injury may require adapted physical education until their normal level of fitness is restored. Medical approval for the student's participation in the adapted activities should be sought before the student begins activity. Most students who have been confined to bed in their homes will not have had convalescent exercises, will return to school with a very low level of fitness, and should not attempt the same amount of activity as they engaged in before their confinement. If there was no injury to a specific area, the exercises and activities described in Chapter 25 for low physical fitness may be used with these students. Some mild and easily regulated games in which these students may participate are:

Volleyball	Bowling
Table tennis	Archery
Shuffleboard	Deck tennis
Horseshoes	Bowling on the green

In situations where there has been injury to a specific area, a special exercise may be given to strengthen the part and to develop total body fitness. The first seven to ten days that a student is on crutches, the activity of walking is in itself sufficient overload for the upper arm area. Isometric muscular contractions can be used to exercise the muscles of the limb which is immobilized in a cast. Students with limbs in casts will want to avoid excessive perspiration in their workouts, because perspiration collects in the cast. If the activities can be performed in a cool area, the excessive perspiration can usually be avoided.

Games recommended for students with orthopedic handicaps are suitable for grade and high school students with legs and arms in casts. Patients in whom a specific area of the body has been weakened by injury or infection require special precautions to protect the area from further injury during exercises which are being given to build up the strength of the area or to increase general body strength. When bones have been broken, joints sprained, or other parts of the body have suffered injuries, activities chosen for participation should be those which will not place undue stress and strain upon the area. In the cases of shoulder dislocation, knee instability, and ankle sprains, which are common injuries, the areas involved can be strengthened by exercise to prevent the recurrence of the injury. Because of their strenuous nature, the exercises are recommended only for older students.

Exercise that increases the strength of the muscles of the shoulder and shoulder girdle, especially the supraspinatus, tends to stabilize a shoulder that is susceptible to dislocation. The supraspinatus tends to hold the head of the humerus in the glenoid fossa, thus preventing displacement during abduction. It abducts the humerus and rotates it laterally. Resistance applied to the arm while abducting and laterally rotating the arm increases the strength of the muscle. All exercises that require raising the arm over the head so that there is a possibility of pressure on the arm, as in basketball, overhand swimming, and volleyball, are contraindicated. Exercises and activities which may be used are:

> Weight lifting (avoid all lifts that raise the arm overhead)
> Pulley weights (same precaution as above)
> Heavy and light bag punching
> Table tennis
> Shuffleboard
> Golf
> Track
> Swimming the side stroke
> Racket games, if the weak shoulder is not involved
> Exercise on the shoulder wheel

Exercises that increase the strength of the quadriceps femoris of the leg tend to stabilize the knee by exerting more pull upon the patella, which in turn holds the tibia in closer contact in the joint with the femur. An exercise that is frequently used to strengthen the quadriceps femoris uses an iron shoe strapped to the foot. The subject sits on a table, straightens the knee, and returns the leg to the original position. Individuals with unstable knees may participate in activities and games which do not place undue stress upon the knee. Among these are:

> Volleyball .   Bowling
> Shuffleboard   Swimming
> Table tennis   Bag punching

Exercises for the ankle that has been sprained tend to promote healing and increase the strength of the muscles involved (peroneus longus and peroneus brevis) in preventing the foot from inverting accidentally. Forced inversion causes the majority of ankle sprains. Suggested exercises and games are:

Standing and walking on tiptoes	Swimming
Toe stands with weights on back	Bag punching
Exercise with ankle exerciser	Shuffleboard

QUESTIONS

1. Trace the development of the exercise program for convalescing patients.
2. What is meant by convalescence?
3. What physiological deteriorations may take place during long periods of bed rest?
4. What are the psychological implications of hospitalization? In what ways can physical education help to alleviate emotional insecurity?
5. What is the purpose of physical education programs in hospitals?
6. List the situations in which physical education may be contraindicated for the patient.
7. What physiological and psychological factors must be taken into consideration when planning a physical education program for an individual who is convalescing?
8. What are the five general areas of convalescence as determined by the nature of the illness? What importance will the area of convalescence have upon the planning of the physical education activities?
9. What is the value of placing students who are returning to school after prolonged illness in the adapted physical education program?
10. Make a list of games and activities that you would recommend for students returning to school after having suffered these conditions:
   a. broken leg; the leg is in a cast and the student on crutches
   b. dislocated shoulder; the arm is not in a cast
   c. mumps
   d. appendicitis
   e. sprained ankle

SELECTED READINGS

Committee on Public Health Relations: *Convalescence and Rehabilitation.* New York, New York Academy of Medicine, 1944.

Frampton, Merle E., and Gall, Elena D. (ed.): *Special Education for the Exceptional*: Vol. II— *The Physically Handicapped and Special Health Problems.* Boston, Porter Sargent, Publisher, 1955.

McCloy, Charles H.: "Physical Reconditioning for the Ill,"—*Science and Medicine of Exercise and Sports.* New York, Harper & Brothers, 1960.

Stafford, George T.: *Exercises During Convalescence.* New York, A. S. Barnes & Co., 1947.

11
NUTRITIONAL
DISTURBANCES

It is an alarming fact that in this country, where there is a greater abundance of food available to a larger portion of the total population than in most other countries of the world, malnourishment is an important problem. Malnourishment, or malnutrition, is a condition in which the body is not receiving the proper nutrients in sufficient quantities. It may be brought about in different ways: the food intake may be inadequate in quantity or quality, or the conditions are such that the body is unable to utilize the nutrients properly. The latter is chiefly a medical problem while the former is one of economics and education.

Individual incomes in modern America are generally sufficiently high so that inability to buy enough food to feed the family is rarely the cause of malnourishment. This is not to be construed to mean that such cases no longer exist. There are, however, more cases in which the family income is spent unwisely and proper foods are purchased in insufficient quantities than there are situations in which the money for the purchase of food is lacking. Consequently, in nearly every community there will be a few children in the schools who are malnourished.

Faulty eating habits constitute a major cause of malnourishment. Adequate amounts of the essential nutrients of a balanced diet are more likely to be obtained if a wide variety of food is eaten. Particularly important is the ingestion of fresh fruits and vegetables and milk. Some families, having failed to develop the taste for a variety of different foods, do not eat well-balanced meals. Traditions and customs of eating passed down through generations of cooks often stress one kind of food, frequently a starchy dish, which is served to the detriment of better balanced meals. Children in such families, while receiving sufficient energy-supplying foods, are likely to become malnourished because of a lack of vitamins and minerals.

Teenagers as an age group represent the segment of the population exhibiting the most faulty eating habits. Many teenagers fail to eat any breakfast; others gulp down a roll and cup of coffee before dashing off to school. Research findings have demonstrated rather conclusively the importance of a nutritious breakfast to body efficiency;[1] moreover, the failure to eat a good breakfast makes it more difficult for the youngster to obtain the necessary daily intake of nutrients, many of which are supplied by a balanced breakfast. Teenagers demonstrate further faulty eating habits in their selection of food for lunch. A sandwich and soft drink become a substitute for a well-balanced luncheon. Although the dinner which is served to the teenager at home may represent the very best in meal planning, the appetite of the teenager is likely to have been dulled by candy bars, ice cream, and soft drinks consumed just prior to the dinner hour. Snacks of sweets, if they do not prevent the consumption of balanced meals, are useful in filling the energy requirements of those active individuals who need large amounts of foods high in calories.

Unfortunately, the poor eating habits of teenagers are sometimes carried over into adult life. High school graduates taking up new lives as college students or employees away from home do not always take up new and better eating habits. The food which they select in restaurants or choose to buy for preparing their own meals is likely to reflect their poor eating habits. For this reason considerable malnourishment may be found among young adults.

Another important factor contributing to malnourishment is the lack of knowledge about the importance of a well-balanced diet and how it may be achieved. Improper cooking methods may have some influence also.

THE NATURE AND CAUSES OF
NUTRITIONAL DISTURBANCES

OVERWEIGHT.   The most common nutritional disturbance in the United States is overweight. Its frequency among the adult population has been a recognized problem for years. The prevalence of obesity among children has come to public attention more recently.

---

[1]W. W. Tuttle, *et al.*: "Effects on School Boys of Omitting Breakfast: Physiologic Response Attitude, and Social Attainment." *Journal of the American Dietetic Association*, Vol. 30, 1954, pp. 674–677.

The basic cause of overweight is that the body is taking in more energy food than it is using, and the excess energy food is stored in the body as fat. The assimilation of food, the metabolic rate, and the amount of energy used in activity are all factors that cause a difference in the amount of fat stored by two individuals who are consuming identical amounts and kinds of food.

Overeating may have a psychological origin. An individual may eat and snack repeatedly throughout the day because he is bored, is under nervous tension, or feels inadequate, and eating becomes an outlet for these anxieties and frustrations. Such "compulsive eaters" do not usually recognize the source of their problem and need help to eliminate the cause of overeating before attempting to lose excess weight.

Much overeating is a matter of habit. Food habits may be established when the energy need is high, and the habit of eating large amounts persists after the energy need has decreased.

Mayer[2] contends that the most important factor in overweight is inactivity. Activity plays an important part in the utilization of calories. His research indicates that the big difference between obese girls and normal girls of the same age group is the lack of activity on the part of the former and not the amount of food consumed. He would recommend, as one important way to control overweight, regular participation in exercises adapted to one's physical potential.

UNDERWEIGHT. Underweight is another significant nutritional problem, but it is less prevalent than overweight. In some cases the cause is poor eating habits. Some authorities[3] believe that certain underweight people inherit a tendency to thinness just as others have tendency to be heavy. A change in fat metabolism and distribution of body fat usually occurs after pubescence, so that we often witness the filling out of the exceptionally skinny girl or the slimming down to normal proportions of the fat boy. Consequently, tendencies to slimness or stoutness in youngsters may not be permanent.

Underweight may be the indirect result of chronic infection, such as tuberculosis or diseased tonsils, or other conditions and diseases, such as hyperthyroidism or diabetes. Poor health habits, such as insufficient sleep and rest, may be a contributing cause to underweight. Loss of appetite may be a possible contributing factor in weight loss, or it may be an indication of some underlying difficulty, usually of psychogenic origin.

PROBLEMS ASSOCIATED WITH NUTRITIONAL DISTURBANCES

The girl or boy who is not eating sufficient amounts of food to provide an adequate caloric intake will usually have other serious problems in

[2]Jean Mayer: "Exercise and Weight Control," in Warren R. Johnson (ed.), *Science and Medicine of Exercise and Sports.* New York, Harper & Brothers, 1960, pp. 301–309.
[3]L. Jean Bogert: Nutrition and Physical Fitness, ed. 6. Philadelphia, W. B. Saunders Co., 1954, p.590.

addition to his poor nutritional state. Since he is likely to be from a family on a low socioeconomic level, he may have problems of social adjustment to face as well as personal problems arising from economic insecurity. He will be easily recognized in the physical education class because of his lack of vitality and endurance. He will usually prove to be a slow learner with no particular interest in activity. Lacking strength and skill, he is highly susceptible to injury. Because poorly nourished muscle tissue become flabby, poor posture is likely to result.

The malnourished student who is suffering from an inadequate consumption of *specific* nutrients, however, may be more difficult to detect. Although body efficiency may be decreased, other easily recognized symptoms of malnourishment are usually lacking in subclinical cases. Students in physical education class who evidence unexplained muscular weakness, poor coordination, and lack of vitality and interest in activity should be referred to their doctors as possible cases of malnourishment.

The extremely overweight girl or boy is at a definite disadvantage in participating in physical education activities. The fat which has accumulated in his body becomes an added weight which must be carried about in the execution of all movements. This, of course, greatly reduces speed, endurance, and some factors of coordination. To better understand the extent of the disadvantage of this additional weight in physical performance, the individual of normal weight should visualize attempting certain physical skills with a 25-pound weight strapped to his body. The difficulty in carrying this weight is not limited to the performance of sport skills for the overweight individual, but is with him throughout the routine activities of daily living, hindering him in most activities that require body movement.

The lowered efficiency contributes to the overweight individual's withdrawal from vigorous activity. This in turn fosters low physical fitness and lack of skill development. Unable to participate on an equal basis with other youngsters his age, he may turn entirely to sedentary activities to fill his leisure hours and so be denied the beneficial effects of exercise. Overweight people have a greater predisposition to diseases of the heart and circulatory system, kidneys, and pancreas (diabetes). Although the incidence of these diseases is higher among adults than children, a definite predisposition is evident among obese children.

The cosmetic appearance of the obese individual is an embarrassment to him. He is the frequent brunt of jokes and inevitably bears the nickname of "Fatty," "Fats," or "Lard."

The underweight boy or girl is often thought to be malnourished, but this is not always the case. The terms underweight and overweight are relative ones, used to describe a degree of variation from the average weight of individuals of certain height and structure. It is possible for an individual to be underweight—that is, below the average—without being malnourished. If, however, the underweight individual has a nutri-

For Girls from 5-18 Years[*]

HGT. (In.)	5 Yrs.	6 Yrs.	7 Yrs.	8 Yrs.	9 Yrs.	10 Yrs.	11 Yrs.	12 Yrs.	13 Yrs.	14 Yrs.	15 Yrs.	16 Yrs.	17 Yrs.	18 Yrs.
38	33	33												
39	34	34												
40	36	36	36											
41	37	37	37	41										
42	39	39	39	42										
43	41	41	41	45	45									
44	42	42	42	48	48									
45	45	45	45	50	50	50								
46	47	47	47	52	52	53								
47	49	50	50	55	55	56	58							
48		52	52	60	61	64	66							
49		54	54	65	65	68	69	71						
50		56	56	57	58	59	61	62	71	78				
51			59	60	61	61	63	66	73	85				
52			63	64	64	64	65	67	77	88				
53			65	67	67	68	68	69	81	93	92			
54			66	69	70	70	71	71	84	95	96			
55				72	74	74	74	75	88	96	100	101		
56	56	56			76	78	78	79	92			103	104	
57					80	82	82	82						
58						84	86	86						
59						87	90	90						
60						91	95	95	97	101	106	108	109	111
61							99	100	101	105	108	112	113	116
62							104	105	106	109	115	115	117	118
63								110	110	112	116	117	119	120
64								114	116	117	119	120	122	123
65								118	120	121	122	123	125	126
66									124	124	125	125	129	130
67									128	129	131	133	133	135
68									131	135	135	136	138	138
69									135	135	137	138	140	142
70										136	138	140	142	144
71										138	140	142	144	145

*Prepared by Robert M. Woodbury, Ph.D., Children's Bureau, U.S. Dept. of Labor.

For Boys from 5-19 Years[†]

HGT. (In.)	5 Yrs.	6 Yrs.	7 Yrs.	8 Yrs.	9 Yrs.	10 Yrs.	11 Yrs.	12 Yrs.	13 Yrs.	14 Yrs.	15 Yrs.	16 Yrs.	17 Yrs.	18 Yrs.	19 Yrs.
38	34	34													
39	35	35													
40	36	36													
41	38	38	38												
42	39	39	39	39											
43	41	41	41	41											
44	44	44	44	44											
45	46	46	46	46	46										
46	47	47	48	48	48										
47	49	50	50	50	50	50									
48		52	52	53	53	53									
49		55	55	55	55	55									
50		57	58	58	58	58	58	58							
51			61	61	61	61	61	61							
52			65	64	64	64	64	64	64						
53			66	67	67	67	67	68	68						
54				70	70	70	70	71	71	72					
55				72	72	73	73	74	74	74					
56				75	76	77	77	77	78	78	80				
57	57				79	80	81	81	82	83	83				
58					83	84	84	85	85	86	87				
59					85	87	88	89	89	90	90	90			
60						91	92	92	93	94	95	96			
61						91	96	96	97	99	100	103	106		
62							100	101	102	103	104	107	111	116	
63							105	106	107	108	110	113	118	123	127
64								109	111	113	115	117	121	126	130
65								114	117	118	120	122	127	131	134
66									119	122	125	128	132	136	139
67									124	128	130	134	136	139	142
68										134	134	137	141	143	147
69										137	139	143	146	149	152
70										143	144	145	148	161	155
71										148	150	161	152	161	159
72											163	155	156	158	163
73											157	160	162	164	167
74											160	164	168	170	171

†Prepared by Bird T. Baldwin, Ph.D., and Thomas D. Wood, M.D.

FIGURE 16. Weight-height-age table for boys and girls of school age.

METROPOLITAN LIFE INSURANCE COMPANY

tional disturbance, this will probably be shown in his listlessness and low fatigue level.

The extremely underweight person has less than the normal amount of fatty tissue necessary for padding the body. This padding provides protection to the nerve plexuses and affects the appearance of the body. Lacking the normal contours of the average person, the underweight person often finds himself, like his counterpart, the overweight individual, the subject of ridicule.

DETERMINING OVER AND UNDER WEIGHT

The correct and desirable body weight for any one person depends upon age, sex, height, bone size, and muscular development. It is, consequently, impossible to construct a table of absolutely correct weights applicable to all individuals because of the numerous possible variations in these factors. However, some basis for determining desired weight is necessary. A useful guide for estimating desirable weights for children of school age is given in Figure 16.

PLANNING THE PROGRAM

Individuals whose extremes in weight affect their progress in physical education activities are readily discovered. Among them will be students who could profit from special counseling and additional information concerning good nutrition, but who are able to take part in the regular physical education class. Some, however, cannot be accommodated in the regular class. For example, a student who has a problem of malnourishment due to lack of energy-supplying foods in his daily diet cannot be greatly helped in the physical education class. It may be advisable to dismiss such a student from participation in vigorous activities until such time as an improved diet effects some physiological changes which enable him to engage in sustained physical activity. Malnourishment which results from a lack of vitamins and minerals presents a similar problem in that a nutritional change which will promote greater capacity for physical performance must occur before the physical education program can be of much assistance to the individual boy or girl. If the student is less than physically fit, he may exercise in the adapted class. However, no great improvement in physical proficiency can be expected until his nutritional deficiency is corrected.

The extent to which the physical educator can be of assistance in helping correct the nutritional deficiency is determined partially by the class time that can be allotted to teaching the facts of good nutrition and encouraging good nutritional habits. If nutritional information is being taught by the elementary classroom teachers and by a health teacher in the high school, the emphasis of the physical education teacher should be one of reinforcing and supplementing the classroom presentation. Where there is evidence of widespread faulty eating habits among the student body, all teachers might join together in a campaign to promote improved nutrition. Cases of nutritional disturbances which are suspected of being due to lack of food should be reported to the school authorities. Frequently, through a program of financial aid to the schools, students in actual need may eat a balanced luncheon at school free of charge.

Traditionally, muscular activity has been linked with the problem of reducing excess weight. The physical education teacher has the responsibility of providing activities in which the overweight student can participate with success. He has the further responsibility of teaching the students how to secure the greatest benefit from physical activity. For the overweight, reduction of weight is one of these benefits.

Students who are only moderately overweight can, as a rule, be accommodated in the regular physical education class, but extremely overweight students cannot usually participate successfully in the regular class and should be enrolled in the adapted class. One of the objectives of these students will be weight reduction. This is not, however, a problem which can be solved entirely by a program of suitable exercises. Control of the amount of food intake and the kinds of foods eaten must be established. All dieting should have the supervision of a medical doctor.

The success in weight reduction through increased work output is directly related to the food intake. Changing long-established eating habits is difficult, and the student must be highly motivated. In some cases these habits have deep-rooted psychological origins beyond the scope of the physical educator. Except in these cases, students will be fairly easily motivated by their desire for improved appearance and by their wish to participate more nearly as an equal with their peers in games and sports.

THE PROGRAM FOR OVERWEIGHT STUDENTS

The activities of the adapted program for overweight students must be those which utilize energy but which do not require more strength and agility than the students possess. Activities in which the body weight must be lifted (e.g., rope climbing and high jumping) are contraindicated both because the heavy student will probably not have sufficient strength to perform them, and because of the chances of injury should he fall. Because obese students are not usually agile and cannot maneuver easily, games early in the program should not require much movement. Table tennis and light bag punching are good in this respect. Other activities suitable for older children are:

Archery
Badminton
Basketball foul shooting
Bowling
Bowling on the green
Calisthenics
Dancing (folk, social, and modern)
Football kicking for distance and accuracy

Jogging short distances
Loop tennis
Shuffleboard
Tetherball
Touch football as linemen
Twenty-one
Volleyball

The selection of activities for younger obese children will not usually present much problem. During the elementary grade school years, there is less possibility that size will be so great as to restrict participation in the respects that it does the older child. The basic skill games and other activities presented in the lower elementary grades are such that a heavy child is not particularly handicapped in their performance, nor do they present any special hazards for him.

THE ADULT PHYSICAL EDUCATION PROGRAM

Physical education for adults who wish to lose weight is becoming increasingly popular and widespread. The classes are sometimes offered in the adult education program of the school, but often they are organized spontaneously by interested members of the community. The physical education teacher is often asked to teach the class or to serve as its consultant.

Adults enrolling in such a class are highly motivated, at least at the beginning. However, because changing habits of long standing is not easy, the participants often need additional encouragement after the initial enthusiasm has worn off. It has been found that participation with others who share the common problem and discussion with them about the difficulties experienced in weight reduction often provide the additional encouragement and motivation to carry the program through to completion.

EXAMINATION.   The participants in such a class should have a physical examination before the first class session. Each should determine just how many pounds he is over the desired weight. In Figure 17, tables are given as guides for estimating the desired weight. In using the tables it must be kept in mind that desired weight for any one individual must take into consideration a number of factors and that the table is, at best, only a basis for making an estimation. The family physician should be called upon to establish the best weight for each person.

Height (in Shoes)	Weight (in Indoor Clothing)		
	SMALL FRAME	MEDIUM FRAME	LARGE FRAME
		MEN	
5' 2''	112–120	118–129	126–141
3	115–123	121–133	129–144
4	118–126	124–136	132–148
5	121–129	127–139	135–152
6	124–133	130–143	138–156
7	128–137	134–147	142–161
8	132–141	138–152	147–166
9	136–145	142–156	151–170
10	140–150	146–160	155–174
11	144–154	150–165	159–179
6' 0''	148–158	154–170	164–184
1	152–162	158–175	168–189
2	156–167	162–180	173–194
3	160–171	167–185	178–199
4	164–175	172–190	182–204
		WOMEN	
4' 10''	92–98	96–107	104–119
11	94–101	98–110	106–122
5' 0''	96–104	101–113	109–125
1	99–107	104–116	112–128
2	102–110	107–119	115–131
3	105–113	110–122	118–134
4	108–116	113–126	121–138
5	111–119	116–130	125–142
6	114–123	120–135	129–146
7	118–127	124–139	133–150
8	122–131	128–143	137–154
9	126–135	132–147	141–158
10	130–140	136–151	145–163
11	134–144	140–155	149–168
6' 0''	138–148	144–159	153–173

(Metropolitan Life Insurance Company.)

FIGURE 17.   Desirable weights for men and women, ages 25 and over, according to height and frame.

The class usually begins each meeting with the weighing of each member and the recording of the weight on the individual charts. Weight will vary from one time to another because of such factors as the time of the last meal, the time of elimination, the amount of water lost, and the amount of work done. If the individual's daily routine does not vary substantially, his weight will be more nearly accurate than if one day he ate a meal just before class but on another day had nothing at all before coming to class. Such variations, which may influence the weight to a considerable extent, should be taken into consideration in the weighing.

DISCUSSION.   Some of the class period is usually given over to a discussion of the individual diets and the problems encountered in holding to the diet. Then the class is put through the exercises. Since the class does not usually meet daily, the class members are given exercises to perform each day at home.

For general body conditioning the following are suggested:
  Side-straddle hop
  Running in place—knees high
  Squat thrust
  Twisting at hips
  Side-straddle touch opposite foot
  Jumping jack
For other suggestions see Chapter 25.

Some adults, particularly women, will be concerned not only with actual weight reduction but with developing a firmer and trimmer body. As muscles increase in strength they develop more tonus, and muscles with more tonus are firmer muscles. Tonus appears in a muscle before there is much increase in muscle size as a result of exercise. Women usually exercise to the point where tonus is developed without a great increase in muscle bulk.

EXERCISES FOR FIRMING THE MUSCLES.   Activities should be selected which place an overload on the muscles involved. A few simple exercises for various areas of the body are suggested below:

Arm muscles:
1. Do modified push-up, using the knees as fulcrum.
2. Hang by the hands and attempt to bend the elbows in a pull-up.

Chest muscles:
1. Bring the palms together in front of the chest and push against the palms.

Stomach and waist line:
1. Lie supine and lift legs four inches off the floor and hold for 3 seconds or more (not to be done by anyone subject to hollow back).
2. Lie supine and raise trunk to touch toes with fingers.
3. Lie on the side with arms overhead; while the feet are being held down, raise the upper trunk.

Hips:

1. Step up on a chair which is about knee height, first with one foot and then the other; step down again very slowly one foot at a time.

2. The third exercise for firming the stomach and waist line also firms muscles in the hip area; for a milder exercise, stand with the feet about one foot apart, arms overhead, and bend first to the left and then to the right.

Thighs:

1. While standing, raise one leg as high as possible in front, keeping the knee straight; repeat with the other leg.

2. Step up on a bench, alternating the feet.

QUESTIONS

1. Define malnourishment.
2. What is meant by assimilation of food?
3. Discuss the predisposing factors in overweight and underweight.
4. How is the obese girl or boy at a disadvantage in physical education class?
5. In what ways can the physical education teacher help encourage students to eat a well-balanced diet?
6. In what way will sports need to be modified for those with nutritional disturbances? The obese? The underweight? The malnourished?
7. What activities are contraindicated for the very obese student?
8. Discuss the contribution muscular activity can make to weight reduction.
9. What is the difference between the terms "firming the muscles" and "reducing"?
10. Develop a set of exercises for firming the muscles in women.

SELECTED READINGS

Beaton, George H., and McHenry, Earl W. (eds.): *Nutrition: A Comprehensive Treatise,* 3 vols., New York, Academic Press, 1964.

Burgess, Anne, and Dean, R. F. A. (eds.): *Malnutrition and Food Habits.* New York, The Free Press of Glencoe, Inc., 1963.

Fleck, Henrietta, and Munves, Elizabeth: *Introduction to Nutrition.* New York, The Macmillan Co., 1962.

Mayer, Jean: "Exercise and Weight Control," in *Exercise and Fitness.* Chicago, The Athletic Institute, 1960.

Morehouse, Laurence E., and Miller, Augustus T., Jr.: *Physiology of Exercise,* ed. 4. St. Louis, The C. V. Mosby Co., 1963.

Morehouse, Laurence E., and Rasch, Philip J.: *Sports Medicine for Trainers,* ed. 3. Philadelphia, W. B. Saunders Co., 1963.

Van Itallie, Theodore B., *et al.:* "Nutrition and Athletic Performance," in Warren R. Johnson (ed), *Science and Medicine of Exercise and Sports.* New York, Harper & Brothers, 1960.

12

OTHER PHYSICAL
CONDITIONS REQUIRING
ADAPTED PHYSICAL
EDUCATION

In addition to the handicapping conditions discussed in the foregoing chapters, there are a number of other incapacitating diseases and injuries with which the teacher of adapted physical education should be familiar. Some of these disabilities, such as minor skin disturbances, are of temporary duration; others, like diabetes and epilepsy, are more permanent in nature. Most of these conditions require certain precautionary measures to insure the protection of the participant from further aggravation of the condition and from possible additional injury precipitated by overexertion and fatigue. Knowledge of the nature of these conditions and the protective and preventive measures which need to be taken during physical activity is essential to those in charge of regular work in physical education as well as to those directing the adapted physical education program. In many cases of permanently incapacitating diseases, a carefully regulated program of physical educating activities can be very beneficial, but the adapted program offered students with permanent disabilities should have medical approval before participation begins.

TUBERCULOSIS

In spite of an impressive decline in the general death rate from tuberculosis in recent years, there has not been a corresponding decrease in the number of cases of tuberculosis. About 115,000 new cases are reported each year; a considerable number of these patients are those 15 to 34 years of age.[1] Consequently, it is likely that the physical educator teaching students in this age group will be faced with the problem of providing special activities for arrested tuberculosis cases.

CAUSE.   Tuberculosis is caused by a tiny rod-shaped bacillus which is found in the body discharges of an infected person. Because the germ is resistant to disinfectants, heat, and drying, it is easily spread by soiled hands, nasal and throat discharges, drinking cups, and flies. When the germs enter the body tissue, they cause nodules or tubercles which increase in size by extension or joining with other tubercles. Sometimes the body is able to build a fibrous wall around the tubercles, thereby preventing the further spread of the disease and making recovery possible. When the body is unable to stop the process of spreading, however, much tissue is destroyed and death eventually ensues.

TYPES.   Tuberculosis appears in a number of different forms and may locate in any part of the body, although the apex of one of the lungs is the most common site. An individual may have such a mild reaction to the presence of the disease that it passes unnoticed. A more severe form of tuberculosis or a re-infection may have serious consequences. In some instances the infection may spread so quickly throughout the body as to cause death in a few weeks; in other cases treatment effectively arrests the infection but the victims must observe certain precautionary health measures throughout their lives.

SUSCEPTIBILITY.   Because the high school and college age group is particularly vulnerable to tuberculosis, the physical educator working with students of this age should familiarize himself with the early signs which indicate *possible* infection. The presence of these symptoms does not mean the student has the disease but that further medical investigation is desirable. Common symptoms during early stages of the infection are:

(1) excessive fatigue, particularly unexplained lack of pep and energy in the late afternoon;

(2) loss of appetite and frequent indigestion;

(3) in girls, scanty or lack of menstrual flow;

(4) afternoon fever and restlessness or inability to sleep well at night.

A sustained and painful cough, possible pain in the side or chest, and the production of sputum with possible evidence of blood are late symptoms of the disease and usually indicate advanced involvement.

The physical education teacher may not have opportunities to observe any of these signs except the first, but if his suspicions are aroused by the lack of enthusiasm and energetic participation of a formerly active, cooperative student, he should do whatever seems advisable to encourage

[1]Public Health Service: *Reported Tuberculosis Data.* Washington, D.C., U.S. Department of Health, Education, and Welfare, 1962.

the student to see his doctor or to take advantage of chest x-ray units which may visit the school or community. In addition to the chest films, two other tests are available for the detection of tuberculosis: the Mantoux test, in which the test material is injected into the skin and produces redness and swelling within two to three days if the germs are present in the body, and the patch test, in which filter paper or similar material is saturated with undiluted tuberculin and applied to the skin with adhesive tape and causes the area to be raised and red after about four days if the test is positive.

TREATMENT.   Treatment for tuberculosis usually requires long hospitalization in a sanitarium, where bed rest and nutritious diet are the key to recovery. The long confinement often produces depression in the patient and considerable anxiety about the future. The patient must take life at a slower and easier pace after his release, and this often produces problems in adjustment, particularly if the former life was vigorous and active. It may be necessary for him to find employment in a less demanding occupation and to change recreational habits from vigorous activities to those more mild in nature.

ACTIVITIES.   As the tuberculous patient begins to show improvement in physical condition, some activity is permitted him. It may be as long as two years before full activity may be resumed, and even then there are usually some restrictions. Students with arrested cases who are returning to school require rest periods throughout the day. The physical education teacher should receive specific information from the student's doctor as to when he may be permitted to participate in a mild adapted program, how long he should work out, and which restrictions and limitations he must observe. With this information to guide him, the teacher can plan a suitable program of activities for the student. Initially the program should consist of games requiring little expenditure of energy: shuffleboard, bowling, archery, casting, table tennis, and horseshoes. Young children may participate in most of the basic skill games appropriate to their age with the exception of those games requiring sustained running. Mild participation in dancing and rhythmic games and in swimming may also be permitted to all age groups. The strenuousness of the program should be gradually increased so that the strength and endurance of the patient may be developed to the desired level. Medical approval should be sought for the planned progression of the activities.

DIABETES MELLITUS

Diabetes mellitus is a disease in which the body exhibits an inability to use properly the starches and sugars which it ingests. The prevalence of the disease is on the rise, a fact which is partially attributable to the stress placed upon detection spearheaded by the American Diabetic Association. The highest incidence is among the late-middle-age population, although it has been estimated that about 10 per cent of the cases occur among children.[2]

CAUSE.   The cause of diabetes mellitus is known to be related to an improper supply of insulin, secreted by the islands of Langerhans in the pancreas and responsible for the breakdown of sugars for utilization and storage by the body. This lack of proper function is not caused by an organic defect; consequently, medical investigation of its cause is being directed toward other possible causes, such as the factors which control the production of insulin in the pancreas.

In diabetics an improper supply of insulin to act upon carbohydrates permits an excessive accumulation of sugar in the blood which is eventually eliminated from the body in urine. The body is consequently denied the heat and energy which might have been produced by the lost sugar, and the individual begins, in severe cases, to exhibit such symptoms as loss of weight, lack of energy, and continual hunger. Other frequently experienced symptoms are unusual thirst, excessive urination, intense itching, and slow healing of injuries.

TREATMENT.   Treatment of diabetes mellitus consists of careful diet control and the addition of insulin to the body. Insulin may be injected in carefully regulated dosages with a syringe and needle, although adults with established cases can often successfully take insulin in tablet form. The amount of exercise and physical exertion of the diabetic influences his insulin requirements because of the amount of sugar burned by the body in physical activity. A carefully established balance between food intake and insulin requirement can be upset by excessive physical activity.

Insulin shock may occur if the diabetic receives too much insulin, if his intake of food is too little, or if his participation in exercise has been too great. Feelings of hunger, trembling, perspiring, and muscular contractions are symptomatic of insulin shock. The body needs more sugar, and the eating of candy or a lump of sugar or an orange gives immediate relief.

Diabetic coma, which results from too little insulin, is a more severe condition. It is characterized by uncontrollable drowsiness or muscular pain, possibly resulting in unconsciousness. A diabetic in coma requires the immediate attention of a physician for the administration of insulin. Individuals under medical care are not likely to experience coma.

ACTIVITIES.   Diabetics are normal in appearance and motor function and so do not usually experience the severe emotional problems that those with more obvious handicaps frequently have. Whenever unsatisfactory adjustment is found in those suffering from diabetes, the cause can usually be found in overprotection or overindulgence by the parents during childhood.

Many doctors emphasize the importance of muscular activity in the

[2]U.S. Public Health Service: *Diabetic Fact Book.* Washington, D.C., U.S. Department of Health, Education, and Welfare, 1962.

lives of diabetics. Exercise is important not only because it decreases the need for insulin but because it contributes to general body health. Moreover, it helps to keep the body weight under control, an important problem with older diabetics, who have a tendency to obesity.

Diabetic children are usually encouraged to participate in normal play activities without restriction or adaptation. Because early fatigue is commonly associated with the disease, the physical educator planning activities for such children should take this factor into consideration. Participation in very strenuous or highly competitive games is usually contraindicated because of the greater possibility of extreme fatigue. As a general rule, diabetics should be guided into types of participation which permit them to stop when necessary to rest for a time. For young children, the games in which turns are taken and considerable time elapses between turns, as in drop the handkerchief, are excellent choices. Bowling, shuffle-board, swimming, and archery are examples of good activities for older patients; skill in such sports should be stressed also for their carry-over value as leisure-time activities.

The physical education instructor should obtain a full medical report on those students who have diabetes. Both he and the student should learn the tolerance of the student for exercise. The instructor should check on the student to make sure that he is carrying extra sugar in some form in the event of an emergency insulin shock. He should be prepared to offer guidance and encouragement to the diabetic in observing the necessarily inflexible adherence to the regulations imposed by the treatment.

The diabetic is particularly susceptible to infection, and great care must be practiced to avoid cuts, abrasions, blisters, and fungus infections. The student in physical education should be impressed with the necessity of showering after class and of carefully drying between the toes to reduce the possibility of athlete's foot. The importance of wearing well-fitting gym shoes and lacing them carefully to avoid the rubbing which may cause blisters should also be stressed.

EPILEPSY

Of all the handicaps with which man is afflicted, none has been more misunderstood or maligned than epilepsy. The seizures which are part of the disorder have been interpreted in various ways throughout the ages as everything from evidence of extrasensory powers to madness. Even today, when more is understood about the pathological nature of the disease than ever before, many people regard the epileptic with fear and prejudice. Consequently, the socially handicapping factors of the disease are more important than the physical incapacity.

In an effort to overcome the misunderstanding and rejection of the epileptic, modern educational practices are directed toward including the child who has epilepsy in the regular classroom. Teachers must be educated about the symptoms of the seizure and emergency measures in caring for the patient. They must be prepared to overcome any undesirable preconceived attitudes they may have about such students and to set the tone for the acceptance of such experience by the rest of the class.

CAUSE.   The exact cause of epilepsy is not known; it is believed to be an improper functioning of the brain-regulating mechanisms which produces lack of consciousness and possible seizures or convulsions. In many cases, as age increases the number of seizures decreases. Medical treatment can effectively reduce the number of seizures. Moreover, as the emotional conflicts of the epileptic are eased, seizures are less prevalent.

The incidence of epilepsy cannot be accurately determined for the general population or for the school population because only severe cases are detected.

TYPES.   The teacher should be aware of the types of epileptic seizures and recognize their symptoms. Not all convulsions are epileptic seizures. Some understanding of the nature, frequency, and severity of the attack is essential.

The most severe type is the *grand mal* (great illness). It is characterized by loss of consciousness, rigidity, and falling. Thrashing of the body, frothing at the mouth and involuntary cries are other symptoms. The tongue may be bitten as the result of the strong contraction of the jaw muscles. Although the attack may last only a few minutes, the stuporous sleep which follows may last for several hours.

The *petit mal* (small illness) results in unconsciousness for a short duration. Mental processes cease during the attack and conscious physical activity is suspended, although automatic action may continue. Muscular twitching and rolling or blinking of the eyes or the fixing of the eyes upon some object are characteristic of this type of attack. Recovery is immediate.

Psychomotor attacks constitute another type of attack affecting a small number of epileptics. Consciousness is not lost during the attack but there is no recall of the attack afterward. The attack is characterized by extremely odd behavior in which the patient may have a temper tantrum or otherwise demonstrate unsocial behavior.

AID TO THE VICTIM OF EPILEPSY DURING A SEIZURE.   Because epilepsy is more socially than physically handicapping to the individual, the physical education for these youngsters should be devoted to eliminating the fear and apprehension experienced by the epileptic who anticipates a possible attack in the presence of his peers. Any teacher who has students with epileptic histories should be prepared for a possible attack during class hours, although epileptics, to be admitted to regular schools, must usually demonstrate relative freedom from attack. Nevertheless, the teacher should know the first aid measures to be taken in the event of a seizure. He should be emotionally prepared to deal with the problem, for his conduct in the handling of the victim will greatly influence the class.

Some epileptics experience warnings of an impending seizure, and in this event the teacher may possibly take the child to a quiet inconspicuous place. He should remain calm and call as little attention as possible to the administration of care to the victim. As first aid measures for a grand mal seizure:

1. Place the victim on the floor away from all possible hazards such as hot radiators, furniture, sharp objects.

2. Loosen any restraining clothing, such as a tie or belt, if this is possible without the use of force.

3. Place a relatively soft material such as a handkerchief or folded paper which is too large to be swallowed at the back of the jaw, if the victim's mouth is open, to prevent injury to the tongue and teeth.

If the victim is hazy following the attack, he should be removed to a quiet place to rest. If he lapses into sleep, he should be kept warm and permitted to rest as long as necessary. It is important that no stimulants or depressives be administered to the victim during the attack.

ACTIVITIES. The epileptic, unless specific activities have been medically prescribed, may be included in all the planned activities of the physical education program. However, students who are subject to frequent seizures should not be permitted to engage in climbing activities in which there is danger of severe injury from falling during an attack. Swimming may be permitted under close supervision.

The development of the heart and vital capacity through exercise appears to have greatly improved some epileptics. Because many of these children may have been greatly restricted in play activities, owing to their social ostracization, they may show evidence of low physical fitness and poor body mechanics. For these children the special program of exercises suggested in Chapters 24 and 25 will be extremely beneficial. Games with a high social and recreational value, such as bowling, golf, tennis, dancing, and the team sports, are extremely valuable for the epileptic because of his need for increased social intercourse.

ANEMIA

A common defect of the blood is a condition called anemia, which is a deficiency in hemoglobin or a reduction of red corpuscles or the quantity of hemoglobin they contain. As a consequence there is a lack of oxygen in the blood, the individual becomes tired more easily, owing to lack of oxidation in the muscles, and appears pale because the blood is less red.

CAUSES. Anemia may be the result of various causes: nutritional deficiency of iron; direct loss of blood by hemorrhage or excessive menstruation; and disturbance in the blood-forming tissue produced by parasitic diseases such as hookworm or malaria.

TREATMENT. Treatment is dependent upon the cause. In the case of dietary deficiency, the diet is improved to include more iron and copper. If blood loss is extremely severe, it may need to be replaced by transfusion. When disease is causing the anemia, it is treated medically. Pernicious anemia, rarely found in school age children, is treated with the addition of liver or liver extract to the diet.

Because he tires easily, the anemic person will not be able to keep up with others in play activities. His lack of success may cause him to withdraw from such contacts.

ACTIVITIES.   During the period of treatment, the student may have to respect certain limitations on his activities. Medical approval will need to be obtained for the types of activities and the strenuousness of his participation. A carefully planned program can be very useful in effecting improved health because exercise stimulates the production of red cells through increased demands for oxygen.

SKIN DISORDERS

There are several types of skin disorders that may require adaptation of the physical education activities while the student is suffering from them.

Blisters on the foot or certain other parts of the body may become so severe that withdrawal from certain types of physical education activities is necessitated. In a blister, pinching or continual irritation causes the epidermis to separate from the dermis, and the area between the two layers fills with fluid. If only the epidermis is involved in the injury, the area fills with the waterlike fluid of blood to produce a water blister. If, however, the dermis is also injured, the area fills with blood, resulting in a blood blister.

Blisters occurring on the feet, usually water blisters, may cause temporary difficulty in participation in activity. First aid measures to open the blister are usually not desirable unless there is indication that the blister will be caused to break open by further irritation of the area. The opening of the blister should be done with a sterile instrument and the wound kept as sterile as possible. Proper padding around the broken or unbroken blister to reduce the pressure on the area will permit the student to participate without further irritation.

If participation in regular physical education is contraindicated because of the additional stress and strain that would be placed on the blistered area by the nature of the activities, the student may be placed in the adapted program temporarily to engage in activities which require little foot movement, such as bag punching, ring toss, table tennis, and shuffleboard. He may remove his shoes for these activities, but other activities in which running is an element should not be permitted without proper shoes because of the danger of slipping.

Students with *corns, calluses, warts, and bunions* may require medical attention before they are able to participate without pain in unrestricted activities. Securing better fitting shoes or a better adjustment of the old shoes may relieve the condition sufficiently to permit participation. Padding to take the pressure off the area is also possible. In situations where such remedial action cannot be taken, the student may be placed in adapted activities of the same nature as those recommended above for students with blisters.

Some *communicable diseases and disturbances* of the skin require dismissal from school until the condition is no longer contagious. Among these are impetigo, a dermatitis with small blisters that break and crust; pediculosis, an infection with head, body, or crab lice; scabies, commonly called the seven-year itch, due to infestation of the skin with a very small mite that buries itself in the skin.

Ringworm of the foot, commonly called *athlete's foot*, once believed to be highly communicable, is not readily transferred. Students affected with ringworm need not be excluded from the use of the shower room and swimming pool as was once a common practice. A severe case may be very painful, and in this event the student should be placed in activities which do not require much foot movement.

Boils are caused by an infection produced by bacteria entering the hair follicle. Boils are readily transmitted from one part of the body to another. They should be protected with a sterile dressing in order to prevent spreading the infection. If a boil occurs in an area such as the groin or axillary region where movement might tend to irritate it, the student should not be required to participate in activities requiring the movement of the involved area but should instead be placed temporarily in the adapted program. Running activities are contraindicated for boils in the groin area, and arm movements for boils in the axillary region.

ALLERGIES

An allergy is a condition of hypersensitiveness to a substance which is harmless in similar amounts to most other people. Why some people are sensitive while others are not is not clearly understood. It is known that the abnormal reaction is in some way associated with protein metabolism; certain proteins cannot be used by some people in the normal way. Allergic reactions occur in various forms, such as eczema, migraine headaches, indigestion, hay fever, asthma. Asthma and hay fever victims have greater problems in physical education than others, as a rule.

In asthmatic attacks there is a swelling of the mucous membrane lining of the bronchial tubes. Expiration is difficult due mostly to muscle spasm. In hay fever there is a nasal discharge and watering of the eyes. Sneezing and coughing are frequent. The nose becomes clogged and breathing through it is difficult.

CAUSES.   There are many substances that cause an allergic reaction in those who are sensitive. Certain foods may cause allergic reactions,

particularly eggs, shrimps, lobsters, strawberries, bananas, melons, to-
matoes, and onions. Pollen and dust are also frequent offenders. Among
the pollens, those from ragweed and certain other grasses are the most
common. Allergic reactions are caused by certain foods, feathers, wool,
and literally hundreds of other things.

TREATMENT.   Treatment involves determining the causative agent
and eliminating contact with it. Some immunization techniques have been
developed and used with some success. Students allergic to dust should
not be required to work on mats unless extreme care has been exercised
to keep them clean. Dusty playing fields should be avoided also.

Physical exertion, fatigue, and emotional upset may precipitate an
asthmatic attack. There is a tendency for an asthmatic victim to withdraw
from physical effort, hence lowering his tolerance for physical exertion.
This sets up a vicious circle: decreased activity lowers the tolerance level
so that attacks may occur more easily, and so the victim avoids attacks
by reducing his activity and further lowers his tolerance. Such students
need progressive developmental activities designed to increase tolerance
so they will be able to participate more normally in play activities. Of
course, the asthmatic student must avoid vigorous and prolonged activity.

HERNIA

A hernia is a protrusion of a loop of an organ or tissue through an
abnormal opening within the body. Hernias may occur in many different
areas of the body, but the abdominal region is the most frequent. The
most common hernia involves the inguinal canal, which is located in the
groin and serves as the passage for the spermatic cord in the male and the
round ligament in the female. In the embryo of the male the testes move
down from the abdomen to the scrotum. This canal normally closes early
in life but undue pressure or exertion may reopen it, resulting in a hernia
or a loop of the intestine protruding through the opening.

If the protrusion remains in the canal, the hernia is called incomplete.
If it leaves the canal and enters the scrotum, it is a complete hernia. In
complete hernia there is a danger that it will become strangulated. The
loop of the intestine becomes constricted, shutting off the blood supply
to the area, which may result in the development of gangrene.

CAUSE AND TREATMENT.   The frequency of inguinal hernia is higher
in the male than the female and higher among the obese. Inguinal hernia
may occur where there is abdominal pressure against weak abdominal
muscles. Lifting heavy weights with the epiglottis closed is a frequent
cause. Blows to the abdominal region may be another cause. Surgery is
indicated in the cure of hernia.

ACTIVITIES.   Students who have hernia should avoid such activities
as weightlifting, boxing, wrestling, or football, which may cause increased
pressure on the abdominal area or in which a blow to that area is likely

to occur. For severe hernia cases, running games are also contraindicated. Rope climbing and activity on the bar and parallel ladders are not recommended. Games in which students may safely participate are horseshoes, swimming, bowling, casting, golf, table tennis, volleyball, and basic skill games which are not chiefly running.

Exercises to strengthen the abdominal walls are of value and offer some protection until surgery can be performed. They are also of great benefit to the patient after surgery. Suitable exercises are described in Chapter 10 in the section on bed exercises to strengthen the abdominal area. Added protection may be given the hernia during exercise by placing the hand over the hernia area. The breath should not be held during exercises.

DYSMENORRHEA

Dysmenorrhea, or painful menstruation, occurs most frequently at the beginning of the menstrual cycle. At this time the abdominal cavity is gorged with an additional amount of blood. This produces increased pressure upon nerves and hence pain. The changes that take place during the cycle within the body may lower the threshold of pain and increase irritability. Dysmenorrhea is often due to lack of exercise, fatigue, constipation, chilling of the body, and poor posture. Sometimes an organic condition such as a displaced uterus may be the cause.

ACTIVITIES AND SPECIAL EXERCISES.   Dysmenorrhea is frequently given as a reason by girls seeking excuse from physical education during menstruation. Most of these girls are unaware that their condition may be relieved by participation in physical education activities which are not extremely strenuous in nature. These girls should be encouraged not only to take part in their physical education classes but to participate regularly in a program of special exercises which are known to be of value in preventing and alleviating dysmenorrhea. These exercises, known as the Mosher, Billig, and Golub exercises, are beneficial because they improve circulation in the abdominal area, increase abdominal muscle tone, increase lumbo-pelvic flexibility, and encourage muscular relaxation.[3]

The *Mosher*[4] exercise is designed to relieve abdominal congestion by "abdominal pumping." To perform the exercise, a supine position is taken with the knees bent and the feet resting on the floor. One hand is placed on the abdomen. The abdominal area is then retracted or pulled in, and a deep breath is taken. The hand massages slowly and heavily from the symphysis pubis up to the sternum (approximately from the region

[3]Eleanor Metheny: "Exercise and Menstrual Pain" in *Symposium on Dysmenorrhea.* Chicago, Phi Delta Pi Fraternity, 1950, pp. 29–32.

[4]C. D. Mosher: "Dysmenorrhea." *Journal of American Medical Association*, vol. 62, 1914, p. 1297.

FIGURE 18.   Mosher exercise.

FIGURE 19.   Billig exercise.   FIGURE 20.   Goleb exercise.

of the pubic hair to the ribs). The abdominal area is relaxed, and the air is expelled entirely. The exercise is repeated several times.

The *Billig*[5] exercise is designed to stretch the fascial ligamentous bands through which the sensory nerves pass. (The fascial ligamentous bands are bands of ligaments that attach the fascia, which covers the muscle, to the bone.) It is theorized that the stretching of these bands relieves the pressure on the nerves and so reduces pain. The effectiveness of the exercise has been demonstrated in a controlled study of girls with dysmenorrhea in which 94 per cent reported their conditions alleviated to some degree by participating in the exercise.[6] To perform the exercise, the subject stands with one side of the body toward the wall, with the feet together and about 18 inches from the wall. With the knees locked and the hips rotated forward, the forearm is placed horizontally against the wall at shoulder height (the palm of the hand, the forearm, and the elbow should be in contact with the wall). The other hand is placed against the hollow of the hip joint and slowly and deliberately pushes the hips forward and toward the wall as far as possible. The return to the original position is made slowly. The exercises should be performed over a period of two or more months three times a day, three repetitions on each side.

The *Golub*[7] exercise stresses systematic twisting and bending of the trunk, activities which were found to be effective in reducing the pain of dysmenorrhea in a study by Golub. The first part of the exercise is done from a standing position with the arms extended straight out from the sides. The body is bent while the knees are kept straight. One hand is lifted up, and with the other an attempt is made to reach around the outer side of the opposite foot until the heel can be touched. The exercise is repeated on the other side. In the second part of the exercise, the individual stands with the arms at the sides. The arms are then swung forward and upward, while the left leg is simultaneously raised backward vigorously. Then the exercise is repeated on the opposite foot. Each phase of the exercise is performed four times on each side.

MENORRHAGIA

Menorrhagia is a condition of unusually heavy flow during the menstrual period. Because of the large amount of blood that is lost, the individual is likely to be tired and somewhat anemic. Exercise, which is helpful to dysmenorrhea because it increases the flow, is not desirable in cases of menorrhagia. Consequently, such girls should be excused from physical education unless permission for them to participate has been given by their physicians.

[5]H. E. Billig, Jr.,: "Dysmenorrhea: The Result of Postural Defect." *Archives of Surgery*, vol. 46, 1943, p. 611.
[6]Eleanor Metheny: *op. cit.*, pp. 29–32.
[7]Leib J. Golub: "A New Exercise for Dysmenorrhea."*American Journal of Obstetrics and Gynecology*, 78, July 1959, pp. 152–155.

QUESTIONS

1. What areas of the body are susceptible to attack by tuberculosis?
2. What techniques are utilized to determine if one has tuberculosis?
3. What types of physical education activities are appropriate for the student who is an arrested tubercular case?
4. What is diabetes mellitus? What is its cause?
5. What is the difference between insulin shock and diabetic coma?
6. What contributions can physical education make to the health of the diabetic patient?
7. Discuss the different types of epilepsy.
8. What limitations, if any, need be imposed upon the epileptic student in physical education?
9. What is anemia? What limitations should be placed upon students in physical education who suffer from anemia?
10. Discuss the skin disorders that may require adaptation of the physical education activities for those who suffer from them.
11. What general precautions need be taken in physical education for students suffering from asthma?
12. List the sports that are generally contraindicated for a student with hernia.
13. What is the value of exercise in preventing and alleviating dysmenorrhea?

SELECTED READINGS

Chao, Dora Hsi-Chih, Druckman, Ralph, and Kellaway, Peter: *Convulsive Disorders of Children,* Philadelphia, W. B. Saunders Co., 1958.

Engle, Earl T. (ed.): *Menstruation and Its Disorders.* Springfield, Ill., Charles C Thomas, Publisher, 1950.

Frampton, Merle E., and Gall, Elena D. (ed.): *Special Education for the Exceptional,* Vols. II and III. Boston, Porter Sargent, Publisher, 1955, 1956.

New York Diabetes Association: *Newer Concepts of Causes and Treatment of Diabetes Melitus, A Symposium,* New York, The National Vitamin Foundation, Inc., 1954.

Phi Delta Pi Fraternity: *Symposium on Dysmenorrhea.* Chicago, Phi Delta Pi, 1950.

Putnam, Tracy J.: *Epilepsy: What It Is, What To Do About It.* Philadelphia, J. B. Lippincott Co., 1958.

13
MENTAL RETARDATION

The years since the turn of the present century have witnessed the development of numerous techniques and procedures for improving the teaching of the mentally retarded. Until the closing years of the 1800's, relatively few mentally defective children were receiving educational instruction geared to their abilities; these were the children enrolled in the private schools and state-supported residential schools which were being established throughout the country. Those in charge of the instruction in these schools became increasingly aware of the varying degrees of potential existing in the subnormal range of intelligence, and by 1900 attention began to be directed toward the development of better methods of meeting the individual needs of these youngsters.

One of the results was the founding of special classes for retarded youngsters within the school system. In the United States, the first classes in public schools were organized in 1896. The growth of special classes since that date has been slow but steady; the success of the initial classes has contributed to their being established in numerous schools in all parts of the country. In many states, state aid to schools establishing such classes has given further impetus to this type of education and has made it possible for many more youngsters to receive special instruction to meet their specific needs.

THE NATURE OF MENTAL RETARDATION

A lack of uniformity in the use of terms describing the individuals who show retarded mental development has resulted in considerable

147

confusion. No one definition of mental deficiency or retardation has been constructed which satisfies all the professional disciplines (medical, psychological, educational, social, legal) concerned with the problem.

The definition accepted by the American Association on Mental Deficiency describes mental retardation as significant "subaverage general intellectual functioning which originates during the developmental period and is associated with impairment in adaptive behavior." In less technical terms, the mentally retarded person is one who, from childhood, experiences unusual difficulty in learning and is relatively ineffective in applying whatever he has learned to the problems of ordinary living; he needs special training and guidance to make the most of his capacities, whatever they may be.

The extent to which the mentally retarded differ from other people depends on the degree of mental retardation. Those who are least retarded are scarcely distinguishable from the "dull normal" (or "slow learner") members of our population, while those whose handicap is extreme may never be able to master such tasks as feeding and dressing themselves.

Degrees of mental retardation are measured by considering both "measured intelligence" and "impairment in adaptive behavior." Since "measured intelligence" usually ties quite closely to learning ability, this factor assumes greater importance in childhood, whereas "adaptive behavior," the ability to make a living and to handle oneself and one's affairs with the prudence ordinarily expected of an adult in our society, is the more important determinant of the degree of retardation in an adult.

The terms *mentally deficient, mentally retarded,* and *mentally handicapped* are used interchangeably to designate a condition in which the individual is incapable of achieving normal mental growth. Such an individual has an intelligence quotient of less than 75, although there are borderline cases on either side of this arbitrary number. Further classification of the mentally handicapped is made in several ways. Formerly, the terms *idiot* (0–20 I.Q.), *imbecile* (20–50 I.Q.), and *moron* (50–70 I.Q.) were used to designate ranges of intelligence in the subnormal group. Today, mental retardation is described as *profound, severe, moderate,* or *mild,* and educators speak of the mentally retarded as *totally dependent, trainable,* or *educable.*

THE TOTALLY DEPENDENT.   Totally dependent children are those who, because of the severeness of their mental retardation, are incapable of being trained for economic usefulness, social participation, or total self-care. These children develop at only one-fourth the rate of average children. They will require nearly complete supervision and care throughout their lives, for they cannot care adequately for their personal needs, protect themselves, or communicate effectively with others.

THE TRAINABLE CHILD.   Those mentally retarded children who have some potential for learning to care for their personal needs, for social adjustment in a group, and for economic usefulness are classified as trainable. These children can be taught enough of the skills of personal care to make them generally independent of care by others. They are capable of learning to get along in the family and in a limited environment. Their mental development is approximately one-fourth to one-half that of the average child, and they are not generally capable of acquiring academic skills beyond the rote learning of simple words and numbers. Nevertheless, they are capable of learning to do simple tasks around the home or for remuneration in a supervised situation outside the home. Some care, supervision, and economic support will be required throughout their lives.

THE EDUCABLE.   Children who, because of slow mental development, cannot profit from the work offered in the regular elementary school but are capable of learning some academic skills are classified as educable. They are generally capable of acquiring from second to fourth grade achievement in reading, writing, and arithmetic by the age of 16. Their development is approximately one-half to three-fourths as fast as the average child; consequently, their academic progress is also one-half to three-fourths the rate of the average child. Although their communication skills are definitely limited, they can be adequately developed for most situations. Most of the educable can learn to get along with others and can acquire enough skills to support themselves economically in adulthood. Emotional and behavior problems may limit their adaptability.

THE EXTENT OF MENTAL RETARDATION

It is estimated that there are more than 5.5 million people in the United States (3 per cent of the population) who are mentally retarded. Between 100,000 and 200,000 of the babies born each year are likely to join this group. By 1970, natural population growth is expected to increase the total to 6.5 million, unless far-reaching preventive measures can be introduced.[1]

Of the total, nearly 2.5 million are children and young people under 20 years of age. At least 2 million of these children are mildly retarded, and many of them may not be singled out and identified until they have been in school for several years. Another 150,000 or more are estimated to be moderately retarded, with an additional 100,000 and 50,000 in the severe and profound categories respectively.[2]

People who are mentally retarded should be identified before they are 15 years of age. Although a significant number of moderate, severe, and profoundly retarded children are found and given help in early childhood, many more are overlooked or not properly diagnosed. The

---

[1]President's Panel on Mental Retardation: *A Report to the President on National Action to Combat Mental Retardation.* Washington, D.C., U.S. Government Printing Office, 1962.
[2]Ibid.

mortality in this group is known to be high but is difficult to document, since frequently a baby may not show definite retardation for months or even years after birth. Usually, however, when parents of retarded children look back, they can recognize that the signs were present from infancy.

Once he has lived to the age of 5 or 6, a retarded child has a good chance of growing up. In fact, the life expectancy of the mildly retarded is probably about the same as that of other people. For the profoundly and severely retarded it is substantially less, although profoundly retarded persons have been known to live to the age of 70 or 80 years. Because the retarded adults of today were born prior to the end of World War II, before the introduction of antibiotics and other modern life-saving treatments, it is likely that the prevalence of moderate, severe, and profound retardation among adults will increase in the next twenty years. Statistics on survivorship among persons with Down's syndrome (mongolism), for example, indicate a much greater life expectancy for this group today than twenty or thirty years ago.

Even so, it is estimated that there are at least 35,000 adults alive today who are profoundly retarded; some 100,000 or more who are severely retarded; and some 200,000 or so who are moderately retarded.

Nearly 3 million adults were once mildly retarded children; these are handicapped members of our society, but, to the extent that they may have been helped to achieve a satisfactory degree of "adaptive behavior" and to attain economic and social independence, they will no longer be "spotted" as mentally retarded. For this reason they are often not identified and counted when community surveys are made, although most of them remain potentially vulnerable to adverse social or economic pressures. Thus, the number of adults who may require help because of varying degrees of mental retardation is probably no more than 1 million to 1¼ million. Many of these persons are receiving disability or general welfare assistance or are dependent on relatives. Thus, as a cause of lifetime disability and as a medical, social, and educational problem of unique extent and complexity, mental retardation today presents an outstanding challenge to science and society in the United States and throughout the world.

THE CAUSES OF MENTAL RETARDATION

Mental retardation can be caused by any condition that hinders or interferes with development before birth, during birth, or in the early childhood years. Well over a hundred causes have already been identified, although these account for only about one-fourth of all identified cases of mental retardation.

Among the specific identified causes are: German measles (rubella) in the mother during the first three months of pregnancy, meningitis, toxoplasmosis, Rh factor incompatibility between mother and infant, lead poisoning in young children, and chromosome abnormalities. Among the commonest and best known of the latter is Down's syndrome (mongolism), which occurs in 1 out of every 600 babies born and usually results in moderate to severe mental retardation. A number of inborn errors of metabolism have been identified which, if untreated, can cause damage to the nervous system and hence mental retardation. Physical malformations of the brain or other organs originating in prenatal life may also result directly or indirectly in mental retardation. Examples include hydrocephalus (a blocking of ducts resulting in an accumulation of fluid in the brain) and craniosynostosis (a premature closing of the sutures of the skull). Inflammation of the brain associated with childhood measles is another cause.

As time goes on, more people who are originally placed in the "undifferentiated" category are found to have specific diagnosable causes of their mental retardation. Nevertheless, even today, in the majority of cases, no clear diagnosis of cause can be made, and in most of these there is no demonstrable pathology of the nervous system. Undoubtedly among the mildly retarded there are many people whose development has been adversely affected by nonspecific influences, such as inadequate diet, inadequate prenatal and perinatal care, and lack of adequate stimulation toward growth and development through learning opportunities. Mental development, like physical development, is promoted by the right kinds of activity and stimulation and retarded when these are lacking. Indeed, the two tend to interact. In this process, the years of early childhood, when the nervous system is maturing and language developing, are certainly very critical.

How many mentally retarded persons actually have brain damage? The term "brain damage" has not been adequately defined and is used differently by different people. Destruction of brain tissue or interference with brain development in the infant or young child frequently produces mental retardation as well as cerebral palsy, convulsive seizures, hyperactivity, and perceptual problems. Such damage accounts for a substantial fraction of moderate, severe, and profound mental retardation. Although it can be definitely shown in most cases of mild mental retardation, the extent of its contribution is not known and expert opinion is divided. Several factors may be at work in the same individual. For example, the premature infant is more vulnerable to brain damage, prematurity is more common among mothers who receive inadequate prenatal care, and inadequate prenatal care in turn is more common in the underprivileged groups in our society; these same children are also more apt to have inadequate postnatal opportunities for growth and development and to be subject to psychological and cultural deprivation.

The extent of psychomotor, perceptual, and sensory handicaps among the retarded points to common causation in many cases. Most severely and profoundly retarded individuals have pronounced motor handicaps, or impairment of hearing, vision, or speech, or a combination of several of these. Although the majority of the mildly retarded would not be readily identified as physically handicapped, their general level of motor coordination is below average, despite the occurrence among them of a few remarkable athletes.

Is MENTAL RETARDATION PREVENTABLE?   Progress is being made in the prevention of mental retardation, but it is proceeding, as might be expected, through a succession of small advances across the broad front rather than by any singular spectacular breakthrough. Each of the many contributing causes must be analyzed specifically, with specific preventive measures devised when the cause has been found. Progress is being made against some of the more serious forms by such techniques as corrective surgery for malformations of the skull and for the diversion of excess fluid in the brain. Children who have inadequate blood sugar in the first few critical days after birth are now more readily identified and given corrective treatment. Damage resulting from Rh factor incompatibility can be prevented by complete blood transfusion in the infant at time of birth. Quick treatment in cases of lead poisoning or, better yet, action to prevent children from eating paint containing lead can also be effective in preventing some cases. The new measles vaccine can help if widely used. Some progress is being made in identifying the characteristics of mothers most likely to give birth prematurely, so that this indirect cause of mental retardation may be reduced. Thus far, however, all of these steps have been effective in eliminating only a relatively small fraction of mental retardation. Increased attention to relevant basic and applied research and to the prompt application of new discoveries are essential to carrying forward this initial progress. Moreover, some of those forms of retardation which stem from physical, emotional, or cultural deprivation will yield only to basic social reform.

NEEDS AND ADJUSTMENTS OF
THE MENTALLY DEFICIENT

Mentally deficient children usually exhibit a number of characteristics of which teachers should be aware. Among these are: lack of ability to concentrate, difficulty in following directions, poor motor coordination, poor body mechanics, low vitality, and social immaturity. Their abilities to see, hear, speak, and their other sensory perceptions, are less than those of normal children. Although they are inferior to the normal child in so many ways, they deviate less in motor ability than otherwise. Because this is so, the physical educator can play an important role in the total educative process of such children.

The need of mentally handicapped children for improved physical fitness and body mechanics is usually very apparent to the observer. Poor eye-hand coordination is typical of these youngsters. A shuffling, inefficient walking gait is representative of the general poorly coordinated body movements. Posture is usually poor and physical vitality low. Some mentally deficient children are subject to excessive and useless movements, while other are subject to diminished motility or muscular asthenia.

The failure of mentally handicapped children to keep intellectual pace with normal children contributes to personality maladjustment and the development of undesirable behavior patterns. Much of the normal child's social maturity and satisfactory adjustment is acquired in play situations throughout his formative years. Not so the mentally retarded child, who finds himself rejected by his normal peers or who, because of his low mentality, has no interest in group play.

The normal child plays spontaneously; he experiments, innovates, exerts himself. The mentally handicapped child, particularly if he is severely retarded, shows little interest in play. Those with higher grades of intelligence desire group activity, although, until they have been taught otherwise, they will usually play as very young normal children do, as individuals within the group rather than as equally participating members of the group. They are capable of learning relatively complex group games and team sports if slowly and carefully instructed. A lack of emotional stability is noted not only in competitive play but also in all circumstances in which more is expected of them than they can deliver. Such instability usually manifests itself in expressions of fear and aggression.

Aggressiveness on the part of the mentally deficient child may also be an attempt to cover his weaknesses, to demonstrate his worth, to attract attention, or to relieve tensions. Rebellious acts and other undesirable behavior are similarly motivated. On occasions the mentally retarded may use their handicap as a protective shield or in an outright bid for sympathy to compensate for their lack of social acceptance.

Perhaps the greatest need of these children is an opportunity for successful participation in group play. Although mentally retarded youngsters cannot generally acquire the high degree of skill of normal players, they can acquire sufficient skills to participate in enough different types of muscular activities to increase their physical fitness and improve their body mechanics. In addition to the physical benefits, there exists in play many opportunities for social development and emotional growth. Adherence to the rule of the game and to the sportsman's code of fair play provides incentive for self-discipline and self-control. Respect for one's own abilities and limitations and those of others is stimulated in the cooperation and sharing necessitated by the game situation. Many desirable learnings are claimed for sports in the training of normal youngsters. However much these have been exaggerated for normal children, they are essentially accurate for the mentally handicapped, whose other opportunities for learning to work and play with others are considerably restricted.

PLANNING THE PROGRAM

Directing the play of the mentally retarded requires the most careful organization on the part of the instructor. To enjoy physical activity and to reap its benefits, the retarded individual must participate to his own satisfaction. He can participate successfully if his interest is aroused and maintained, if he can grasp the nature of the activity, and if he isn't required to remember too many directions.

STUDENT INTEREST.   The youngsters will probably come to the physical education class with high initial interest because the change to another type of class activity is interesting in itself. Moreover, if previous physical education periods have been fun, interest is high in anticipation of more fun. If natural initial interest does not exist among the students, it can be aroused in various ways. Simple, colorful pictures may be shown to introduce a game. A short story related to the activity which is to be presented may be told the class. Or, if a song or music is to accompany the activity, this may be introduced in an interesting way before the actual activity is presented.

The intial interest, while it may be very strong, is usually not sustained because the interest span of these youngsters is relatively short. When interest lags, a change in activities is indicated.

EQUIPMENT.   A wide variety of play equipment is desirable because of this lack of sustained interest. There should be enough toys or items of playground equipment so that no child need sit around idly waiting for a turn. The items can be exchanged from time to time to afford renewed stimulation and interest. Teachers may find their ingenuity taxed to provide toys suitable to the mental ages of the youngsters yet capable of withstanding their physical strength. Most commercial toys are geared in interest appeal and durability to the handling of normal youngsters. Such toys do not last long in the hands of a ten-year-old with the mentality of a two-year-old, and the physical education teacher must be prepared to improvise sturdy equipment for older children. It is recommended that some of the play equipment be the type on which the youngsters may vent their aggressive tendencies. Large inflatable plastic toys which can be struck and kicked without damage to the toy or to the participant are excellent. Water play also provides a harmless outlet.

NATURE OF ACTIVITIES.   The nature of the program offered by the physical education teacher must be based upon their specific needs and upon their intellectual capacities for learning. Some of the youngsters will, of course, be incapable of learning more than very rudimentary motor skills. Others of higher intelligence can learn complex skills if they are slowly and carefully instructed. In presenting such skills it is often necessary to break them down into their components so that, for example, the act of turning, jumping, and shooting a basketball might be taught as three separate skills first and gradually put together. Many mildly retarded individuals can learn to perform motor skills exceptionally well. As a general rule, however, games should be chosen for them which require little in the way of memorization of playing rules, strategy, or movement patterns.

TEACHING HINTS.   Verbal directions should be few and simply stated. It may be necessary to repeat them several times with the words spoken slowly, distinctly, and in the same general word pattern. Replies to questions must also be as brief and direct as possible. Like the very small child, the mentally retarded individual is not interested in, and his attention cannot be held by, detailed explanations.

Demonstration is perhaps the most effective method of instructing mentally retarded children. These youngsters are great mimics, and by encouraging them to imitate the demonstrated skill much can be accomplished. The demonstration must necessarily be adapted to the intellectual abilities of the students. Kinesthesis is effective in many situations, such as teaching a child to ride a tricycle. Here the child may not be able to perceive the nature of the action required to pedal the tricycle until the teacher moves his feet alternately through the proper movements.

Visual aids can be used in teaching handicapped youngsters, but they are generally not as effective as with children of normal intelligence. Retarded children cannot make sufficient interpretation of the skills they have seen to incorporate the techniques in their own performance. The appeal of the visual presentation is very significant, however, in arousing interest in an activity and in motivating skill performance. Consequently, the use of visual aids should not be excluded as a teaching technique but should be simplified as much as possible.

Participation in the play activities by everyone should be actively encouraged by the teacher. There should, of course, be no resort to pressure tactics. The retarded child needs and seeks approval, and he can be led to cooperate and participate if he knows that this is what the teacher wants and gives approval for.

Praise should be offered generously for the efforts of the youngster. The effort may not result in successful performance, but the effort that is exerted should be approved by the teacher. Sincere praise for effort can be one of the teacher's most effective motivators and helps to create the kind of learning situation most conducive to progress.

The teacher should exercise firm discipline without resort to threats and corporal punishment. The disciplining must take a form which the group is capable of comprehending, such as withholding approval. Those who present a disruptive influence may be temporarily removed from the class and dealt with in a small group or on an individual basis.

Retarded individuals perform best the first few times they do a skill. Consequently, it is to their advantage to end the practice period on any one skill before frustration at the inability to do the skill well sets in. After the skills of a game have been mastered over a gradual period of time, the skills should be reviewed briefly each time before the game is played. These drill periods should be just long enough to refresh their memories.

Because many retardates have low physical vitality, they fatigue easily. This has important implication for the teaching situation. First, it means that new and complex activities should be planned for the early part of the period while the students are fresh and alert. Then, too, a greater chance of injury exists after fatigue has set in, so it is extremely important for the instructor to watch for signs of fatigue.

Special efforts may be required to evoke responses from torpid youngsters. Such students are particularly in need of physical activity but show no interest in play. The physical education teacher must endeavor to arouse interest and awaken their sensibilities. To do this it may be necessary to force the torpid child to display a physical response such as tossing balloons at him so that he will raise his arms to protect himself or will attempt to catch or dodge the balloons. From the use of balloons, the instructor may progress to beanbags and large soft balls which would not seriously hurt the child if he failed to ward them off. Eventually the child can be taught catching, throwing, and other simple motor skills.

In some instances, physical education teachers have obtained the assistance of outstanding high school students on a volunteer basis in providing individual attention for retarded youngsters in physical activity. This has proven to be a worthwhile learning experience for both the helping student and the retarded youngster.

The physical educator has the opportunity also of teaching certain health and safety facts and of encouraging the development of good habits pertaining to personal care and protection and in the wise use of leisure time. Specifically in the area of health are such personal hygiene matters as showering after activity, care of the feet to prevent athlete's foot, cleanliness of gym clothes and socks. Good safety practices, such as not throwing the bat, should be clearly and firmly established so that they will be observed not only in supervised play but also in free play. By providing in the physical education curriculum opportunities to learn games which can be played during leisure hours, the wise use of such time can be encouraged. Because of their generally restricted interests and recreational opportunities, the mentally retarded often pursue undesirable leisure-time activities or idle the time away, which is undesirable from the standpoint of their development and may become harmful to themselves and to society.

THE PROGRAM FOR MENTALLY DEFICIENT CHILDREN

The physical education program must present a variety of activities directed toward the special needs of the mentally retarded. Because these youngsters have poor body mechanics and low physical fitness, much attention must be focused on exercises and activities which will improve these conditions. Those with specific muscular weaknesses may need additional work to strengthen these areas of the body. The exercises and games suggested for improving fitness and body mechanics in Chapters 24 and 25 are applicable to all except the most severely retarded.

For very young children and those who cannot participate with success in more complex exercises and games, a variety of simple activities which will achieve the goal of desired physical development should be introduced. Among the very simplest of these activities are the basic motor skills of everyday living: walking, balancing, twisting, turning, bending, climbing stairs. Slightly more involved are the basic play skills: running, hopping, jumping, skipping, kicking, hanging, catching, and throwing. These skills must be presented to the children so that they will take pleasure in performing them. Variety in their presentation is also vital to achieving interest in their performance. The following suggestions are ways in which this may be accomplished:

1. Walking at varied tempos and with different sizes and kinds of steps, such as short quick steps, slow giant strides, tiptoeing.

2. Running at varied tempos.

3. Jumping on both feet, alternating feet, one foot; attaining various heights.

4. Hopping on one foot and on alternate feet.

5. Skipping at varied tempos.

6. Marching at varied tempos; alternating with running, skipping, and jumping; accompanied by hand clapping.

7. Climbing stairs, alternating the feet.

8. Catching and bouncing the ball.

9. Throwing the ball for distance and at objects; throwing the ball to a catcher.

10. Kicking, with the leg swinging freely, at a large ball, at a small ball.

11. Hanging from a bar or the rung of a ladder, with both arms, with one arm; climbing the ladder with the hands only.

12. Balancing on a balance beam, walking along a chalked line, stepping on the rungs of a ladder placed on the floor.

13. Springing up and down on a jouncing board; leaping from the board to the ground.

Play on playground equipment may begin as soon as children demonstrate sufficient balance and strength to perform with safety. As balancing skills improve, tricycle riding, propelling a wagon, jumping rope, and roller skating may be introduced. Roller skating should usually be confined to one skate until the child has the confidence and ability to attempt two skates.

The possibilities for big-muscle activity in mimetic play are practically limitless. Pretending they are animals, the class can waddle like ducks, hop

158   SPECIAL PHYSICAL EDUCATION

FIGURE 21.   The Mansfield State Training School and Hospital successfully fields a football team. It is the only residential school of its kind in the country to have varsity football. (Mansfield State Training School and Hospital, Mansfield Depot, Conn.)

like bunnies, leap like frogs, and walk softly (on tiptoes) like kittens. Imitating the actions of people, they may vigorously chop wood, march in a band, sweep the floor, iron clothes. At times the mimetic activities may be done to musical accompaniment, both for the added interest provided by the music and for the introduction it provides to instruction in dance.

Relays and simple games[3] may be introduced as skills improve. The following guide is offered for the selection of simple activities. The more capable the students are of participating in complex activities, the less necessity there will be for the games to meet all of the suggested criteria. A very simple game is one in which:

(1) all children do the same thing;
(2) the space is relatively small;
(3) choices which must be made are few in number;
(4) positions are fixed;
(5) quality of performance brings no penalties or privileges;
(6) the possible directions of movement are restricted;
(7) personnel remain the same;
(8) motor skill requirements are limited.

These children also enjoy doing simple calisthenics to the count of the instructor. Included may be such simple activities as bending, squatting, twisting the trunk, rotating the arms. Educable youngsters can achieve considerable skill in the performance of more complicated

[3]For a description of basic skill games see Chapter 16.

calisthenics such as the push-up and the squat thrust. They can also perform satisfactorily in more complex games such as badminton, basketball, softball, tennis, table tennis, football, and volleyball. Track and field events and tumbling and gymnastics can also be taught to these youngsters. The physical education program should provide as many of these sports and games as possible. They provide the vigorous muscular activity essential to improved physical fitness in these youngsters, so many of whom are physically deficient. In addition to the physical benefits are the recreational and socializing values which have already been stressed.

Capable teachers have been able to teach the skills of team play well enough to mentally retarded students that they have been able to compete against teams of normal students. Some residential schools field baseball and basketball teams. The mentally retarded enjoy competition of this nature and desire it for the social approval which it brings them, but they do not always respond well. Defeat may promote undesirable aggressive behavior on the one hand or cause them to lose interest entirely on the other hand. The teacher coaching a competitive team should attempt to prevent these possible reactions through careful development of the best possible attitudes toward competitive play.

The mentally deficient enjoy music and rhythm and respond well to dance and rhythmic activities. Such activities are valuable in improving coordination, flexibility, and body carriage. Extensive dance activities, ranging in complexity from simple movements to musical accompaniment to folk dances of complex patterns, should be included in the physical education program. Moreover, they provide a release from tensions and anxieties, which is in itself extremely valuable for these students. The listening experience also heightens auditory perception.

QUESTIONS

1. Define these terms: totally dependent, trainable, educable.
2. What are the causes of mental deficiency?
3. Why does the physical education teacher play such an important role in the education of the mentally retarded?
4. What is the chief contributing factor to personality maladjustment in the mentally retarded?
5. Why is it important that the program of physical education for the mentally retarded provide a maximum amount of success in participation?
6. Discuss the techniques which may be used to motivate the mentally retarded in physical education.
7. Discuss the value of demonstration and kinesthesis as teaching methods in physical education for the mentally retarded.
8. At what time during the practice period should new skills be introduced? Why?
9. What implication does the fact that mentally retarded individuals frequently have low fitness have for the physical educator?
10. Refer to the suggested criteria for game selection for the mentally retarded. Explain why each suggestion is important.

SELECTED READINGS

American Association on Mental Deficiency: *A Manual on Terminology and Classification in Mental Retardation.* Monogram Supplement Journal 64, No. 2, 1958.

Dybwad, Gunnar: *Challenges in Mental Retardation.* New York, Columbia University Press, 1964.

Frampton, Merle E., and Gall, Elena D. (ed.): *Special Education for the Exceptional:* Vol. III — *Mental and Emotional Deviates and Special Problems.* Boston, Porter Sargent, Publisher, 1956.

President's Council on Mental Retardation: *A Proposed Program for National Action to Combat Mental Retardation.* Washington, D.C., U.S. Government Printing Office, 1962.

Robinson, Halbert B.: *The Mentally Retarded Child.* New York, McGraw-Hill Book Co., Inc., 1965.

Stevens, Harvey A., and Heber, Rick (ed.): *Mental Retardation: A Review of Research.* Chicago, University of Chicago Press, 1964.

Wallin, J. E. Wallace: *Education of Mentally Handicapped Children.* New York, Harper & Bros., 1955.

14
SOCIAL MALADJUSTMENT
AND MENTAL ILLNESS

The problems of those in our society who deviate from normal because of their inability to adjust to the circumstances of their environment are receiving increasing attention as the sociologists, psychiatrists, psychologists, and social workers expand the body of knowledge about the causes of social maladjustment and mental illness. In former times such people were labeled *criminal* and *insane* and were considered outcasts of society. Their treatment was, until modern times, usually harsh and cruel in the extreme as was thought to befit their status as outcasts. During the ancient and medieval periods of history, the mentally ill were regarded as being possessed by the devil and were often subjected to death by slow torture. Criminals received extremely harsh penalties for even very minor offenses. and brutal treatment was frequently administered publicly as a lesson both to the prisoner and to the witnesses. Gradually, as the nature of abnormal behavior in those who suffer mental illnesses and those who commit crimes against society came to be better understood, a more humanitarian approach was achieved toward the problems such individuals present. Institutions and hospitals were established for the custodial care and treatment of the mentally ill. Prison conditions were improved, and punitive measures began to be replaced with a more positive approach designed to rehabilitate the offenders. The modern-day concept of the treatment of those who demonstrate abnormal behavior is largely one of seeking out the causes and eliminating them; helping the individuals to achieve satisfactory adjustment and to develop normal behavior patterns, and providing the means by which they can return to society as useful, responsible, and contributing members.

In the rehabilitation of the socially maladjusted and the mentally ill, the provision of opportunities for fun and exercise through games, dancing, and sports is a very important facet of the over-all program, which usually also includes medical and psychiatric treatment and vocational and educational instruction. Because of his special knowledge of many types of games and the contributions which they can make to physical and emotional well-being, the physical educator is often called upon to direct the physical education programs for those housed in institutions for the mentally ill and for those whose behavior has caused them to be confined to penal institutions.

Programs for these types of institutions will be examined in detail in two sections of this chapter. A third section will be devoted to a pattern of abnormal behavior which, while it is of less consequence to society than the other two, may nevertheless be very damaging to the individual. It is that conduct which results from extreme fear or hatred of muscular activity. Students with violent dislikes for participation in physical education activities or with great fear of certain types of muscular activities need special help from the physical education teacher to dispel these extreme emotions so that they may participate with pleasure and gain for themselves the benefits of vigorous play. Such students may profit from the greater attention and more individually planned activities of the adapted physical education program.

THE NATURE OF MENTAL ILLNESS

Mental disorders are divided into two categories: *organic,* or *structural,* and *functional.* A structural disorder is produced as the result of injury or change in the nerve cells. The actual cause of the functional disorder is unknown; it appears not to be caused by any structural changes of the nervous system. It is undoubtedly influenced by the interplay between the individual and his environment and the nature of his adjustment. It is possible, also, that the disorder may be due to structural causes as yet undiscovered by medical science. The functional disorder can be further broken down into the two types in which most cases of functional disorder fall, schizophrenic and manic-depressive.

SCHIZOPHRENIA.   Schizophrenia is commonly known as the "split personality." This is very descriptive of the disorder, for in schizophrenia there is a splitting of intellect and emotion. The intellectual ability is divorced from other phases of the personality. Schizophrenics do not lose their mental capacities, as measured by intelligence quotient tests, but they no longer possess the ability to utilize their intelligence in solving their emotional problems.

The schizophrenic attempts to escape reality and the emotional conflicts he cannot resolve by seeking refuge in a world of fantasy. He tends to avoid all social contact and prefers privacy and solitude. Dissatisfied with himself or his position in life, he at times assumes the identity of another person, usually someone who is a famous and successful personality.

Schizophrenia may manifest itself in one of several different forms or in a combination of two or more of these. Classified as types, these forms are: simple, paranoid, hebephrenic, and catatonic.

The individual with the *simple* type of schizoid personality seems apathetic and indifferent but does not exhibit any other strikingly abnormal behavior. His reaction is occasionally misinterpreted as laziness. The individual with simple schizophrenia tends to withdraw and become seclusive, although he may adjust fairly well in a situation which does not demand too much of him.

Paranoid schizophrenia is characterized by delusions of grandeur and persecution. The paranoid patient is in touch with reality in certain areas of his life, but reasoning will not dispel his delusions. He frequently believes he hears strange voices and that certain people are exerting unnatural and damaging influences over him. Often these people take the form of enemies who are persecuting him.

Hebephrenic schizophrenia is marked by rapid deterioration, hallucination, and absurd illusions. Senseless laughter and silly mannerisms, such as the wearing of bizarre clothing, are common characteristics.

The *catatonic* is characterized by a morbid inclination to do the opposite of what normal desire would suggest or what most people would do. There are phases of stupor and excitement. The movements may be characterized by rigidity or sudden explosive movements. A static position is often assumed or a particular movement continually repeated.

MANIC-DEPRESSIVE PSYCHOSIS.   Manic-depressive psychosis involves marked disturbances in emotions, varying from extreme excitement and elation to fits of depression and despondency. The patient may alternate from one extreme to the other periodically. Some periods of emotion are relatively short, while others are as long as several months or even years.

When the patient is in the manic stage he may talk continually, pursue many thoughts at once, change interests frequently, and usually he is very active. In most cases he is extremely satisfied and happy. He is somewhat insensitive to fatigue, sometimes continuing activity for days without showing signs of tiring. He is difficult to calm in this state. He may be either very cooperative or very irritable and even belligerent. He is usually sensitive to the reaction of others to him.

In the depressive state the patient is less active. He usually experiences strong guilt feelings and uselessness and is very remorseful and sad. In this state he is difficult to stimulate and may demonstrate suicidal tendencies.

As a group, the physical health of mental patients with severe psychosis is poor. Physical fitness is frequently very low, particularly for those who have withdrawn from social contacts and hence from active participation in physical activities. Confinement to hospital wards does not permit sufficient physical activity to maintain a minimum level of physical fitness, unless special consideration is given to planning for muscular activity. Although it is not known how close the relationship may be between physical fitness and mental health, an interrelationship has been well established and it would appear to be advantageous to the mental patient to maintain good physical fitness.

Aside from improving physical fitness, the role that meaningful activities can play in the lives of these patients is well recognized. Hospital routine which is unbroken with pleasant activities tends to produce boredom and lack of ambition. Mental patients who have no interesting activities to fill their long hours have been observed to lose all interest in their appearance, to become slovenly and untidy in their personal care, and to give little heed to the treatment and care provided for them. A program of physical education is able to provide for this dual need for vigorous muscular activity to improve physical fitness and for meaningful recreational activities which add to the zest of living.

Muscular activity following emotional stress tends to nullify some of the physiological reaction to extreme emotion. It is known that anxiety or other strong emotions cause the body to undergo certain changes preparatory to action, such as increased flow of epinephrine, change in the size of capillaries, increased rate of blood flow, and disturbances in the flow of gastric juices. As a result, such functional disorders as indigestion and stomach upset may occur. But they are not usually evident if the strong emotions are followed by physical exertion. It would appear, then, that some of the physiological disturbances resulting from frequent emotional stress might be removed by vigorous workouts. Participation in physical activity also provides an acceptable outlet for pent-up emotions and release from aggressive tendencies. For those who have difficulty expressing themselves to their emotional satisfaction, kinesthetic or muscular movement offers a satisfying outlet.

Depressed patients need to be motivated to participate in muscular activity. This is the first step in rehabilitation. Disinterest and depression are often alleviated when patients engage in play activities. It has been postulated that play activities awaken in the patients pleasant childhood memories of play and create an association of pleasantness with their current activities.

THE PROGRAM FOR THE MENTALLY ILL

In developing a physical education program for the mentally ill, one must consider the individual needs of the patients. The kind of mental illness is not the chief factor in determining the types of activities that will be of the most value to them. Individual differences in abilities and interests are just as prevalent among the psychotic as among the normal. However, the classification of the patient will give the physical educator some clue as to the type of activities which the patient can engage in with success and pleasure. For example, the catatonic who exhibits some degree of rigidity in muscular movement is not able to participate in highly organized team sports but probably can and should participate in such activities as ball (or, if very severe, balloon) tossing and catching. Patients in a very hyperactive state respond fairly well to strenuous physical activities that make them tired physically. Strenuous activities also aid in stabilizing the physiological reaction of the body to strong emotions, as was discussed earlier.

It should be remembered that the total number of patients for whom the program is to be planned will usually be fairly large and will contain all types of mental disorders. Consequently, the program must be carefully organized with the advice of the hospital's medical staff.

The activities which are offered should include those with which the patient has had experience before coming to the institution. New games should be offered and can be taught successfully if properly motivated. As part of the motivating process, a wide variety of game equipment can be displayed for the patients to look at and handle. When an interest in a particular piece has been kindled, the instructor may talk to the patient about it and show him how to use it. As the patient tries it out, he is encouraged to continue to play with it. Instruction should be simple and informal.

Group participation in play activities is highly desirable for the social contacts it makes possible. Some patients may experience considerable strain in social adjustment, so it may be necessary to work gradually toward group activities, progressing from spectatorship to individual sport to dual sport and eventually to small group activity. As the patients become accustomed to group play, staff members and volunteer assistants who visit the hospitals may be included in the group to increase the scope of the patients' social contacts. Having such individuals join in the activity also provides an incentive for approved social conduct, but they should be very careful not to dominate the game or detract in any way from the successful performance of the patient.

Basic skill games and exercises which do not require fine coordination are usually the most suitable. Patients who are very regressed are easily frustrated by activities requiring numerous movement patterns and detailed directions. Activities of limited responses and simple structure which may be successfully used are: shuffleboard, casting, croquet, horseshoes, ring toss, bowling, weightlifting, bag punching, and the basic sport skills of throwing, catching, dribbling, and hitting a ball. A certain element of competition in the games is usually not disapproved. For most patients, contact sports and highly competitive games which tend to encourage the expression of aggression directly toward others are contraindicated.

Not all of the play activities should be organized for the patients.

They should be provided with opportunities to check out equipment and play on their own; they should also have the chance for passive and spectator participation in sport activities. Patients engaging in impromptu play must be made to understand the regulations which have been established in regard to their use of the equipment and facilities during unsupervised periods. Strict adherence to safety precautions should be expected and received from the patients. If a patient must be denied permission to use the equipment or refused any other request made of the physical education instructor, this should be done upon an impersonal basis so the patient will not feel hurt or discriminated against.

Co-recreational activities in which the two sexes can mingle socially should be given appropriate attention in the program. Because of the appeal of music to the emotions of the patients, one of the most successful co-recreational activities is social dancing. Those who do not wish to dance often enjoy watching the others, and a dance can become a very special event in the lives of the entire hospital population. Square and folk dances are usually too complicated in structure for most patients, although they are greatly enjoyed by some. Those who cannot participate in these forms of dance can be encouraged to perform simple rhythmic activities to music. Modern or interpretative dance appears to hold interesting possibilities as a therapeutic aid for patients whose other means of expression are blocked. Because of the strong emotional involvement in this type of dance expression, it is recommended that this form of dance be approached only with the consultation of the hospital's medical personnel.

Swimming should be included among the activities of the program because of the desirable effects which water has upon the patients. It frequently acts as a stimulant to the depressed and encourages movement in catatonics. Hyperactive patients are often greatly relaxed by the water, particularly if it is warmer than normal.

The instructor must plan for successful participation in the activities by the patients. Success is extremely important to them. To be successful does not necessitate being a winner, but it does require that the activity be fun and self-satisfying. To insure success the instructor must consider the special needs of each patient and any sports interests he has displayed; he must give him friendly, patient instruction in the skills; and he must continually encourage the patient toward a wider interest in play and the people who play. Above all, the patient should be treated as an individual who is deserving of respect and consideration.

THE NATURE AND CAUSES OF SOCIAL MALADJUSTMENT

Social maladjustment resulting in abnormal behavior constitutes one of the greatest social problems of our day. It is not always easy to determine the dividing line between normal and abnormal behavior, although the difference at the extremes is readily observed. Extremely abnormal conduct is antisocial, destructive to the personality, and often ends in actual criminal action. It varies in degree from very slight deviation from accepted conduct to serious breaches of the law.

When does abnormal behavior become delinquency? The National Probation and Parole Association has established these conditions as indicative of delinquent behavior: (1) violation of any laws; (2) habitual waywardness or disobedience which cannot be controlled by the parents, guardians, or custodians; and (3) conduct which injures or endangers the morals or health of the individual or others.

It is recognized that there is no one universal cause of delinquency. It is the result of many different influences of the environment upon the individual. Statistics indicate that a large majority of delinquents come from underprivileged homes, broken homes, or homes with poor discipline (lax, overstrict, or erratic).[1] Lack of parental love and leaving a child to his own devices without supervision or the provision for meaningful use of leisure time are other important factors in the development of delinquent behavior. Considerable attention has been directed toward the violence depicted in the entertainment media as an influence upon delinquent conduct; the extent of the influence has not been established, although some authorities are inclined to feel that it may certainly tip the scale in that direction. It is also frequently stated that lack of recreational facilities is a factor, but this appears to be chiefly an excuse for delinquency rather than a basic cause.

The presence of any or all of the contributing factors in the life of any one person does not necessarily result in delinquent behavior on his part. The significance of the influence exerted by any unfavorable conditions varies from person to person, depending upon his previous background and training and his individual nature. Many children grow up under these conditions without ever exhibiting delinquent behavior, while many others become delinquents in their youth and criminals in their adult lives.

Drawing upon this evidence, it would appear that there are two motivating forces in delinquency. One of these is the adherence of the individual to group mores which do not conform to the general mores of society. The group has a distorted sense of values; its concept of right and wrong is not in agreement with generally accepted standards and with established laws and regulations. The group is likely to consist of a gang of contemporaries but it may also be a family group. Antisocial conduct is actually encouraged by some families, in which children are taught to steal and to "get by" the law, while in other families the lack of moral example and instruction contributes to the social maladjustment of the children.

The other motivating force stems from conflict. In this situation,

[1]Harry J. Baker: *Introduction to Exceptional Children*, ed. 3. New York, The Macmillan Co., 1959, pp. 60–68.

delinquent behavior is a neurotic expression of the conflict. Early childhood conflicts resulting from unsatisfactory family relationships may develop in a person a lasting sense of hostility toward the world or toward himself. Studies comparing delinquent and nondelinquent siblings have shown that the delinquents had a very unsatisfactory relationship with their parents while their brothers and sisters did not. Conflicts with parents in disciplinary matters and conflicts with siblings for the love and attention of the parents give rise to feelings of inadequacy and inferiority which find outlet in forms of undesirable behavior.

Peculiar characteristics of the behavior of delinquents and potential delinquents which have been noted are marked willfulness, defiance, suspicion and hostility without cause, desire to destroy and hurt others and themselves, and desire for excitement, change, or risk. Feelings of insecurity and worthlessness are common to these individuals.

Many programs are organized with the expressed purpose of combating delinquency among youngsters by providing them opportunities to gain attention and success in socially acceptable ways. It is hoped that in this way they will gain the respect for themselves and others which their home training and environment have denied them. A large part of such programs consists of sports activities designed to promote both the physical and social well-being of these youngsters, who are often as much in need of physical improvement as social rehabilitation. Numerous physical educators have found their life work as directors and instructors in such programs; many more give their free time to volunteer instruction in sport skills.

Delinquent behavior in the classrooms is a constant problem in many schools. The physical education teacher often has a better opportunity than other teachers to contribute to the solution of this problem, owing to the universal appeal of sports for young people. Using this appeal as a motivator, the teacher of physical education is often able to involve a delinquent in constructive play from which some degree of personal success is likely to result. This success, for one who has never known success, often provides the motivation and incentive for a more desirable and acceptable mode of conduct.

It is, of course, beyond the scope of his training for the physical educator to give treatment to the individual delinquent. However, his patience and understanding, his general philosophy, and his method of control may have a far-reaching effect upon such a student. Toward this end, the following suggestions are offered to the teacher:

(1) aim to understand the delinquent and his problems so that you will know why he acts as he does;

(2) isolate his chief grievance, help him to understand why it irritates him, and then help him determine acceptable ways of alleviating it;

(3) discover some things that he is able to do well, for which he will receive favorable recognition;

(4) enlist the cooperation of a small group of classmates to help develop his self-confidence;

(5) try to find a way to have any physical defects corrected, including minor ones;

(6) keep the program for helping him flexible, letting him know that it is an attempt to help him become a better person;

(7) do not become discouraged by relapses in conduct but continue to express confidence that the delinquent will improve;

(8) secure professional help when it is needed and is available.

THE PROGRAM FOR DELINQUENTS

The physical education program in reformatories and prisons is largely a recreational sports program. While it is recognized that participation in sports does not contribute directly to the control of delinquent behavior, it does provide a certain degree of motivation and incentive for a certain mode of conduct during the game. Sometimes the desire to participate can be used to motivate desirable conduct at other times as well. If the sports program is particularly effective and enjoyed by the participants, it can be a strong incentive to better conduct so that the opportunities to play will not be jeopardized.

The sports program for these people has benefits other than its possible influence upon behavior. It provides invigorating activity which has wide interest appeal, it makes possible social intercourse in a controlled situation, it encourages the release of strong emotions and aggressive tendencies, and it provides some measure of success in lives which are largely filled with failures.

Greatest benefits are secured from the sports program that offers as wide a variety of different sports and games as possible, so that all interests can be met and everyone given an opportunity to play, or learn to play, one or more games successfully. Competition should be equalized by division of players into squads of like ability. Competition is good because it heightens interest and may provide an outlet for aggressive tendencies. Intramural competition can be easily arranged, and a varsity team may be possible if games can be scheduled with teams in neighboring towns who are willing to come to the institution to play. Scheduling may present difficulties, but it is extremely worthwhile for the contact that it establishes with the outside world.

Any link with the world from which they have been removed is important to the morale of those confined in penal institutions. Consequently, the celebration of holidays with special sports events is desirable. Fun and activity are associated with holidays at home, and special provisions for holiday observances help to create a necessary link between home and institution.

EXTREME HATE OR FEAR OF PHYSICAL EDUCATION

Extreme hate and fear of physical education manifest themselves at all educational levels, from elementary school to college. Hatred of muscular activity can usually be traced to unfavorable experiences in physical education. Fears are most often stimulated by particular types of activities which are associated with danger in the minds of certain students, swimming being the most common. Fear of swimming ranges from a more or less normal reaction to water, because of lack of swimming skill, to aquaphobia in which there is extreme fear of water. Contact sports elicit great fear in some students while activities such as rope climbing, tumbling, and apparatus work may evoke fears in others.

In young children a reaction of dislike usually stems from fear of the activity or factors inherent within the situation itself. Overprotectiveness of parents and inexperience in play activities are chiefly responsible for abnormal emotional reactions to physical education activities. In older children the fears are usually more deep-seated than in the younger child. Lack of experience may be the reason, although unsatisfactory experience in such activities is the more usual cause. Fear of ridicule and continual defeat in achievement of physical performance are important contributing factors. Fear of physical injury is yet another factor.

Dislike and hate in older students may develop from a long history of continual fear as well as from experiences in poor physical education programs which promoted none of the values inherent in well-planned programs. This reason for dislike is more prevalent among high school upperclassmen and college students. In the majority of cases this dislike does not result in any great deviation in behavior; however, some students go to great lengths to avoid class participation. Malingering is the method most frequently used, in the hope of being excused from participation for physical reasons.

Students who experience extreme dislike, fear, and hate for physical education need special help in overcoming their strong emotional reactions to muscular activity. If circumstances permit, they should be placed for a time in the adapted program, where attention can be given to seeking out the cause which has prompted the emotion and overcoming it. When it is not possible to accommodate these students in the adapted program, individual conferences with the students can achieve the same objectives.

In either situation, the student should be indoctrinated with the values of physical education. The facts of the physiological benefits of exercise should be described dramatically and in a vocabulary appropriate to the student's educational achievement. The fun of playing and the social benefits to be derived from it should be given special emphasis. If fear of injury is the basis of the strong emotional reaction, the student should be given every reassurance that the possibility of injury is minimal. All the various precautions that are exercised to insure the safety of the players should be demonstrated to him. He should also be given instruction in falling to avoid injury to help him realize that there is little danger of personal injury even in vigorous activity. Exposure of such students to actual participation should be very gradual. The technique of helping a student overcome a fear will be described here in detail, in order to suggest ways in which a student can be led gradually into an activity which he fears.

Perhaps the most common fear of students in physical education is of water. Unless the student has an actual water phobia, he can usually overcome fear of the water through a careful process of introduction to it. A student with a phobia cannot as a rule be persuaded even to enter the pool area and will require special help from a psychiatrist or psychologist. The others should be requested to come to the pool and sit on the edge with their feet in the water. They are informed that nothing else is expected of them, but if they feel like getting into the water they may do so. After a day or two of sitting on the pool's edge it is likely that even the most reluctant student will venture into the water. From here on, the techniques are much the same as those recommended for introducing any beginner to the water; however, progress may be considerably slower and the instructor should never force or rush the students. It may, for instance, take much longer before a student who is mastering fear of the water will splash water into his face than for the normal beginner. Care must be taken to prevent splashing and commotion by experienced swimmers who may be in the pool at the same time; and, above all, no ridiculing remarks should be tolerated. It is easier, of course, if those with water fears can be alone in the pool until they overcome their fears, but this is not usually possible. Hence it is very important that careful control be exercised over the other students who are present.

Lack of success in performance and generally unfavorable physical education experiences are the usual underlying causes of extreme dislike of physical education activities. Students who hate physical education class because they are always last in the race and repeatedly in error when playing the ball are very numerous. Subnormal coordination, strength, and endurance are the usual basis of failure to perform well, and work in the adapted program on fitness exercises will greatly benefit these students. The instructor should also encourage these students to practice skills during their free hours. He might also refer them to visual aids and reading materials which may be used to learn more about the techniques of skill performance. He should give them as much individual instruction as possible in helping to analyze and overcome skill faults. Those whose dislikes stems from former poor physical education experiences may need a period of indoctrination to convince them of the values of physical education. Every effort should be made to arouse the interest of these students in a special game or sport which they will learn to perform with success and pleasure and which can then be used as a springboard to broader participation.

QUESTIONS

1. Trace the public attitude and treatment of the criminal and the insane throughout the history of civilization.

2. Describe the difference between functional and structural mental disorders.

3. List the different types of mental disorders and describe the common characteristics of each.

4. What place does physical education play in the health and welfare of the mental patients in hospitals?

5. Discuss possible ways of motivating the depressed patient in physical education activities.

6. Define social maladjustment and delinquent behavior.

7. What are some of the factors contributing to delinquency?

8. What part does wholesome recreation have in the prevention of delinquency?

9. Compare the use of highly competitive sports in institutions and schools for delinquents with their use in mental hospitals.

10. What techniques may be utilized by the physical education teacher in helping students to overcome their fears of certain aspects of the physical education program?

11. What are some of the possible reasons for the extreme dislike of physical education by some students?

SELECTED READINGS

Clinard, Marshall B.: *Sociology of Deviant Behavior*, ed. 2. New York, Holt, Rinehart & Winston, Inc., 1963.

Frampton, Merle E., and Gall, Elena D. (ed.): *Special Education for the Exceptional*; Vol. III—*Mental and Emotional Deviates and Special Problems*. Boston, Porter Sargent, Publisher, 1956.

Glueck, Sheldon and Eleanor: *Delinquents in the Making. Paths to Prevention*. New York, Harper & Brothers, 1952.

Haring, Norris G., and Phillips, Ewing L.: *Educating Emotionally Disturbed Children*. New York, McGraw-Hill Book Co., Inc., 1962.

Heck, Arch O.: *The Education of Exceptional Children*, ed. 2. New York, McGraw-Hill Book Co., Inc., 1953.

Hunt, Valerie V.: *Recreation for the Handicapped*. New York, Prentice-Hall, Inc., 1955.

Lewis, Hilda: *Deprived Children: A Social and Clinical Study*. London, Oxford University Press, 1954.

Patterson, Charles H.: *Counseling the Emotionally Disturbed*. New York, Harper & Brothers, 1958.

Redl, Fritz and Wineman, David: *Children Who Hate: The Disorganization and Breakdown of Behavior Control*. Glencoe, Ill. The Free Press of Glencoe, 1951.

15
AGING

Until very recently in man's history, death at an early age was the common expectation. Lack of sanitation, famine, and pestilence took a heavy toll among young and old alike. But as man learned to control his environment, he reduced the mortality rate and increased life expectancy. The probable life span of an infant born today is nearly twice as great as that of a baby born during the 18th century. This great statistical increase is due largely to the decrease in the number of deaths among infants and young children. However, the declining mortality rate has benefited all age groups, and a considerable proportion of those who reach the age of 65 can expect to be alive 20 years later.

The number of aged men and women in our population has continually increased during the past two centuries but particularly during the last half century. The total population of the United States has doubled since 1900, but the number of persons over the age of 65 has quadrupled. There are more women than men in this upper age bracket; over the age of 65 there are approximately nine men to every 10 women. The substantial increase in size of the older segment of our population and the reliable indications of its continued increase have aroused nationwide interest during the past decade in the problems of aging. Conferences and workshops have been held to study and make recommendations for solving the problems of the aged. Governmental and private agencies have been organized to provide services. Much research is being conducted in the area of gerontology, the study of aging; geriatric medicine has become both a challenge and a major concern.

173

Among the problems of the aged, the satisfying use of increased leisure time has received particular attention. However, consideration of sports and games and other physical education activities in this connection has been largely in terms of leisure-time recreation. The value of these activities in improving and maintaining physical conditioning has not received deserved attention. It is anticipated, however, that as the contributions of physical activity to the psychological and physical well-being of the aged are more fully recognized, physical education for elderly persons will become an important area of consideration.

THE NATURE OF THE AGING PROBLEM

Chronological age is not an exclusive indicator of the extent and degree of aging. In comparing the chronological with the physiological, emotional, and intellectual ages, one often finds considerable discrepancy. The process of aging is not completely understood, but certain changes are known to take place. Changes observed to occur in aging include cellular atrophy, retardation of cell growth and tissue repair, degeneration of the nervous system, gradual reduction in basal metabolic rate, reduced capacity to produce immune bodies, and gradual impairment of the homeostasis. An older person becomes more susceptible to chronic disabling diseases, cardiovascular ailments, malignant neoplasia, and cerebral vascular accidents. The decrease in the immune bodies makes old people, in many instances, more susceptible to infections. Their bones are more prone to fracture and repair more slowly following injury. Diminished acuity of the sense organs also accompanies aging; hearing ability decreases and vision becomes impaired. There is an increased tendency for the development of farsightedness; in instances where a person has been nearsighted in youth, this sometimes effects an improvement in vision.

There is also a decrease in motor efficiency. Speed, strength, endurance, coordination, and flexibility diminish gradually as one grows older. How much this decline is dependent upon the aging process and how much upon decreased muscular activity is not clearly established. It has been demonstrated in many cases that those who continue to participate extensively in physical activities lose their motor abilities at a much slower rate than those who do not. Some of the physical degeneration that occurs in the aging process can be duplicated in the young by enforced inactivity: decrease in muscle size and strength, endurance, power, coordination, flexibility, deterioration of bone cells, and the development of poor digestion can be produced at any age.

Psychological changes in aging follow an even less uniform pattern than physiological changes and, as a rule, do not usually occur as early. Loss of memory of recent events is a psychogenic phenomenon of aging. Speed in recall and organization of thoughts is diminished in some older people. Conservatism is a characteristic mental attitude commonly ascribed to older people; this is probably true only to the extent that anyone hesitates to change a mode of conduct which he has formerly found satisfying. It is apparent, however, that as people grow older, they lose faith in their ability to acquire new skills and, consequently, tend to cling to familiar activities. It seems likely that many of the emotional and mental characteristics of the aged are not the direct result of aging but are, rather, related to the role they are expected by society to take as old people.

NEEDS AND ADJUSTMENTS OF THE AGED

A large portion of our population past the age of 65 is constituted of those who have been retired from the jobs at which they earned their livelihoods. While retirement does afford the retired worker an opportunity to take life easier and to relax and enjoy such anticipated pleasures as extended traveling, it is usually not long before he is forced into a realization of his new role. Where he was once accorded recognition as the head of a family, he is now likely to be thought of as an elder in need of care and protection. Where he formerly enjoyed status as a contributing member of society, he is now likely to feel unwanted and unneeded. Freedom from the workday routine liberates a large portion of the day for the retired worker and for the housewife, but this time becomes increasingly difficult to fill with satisfying activities in a society which relegates the aged to the side lines. Adjustment to these circumstances is likely to be further complicated by the death of the spouse, particularly the husband, and possibly of friends and associates.

Without these companionships and without the former demands on his time, the day becomes a series of long lonely hours. Unless activities can be found to fill the hours, boredom is certain to result. Daydreaming and reminiscing become favorite escapes from loneliness and boredom. Such mechanisms are undesirable from the standpoint of good mental health; they are also detrimental to physical health because they discourage the physical activity necessary to maintaining a satisfactory standard of fitness. Active participation in play activities could provide physically beneficial and mentally and emotionally stimulating use of leisure time. However, it is extremely difficult for people who have been increasingly physically inactive over a period of two or three decades to become interested in muscular activity after retirement.

Vitally needed in present-day society is a positive promotion of the understanding among youngsters and young adults of the importance of continued muscular activity to total well-being. A large proportion of present-day youngsters leave school without a proper appreciation of the contributions which physical activity makes to their lives. They then become so involved in their own problems after leaving school that they

FIGURE 22.   Opportunities for social intercourse and for beneficial exercise are provided by a game of croquet. (National Recreation Association.)

give up active participation in sport and play activities. The sedentary occupations of the technological age deprive many workers of the vigorous physical activity which was once essential to earning a living. Other changes, such as modern transportation and mechanized homes, further reduce the necessity for physical exertion. A lack of muscular activity characterizes the life of the young wage earner and becomes a pattern of living until retirement. By then habits are established, physical fitness is lowered, and motor skills are greatly reduced.

In a society in which mechanization is increasingly eliminating the necessity of muscular activity in the daily routine of living, other means must be interjected to provide the benefits to the body of a vigorous physical workout. Sports and play activities seem to offer the best opportunity of doing this. And our schools offer the best place in which to educate the citizenry about the importance of physical activity to well-being. The physical education program at all levels, but particularly in the late high school and college years, should concentrate on giving students a broad skills program, with many sports and games which can be played long after the school years. If a student learns to play several games well, he is very likely to continue to play them during his leisure hours throughout his adult life, and he will not then need to be convinced of the importance of continuing to be physically active after he reaches retirement age.

Participation in play activities does more than help the aged individual to keep physically fit. It provides him many opportunities for socialization with others of his own age who enjoy the same games, and with younger players whom he can meet on a common ground in a shared interest. Making new friends among different age groups eases the emotional strain of having lost friends and relatives in the contemporary age group. Moreover, the mere knowledge that he is able to play with others and that he is still capable of learning new skills reinforces his self-esteem and helps to negate the feelings of uselessness intrinsic to his role as an aged member of our society.

PLANNING THE PROGRAM

As has been indicated, the best solution to the problem of encouraging participation in physical activity among the aged of the future is the development of positive attitudes and numerous carry-over sports skills in the physical education programs in which they are enrolled as elementary school, high school, and college young people so that, as young adults, they will not completely divorce themselves from physical education activities upon leaving the school environment. The school program must be planned so time may be devoted to instruction on the necessity for physical fitness and the ways in which it may be achieved and maintained; this to be complemented with practical conditioning activities and broad experience in sports and games.

Our present aged group contains many who have not been educated to the need for physical activity and who have no confidence in their ability to learn new motor skills, even though they may become convinced of the value of muscular activity. These people can often be reached through city recreation programs, "Golden Age" clubs, and other community organizations promoting projects for the aged. The physical educator is often invited to speak at programs for the aged or to help instruct them in the use of recreational facilities such as croquet and shuffleboard courts, pitch and putt courses, and casting pools which have been made available to them. Given such opportunities, he can stress the importance of physical activity and give them the confidence and encouragement they need to begin a program of increased muscular activity.

Recreational opportunities are being expanded for old people confined to their own homes or to convalescent homes largely through volunteer leadership. The physical educator may wish to contribute time to such a project either in working directly in an activity program with patients or in training other volunteer workers in the presentation of physical education activities to those who are confined. A few of the more advanced homes for the aged employ trained personnel to direct their activities programs. In some communities several "homes" employ a director cooperatively, sharing the cost and the services. The director usually recruits and trains volunteers to assist him in the programs.

Before active participation in physical education activities begins,

FIGURE 23. Active participation through the years helps to maintain a high level of tolerance for exercise. (National Recreation Association.)

older players should be made thoroughly aware early in their program of muscular activities of the necessity for moderation. A thorough physical examination is recommended to determine any specific limitations or restrictions upon physical activity. The tolerance to exercise must also be clearly identified. Years of inactivity create a physical condition of the body which cannot tolerate excessive exercise. Those who have once participated in the more vigorous sports have a tendency to over-do when beginning a program of physical activity, because they do not recognize that their capacity for strenuous work has decreased.

Some older people will be extremely difficult to motivate. A thorough understanding of the benefits that may be expected from physical activity is an excellent motivator, because almost everyone wishes to experience the joys of increased well-being. Visual aids of various types illustrating the benefits of exercise to the human body may be used to good advantage in convincing a reluctant group. The very best motivation, however, is the fun of playing. The benefits of physical activity will not be immediately apparent; consequently, some motivation for continued exercise is necessary, and the sheer pleasure of the activity is probably the best guarantee that it will be repeated. Then, as the physical benefits of the increased muscular activity begin to manifest themselves, special motivation will no longer be necessary.

The physical educator planning a program for the aged might use the following as a guide to insure the safety and fun of the participants:

1. Areas of the body weakened or damaged by injury or disease should be adequately protected.

2. Medical recommendations for limitations and restrictions in activity should be strictly observed.

3. Frequent rest periods should be enforced. A player who shows signs of fatigue or breathlessness should cease activity immediately.

4. Players should be discouraged from giving undue concern to the perfection of skills. Having fun is more important than good form.

5. Encouragement and praise should be offered generously; confidence in themselves and pride in accomplishment are extremely important to the emotional stability of old people.

6. Some time should be devoted to introductions and socializing so that the participants may become acquainted.

7. Part of the play period may be spent in planning activities in which the group has an interest; assuming responsibility in planning and organizing the games and activities helps to promote self-esteem.

THE PROGRAM FOR THE AGED

Of all the factors in sports performance, speed decreases the most rapidly with advancing years. Endurance diminishes considerably but usually not to the extent of speed. Strength in most instances decreases less than either speed or endurance. The program of activities which is planned for a group of aged participants should give recognition to these facts, and games which place great demand on speed, sudden explosive power (in which speed is a factor), and endurance should not be included. Activities which are largely a matter of skill hold the most appeal and promise of success in performance.

The success of a program often depends upon the way in which is is introduced. All of us like to go from the known to the unknown, from the easy to the difficult. It becomes essential, therefore, to begin a program for older persons with activities which they already know or which they can learn easily. Pitching quoits and horseshoes are sports known and enjoyed by most men. Shuffleboard has proved very popular with oldsters and is another good activity to initiate the program. For those who require less demanding activity, the ring toss or beanbag toss makes a good opening activity. The important thing is that the activity be one the participant can perform or learn to do easily and with enjoyment. Upon this successfully established base, then, other activities more demanding and perhaps more beneficial can be built.

Possibilities for the activities program for the aged follow, with suggested adaptations for those with very low physical fitness. Attention is directed toward the fact that the temperament of each individual greatly influences how vigorously he performs an activity, so that a game which may be only mildly or moderately active for one may be quite strenuous for another who goes "all out" in sports performance. Allowances for these individual differences must necessarily be made in the program.

Archery: May be played without modification; a lighter bow may be used by those lacking strength and the distance to the target reduced.

Bowling and Bowling on the green: May be played without modification; emphasis on form is not important.

Canoeing and Rowing: No modification is necessary, but special safety measures may be necessary for getting in and out of the canoe or boat. The wearing of life preservers may give a greater feeling of security.

Shuffleboard: May be played without modification.

Croquet: May be played without modification. Wickets should be painted white so they can be easily seen.

Deck tennis: May be played without modification.

Fly and bait casting: No modification is necessary; participants unable to stand for long periods may be seated in chairs.

Skish: An excellent casting game for those for whom fishing expeditions are too strenuous.

Horseshoes: May be played without modification. Ring toss may be substituted for any who find horseshoes too difficult.

Dancing (folk, social, and square): Strenuous dances may be modified by slowing the tempo. Circle dances which require no partners are good for groups in which the women outnumber the men.

Skating and Skiing: Suitable for participation by experienced participants; there is too much risk of serious injury in falling for beginners.

Handball and Squash rackets: Suitable for experienced players in good physical condition; doubles will be less strenuous.

Swimming: Suitable for experienced swimmers if endurance is not taxed in swimming long distances; the learning of the strokes will probably be too strenuous for oldsters who are out of condition, although they can participate in water play.

Badminton: Suitable as doubles for experienced players in good physical condition; may be further modified by reducing the width of the court by one half and eliminating the drop shot. A game can be equalized for a young player and an older opponent by permitting the latter to play on a reduced court while the former plays the full court.

Tennis: Suitable as doubles for experienced players in good physical condition: further modification consists of reducing the width of the court by one half and eliminating the drop shot.

Volleyball and Softball: Suitable for play by all those in moderately good physical condition.

Golf: Suitable for those in good physical condition; if endurance is low, the number of holes played may be reduced. Those not able to play regular golf may participate in such adaptations as pitch and putt or miniature golf. Driving balls into a wire practice cage and placing chip shots into a wastebasket are other possibilities for employing golf skills.

Calisthenics: Very mild calisthenics are suitable for all; their strenuousness may be gradually increased as the physical fitness level rises. Flexibility exercises are particularly valuable. Exercise suggestions applicable to the aged may be found in Chapters 24 and 25.

Bed and wheelchair exercises: For old people confined to bed or wheelchairs, the exercises and activities suggested in Chapter 10 for convalescing patients may be used.

Games[1]: Many of the basic skill games learned in childhood are enjoyed by oldsters and provide good exercise for them.

[1]For a description of basic skill games see Chapter 16.

QUESTIONS

1. Explain why the approximate age span of man has nearly doubled in the last century.
2. How do the problems of physical education for the aging differ from those in recreation for the aging?
3. Discuss the statement that chronological age is not an exclusive indicator of the extent and degree of aging.
4. What is the nature of the aging process?
5. Which characteristics of aging can be duplicated in the young through enforced inactivity? What is the significance of this?
6. What are the chief psychological problems of the aging? In what ways are they significant to the physical educator?
7. What opportunities does the school of today have to promote a better understanding and to shape attitudes toward the need of continued physical activity for the aged of tomorrow?
8. List the values that may occur in a well-planned physical education program for the aged.
9. What opportunities exist in most communities for the promotion of physical education among the older age group?
10. In what ways can older people be motivated to participate in muscular activities?
11. Look at the guide for planning a physical education program for the aged on page 179. State why each of these principles is applicable.
12. Which of the factors in sports skills performance decreases most rapidly? What influence does this fact have upon physical education programing for the aged?
13. What physical education activities usually hold the most interest for the aged?
14. What criteria would you use in recommending activities for old people?

SELECTED READINGS

Arthur, Juliette K.: *How To Help Older People: A Guide for You and Your Family.* Philadelphia, J. B. Lippincott Co., 1954.
Cratty, Bryant J.: *Movement Behavior and Motor Learning.* Philadelphia, Lea & Febiger, 1964.
Donahue, Wilma T. (ed.): *Education for Later Maturity.* New York, Whiteside, Inc., 1955.
Donahue, Wilma T., *et al.* (eds.): *Free Time: Challenge to Later Maturity.* Ann Arbor, Mich., University of Michigan Press, 1958.
Frampton, Merle E., and Gall, Elena D. (ed.): *Special Education for the Exceptional:* Vol. III— *Mental and Emotional Deviates and Special Problems.* Boston, Porter Sargent, Publisher, 1956.

Kubic, Susan H., and Landau, Gertrude: *Group Work with the Aged.* New York, International Universities Press, Inc., 1953.

Lansing, Albert I.: *Problems of Aging,* ed. 3. Baltimore, The Williams & Wilkins Co., 1952.

Lowry, Louis: *Adult Education and Group Work.* New York, Whiteside, Inc., 1955.

Shock, Nathan W.: *Trends in Gerontology,* ed. 2. Stanford, Cal., Stanford University Press, 1957.

Welford, A. T.: *Ageing and Human Skill.* London, Oxford University Press, 1958.

Williams, Arthur M.: *Recreation in the Senior Years.* New York. Association Press, 1962.

16
BASIC SKILL GAMES

The familiar games of childhood have a definite place in the physical education program of all elementary school children, regardless of their mental and physical capacities. Most of these activities require little or no equipment and are easily organized for play. For this reason, they are often called *low organized games*. It seems more fitting, however, to refer to them as *basic skill games* because of the important contributions they make to the basic development of the physical, mental, and social skills of young children. To fail to provide any child with the opportunities for development engendered by play in the basic skill games is to deny him entrance to one of the best avenues to optimum growth and development.

ORGANIZING THE INSTRUCTION

Because the space required for playing the basic skill games need not be large, the games can be organized for play almost anywhere—on the playground, in the classroom, in the gymnasium or all-purpose room, even in hallways. Equipment is relatively simple and inexpensive: balls, beanbags, boxes, batons, and Indian clubs. Most of these items are easily obtained or readily improvised. Beanbags, for example, can be made from scrap cloth sewn into a bag and filled with dried beans or rice. Pieces of wood of suitable size and free of splinters may be substituted for Indian clubs and batons.

In situations where normal and handicapped children are playing together, it is usually more desirable to integrate the handicapped with their normal peers. Sometimes this will not be feasible, and then the handicapped children may be grouped separately to play one game while the other children play another game. A game to be played by the handicapped may be totally adapted or modified in part as required by the limitations of the players. For example, if no one is able to run, the game is modified to substitute a slow walk for the running. However, if, for example, only one child in the group is unable to run, the game may be adapted to permit this child to choose another child to run in his place when his turn comes.

CHOOSING THE RIGHT GAME

The selection of games for use in the program for any given class depends upon the objectives being sought, the abilities of the children, and the space, time, and equipment available. An analysis of the nature of a game indicates which objectives the game may be expected to accomplish. A game that centers around the use of a ball or beanbag probably contributes to the development of the basic skills of catching and throwing and so satisfies that particular objective. The abilities of the children can be determined both by observation and testing. Procedures for the latter are discussed in Chapter 25.

To facilitate the selection of appropriate games for each grade level, the games that follow have been labeled according to the levels for which they are most suited as determined by the abilities, interests, and needs of young children. It must be remembered, however, that the manner in which a game is presented has a direct bearing on its acceptance by any age group. In the case of mentally retarded children, the chronological age cannot always be relied upon as an effective guide for choosing appropriate games. Games for younger children, however, may be considered too babyish by the retarded, and they will refuse to play them or be so embarrassed while playing them that the potential value of the game is lost. Care must be exercised in selecting games that these children, particularly the older ones, are willing to accept as fitting for their age.

RINGMASTER (Grades K–1).   Players form a circle, with one player called the *Ringmaster* in the center. The *Ringmaster* pretends to snap a whip and calls out the name of an animal. All those in the circle imitate the animal named. This procedure continues with different animals. Finally the *Ringmaster* calls, "We will all join in the circus parade," and everyone moves around the circle imitating any animal. *Ringmaster* then picks another player to take his place.

BOUNCING BALL (Grades K–1).   Children choose partners, with one becoming a *ball* and the other the *bouncer*. The one who is the *bouncer* pushes on the partner's head as he would in bouncing a ball. The partner does a deep knee bend and returns to standing position.

PUSSY WANTS A CORNER (Grades K–1).   Circles are drawn on the floor for each player. One player, called *Pussy*, walks to different circles saying, "Pussy wants a corner." The player in the circle answers, "Go to my next-door neighbor." Meanwhile, as *Pussy* is at other circles, the remaining players signal each other and attempt to exchange places. *Pussy* tries to occupy a circle left by another player. The one left without a circle becomes the new *Pussy*. If one player continues as *Pussy* too long, he may call "All change" and quickly find a vacant circle as everyone changes circles.

CIRCLE BALL (Grades K–1). Players form a circle with a leader in the center. The leader tosses the ball to each player in the circle, who then tosses it back. When the leader drops the ball, he exchanges places with a player in the circle.

SPIDER AND FLIES (Grades K–2). Mark off two goal lines 40 feet apart. Draw a circle between the goal lines large enough to hold all the players. One player is a *Spider* and squats in the circle while the rest of the players are *Flies* and stand behind the goal lines. All *Flies* advance toward the circle and walk around to the right. When the *Spider* jumps up, all *Flies* run toward a goal while the *Spider* tags as many *Flies* as possible before they get back behind either goal line. Those tagged join the *Spider* in the circle and help catch the remaining *Flies*. The last *Fly* caught is the *Spider* in the next game.

JOUNCING ON JOUNCING BOARD (Grades K–2). A two by eight-inch board several feet long is rested on two sturdy uprights. Participant stands in the middle of the board and bounces.

CIRCLE RELAY (Grades K–2). Players form circles of six to eight players. Number one in each circle is given a handkerchief. He runs to his right around the circle and gives the handkerchief to number two, who repeats the same procedure. The relay continues until each person has had a turn. The first circle finished is the winner.

MAGIC CARPET (Grades K–2). Large circles called poison spots are drawn in the play area. On signal, eight to twenty players march or skip to the right, stepping in each spot. When "stop" is called, players stop promptly in position. Players with one or both feet in a poison spot are out. The last player remaining is the winner.

ELEPHANT WALK (Grades K–2). Each child stands and bends forward at the waist. He clasps his hands and lets his arms hang in imitation of an elephant's trunk. The arms are swung from side to side as the child walks with back rounded and knees slightly bent.

BRONCO RELAY (Grades K–2). Players form lines of even numbers of players. Each line divides into partners. The first couple, one behind the other, straddles a broomstick at the starting line. On the signal, they ride the broomstick to a specified turning line and back to the starting point, where they give the broomstick to couple number two, who repeats the same action. The line in which all the couples complete the relay first is the winner.

MIDNIGHT (Grades K–2).   For this game two players are designated as *Mr. Fox* and *Mother Hen* and all the other players are called *Chickens.* The *Hen* and *Chickens* have a goal line 30 yards away from the *Fox. Mother Hen* leads the chickens to *Mr. Fox* and asks, "What time it it?" *Mr. Fox* replies with any time he chooses, but when he answers "Midnight" the *Hen* and *Chickens* run toward their goal with *Mr. Fox* chasing them. Those tagged become *Mr. Fox's* helpers. The last one caught is the winner.

FARMER AND THE CHICKENS (Grades K–2).   One player, the *Farmer,* pretends to toss out seed and lead other players, the *Chickens,* away from their safety area, or *Pen.* When *Farmer* has taken them far enough from the *Pen,* he calls, "Today is Thanksgiving," and chases the *Chickens,* who run for the *Pen. Chickens* caught become *Farmer's* helpers. The last *Chicken* caught is the winner.

JUMPING JACK (Grades K–2).   Each person squats down and crosses arms on chest. He jumps to standing position with arms out to the sides. The movements are repeated to create jumping jack. Legs may also be spread in the jump to increase the difficulty of the exercise.

WALKING, BALANCING BEANBAG ON HEAD (Grades K–2).   Players form even-numbered teams about four feet apart. The first person in each line places a beanbag on his head and walks to a line 20 feet away. He touches the marking, walks back to the starting line, and gives the beanbag to the second player, who repeats the same procedure. Players dropping the bag must start over. The first team finished is the winner.

WONDER BALL (Grades K–2).   Players form circles of six to ten players. A ball is passed around the circle while players repeat:

> "The wonder ball goes round and round,
> To pass it quickly you are bound,
> If you're the one to hold it last
> You — are — out!"

The player holding the ball on "Out" is out until the next game.

TARGET TOSS (Grades K–2).   Players form groups of four to eight players. Each group has a beanbag and a circle drawn on the floor. Each group forms a straight line 20 yards from the circle. Each child tosses the beanbag at the target and receives one point for getting it in the circle. The group with the greatest number of points at the end of the playing time wins.

LINE RELAY (Grades K–2).   Players form teams in parallel lines and number off. A leader calls a number, and this player steps out to the right and runs counterclockwise completely around the team, back to his original position. The player who returns first is the winner. The team with the highest score wins.

SKUNK TAG (Grades K–2).   Eight to ten players spread around the playing area. One person who is *It* runs around trying to tag someone.

To avoid being tagged, a child must hold his nose with his right hand and his left foot with his left hand. If he's tagged before getting into this position, he becomes the new *It*.

EAGLE AND SPARROWS (Grades K–3).   One player is chosen as the *Eagle*. Other players, six to eight, are *Sparrows*. *Sparrows* stretch their arms to the sides and circle them up, back, down, and forward. The *Eagle* chases the *Sparrows* as they run while rotating arms in the described fashion. *Sparrows*, when tagged, become *Eagles*.

CAT AND MICE (Grades K–3).   Players form a large circle with four *mice* in the center and a *cat* on the outside. On the signal, the *cat* runs into the circle and tries to tag all the *mice*. The *mice* may run anywhere within the circle to avoid being tagged. When tagged, the *mouse* takes his place in the circle. The last *mouse* caught is the *cat* for the next game. The leader then chooses four new mice.

PARTNER TOSS (Grades K–3).   Players choose partners. The pair throws the ball back and forth. Each time the ball is caught, the partners move farther apart. When the ball is missed, they start over at the original positions. Partners farthest apart at end of playing time win.

WRING THE DISH RAG (Grades K–3).   Partners stand facing each other and join hands. One raises his left hand and grasps the raised right hand of the other. Partners lower the other arms and turn under the raised arms ending in a back to back position. They then raise the other pair of arms, turning under them to face each other again. Repeat several times.

COWBOYS AND INDIANS (Grades K–3).   Players divide into two teams called *Indians* and *Cowboys*, which stand 30 yards apart on their respective goal lines. Each team chooses a leader. All *Indians*, except the leader, turn around. The *Cowboys* walk up, and when the leader of the *Indians* thinks they're close enough he calls, "The *Cowboys* are coming!" The *Indians* chase the *Cowboys*, attempting to tag them before they reach their goal line. All *Cowboys* tagged become *Indians*. The procedure is reversed for the next game. The team having the largest number at the end of the playing time wins. If leaders are caught, the teams pick new ones.

CALL BALL (Grades K–3).   Players form a circle of six to ten players. One player who is in the center is *It*. He tosses the ball into the air and calls a player's name. This player must catch the ball before it bounces more than once. If the player succeeds, he becomes the new *It*. If not, the one in the center remains until a player successfully catches the ball.

HOP TAG (Grades K–3).   Eight to ten players spread around the playing area. One player who is *It* hops around trying to tag another player who is also hopping. When another player is tagged, he becomes the new *It*.

THREE DEEP (Grades K–3).   Two circles of from ten to twenty-five players are formed, with one circle inside the other. Each child in the inside circle stands directly in front of a child in the outside circle. One child is chosen to chase another around the outside of the circles. The one being chased may step in front of a child on the inside circle to avoid being tagged. The outside player of this group then becomes the one being chased. If the runner is tagged, he turns and chases the tagger.

SIMON SAYS (Grades K–4).   The leader performs simple activities, such as putting his hands on his shoulders, which the children imitate if the leader prefaces the activity with the words, "Simon says do this." However, if the leader says only the words, "Do this," the children must not execute the movement. Anyone who does is eliminated from the game. The last one to be eliminated is the winner.

DROP THE HANDKERCHIEF (Grades 1–2).   Eight to ten players form a circle. One player who is *It* has a handkerchief and walks around the outside of the circle. He drops the handkerchief behind a player in the circle, who picks it up and chases *It* around to the right and back to the open space. If *It* reaches the space safely, the one chasing him is the new *It*. If tagged, *It* walks around and repeats the same procedure.

RED LIGHT (Grades 1–3).   Eight to twenty players form a line side by side. One player who is *It* stands about 25 yards in front of the line. *It* turns his back and rapidly counts to ten, during which the line of players runs toward him. Upon reaching ten, *It* calls "Red Light" and all players must stop running before he turns around. If he sees anyone moving, he sends him back to the starting line. The first player to tag *It* becomes the new *It*.

POST BALL (Grades 1–4).   Two or more teams participate. They form parallel lines with each player about three feet behind the other. A leader stands facing each line 12 feet away. On signal, the leader tosses a ball to the first player in line, who catches it, throws the ball back, and squats in line. The leader repeats the same procedure with each one in the line. The team finishing first and dropping the ball the least number of times wins.

DRIVING PIG TO MARKET (Grades 2–3).   Players form even-numbered lines. The first person in each line is given a wand, and a dumbbell or ball is placed at his feet. On signal, he pushes the dumbbell by sliding the wand back and forth. He must go around a stool 20 feet away and return to the starting line. Here he gives the equipment to the second one in line, who repeats same action. First team finished wins.

STORK STAND (Grades 2–4).   Child places hands on hips, raises one foot and places it against the inside of the opposite knee. To eliminate the role of the eye in achieving balance, the participant may close his eyes while he attempts to maintain balance.

MEASURING WORM (Grades 2–4).   Child bends over and places his hands on the floor and extends his legs to take a front leaning position. With the hands in place, he walks up to his hands. Keeping the feet in place, he walks on the hands away from the feet. The elbows and knees remain straight as he repeats these actions several times.

FIRE ON THE MOUNTAIN (Grades 2–4).   Players form two circles with one circle, called the *Trees,* standing inside the other circle, called *Boys.* In the center is one player who is *It.* He begins clapping his hands as he calls, "Fire on the Mountain. Run, *Boys,* run!" The *Trees* remain standing while the *Boys* run to the right behind the *Trees.* When *It* stops clapping, he and the *Boys* run to stand in front of a *Tree.* The one who does not find a tree is the new *It.* In the next game, the *Trees* and *Boys* change roles.

CHAIN TAG (Grades 2–4).   One player is *It.* He tags another player, and the two join hands and run to tag other players. Each player who is tagged joins the chain at the end. Hands must remain joined and only the first and last players in the chain are allowed to tag.

CIRCLE WEAVE RELAY (Grades 2–4).   Players form circles, six to eight players to a circle. One player from each circle starts the relay by running to the outside of the player to his right, to the inside of the next, and continues weaving in this pattern around the circle to the starting position. He tags the next player to his right, who similarly runs to his right around the circle. The relay continues until everyone in the circle has had a turn. The first circle to complete the relay is the winner.

STEAL THE BACON (Grades 3–4).   Players divide into two teams with the players standing side by side behind the goal line. Teams number off beginning at diagonal ends. A ball, called the *Bacon,* is placed on the floor midway between the lines. The leader calls any number. Both players having this number run in and attempt to steal the ball and return to own goal line before being tagged by the other player. One point is scored for each safe return. When opposing players reach the *Bacon* at the same time, they should wait for an opportune moment to steal the ball. The team having ten points first wins.

CROSS TAG (Grades 3–4).   Eight to ten players scatter around the playing area. One player who is *It* runs and tries to tag another player. If another player crosses between the chased player and *It, It* must change and chase the crossing player.

WALL BALL (Grades 3–4).   Players divide into groups of four to six players. Groups form lines about four feet apart facing a wall. Distances are marked off every foot, beginning at three feet from the wall and ending at eight. Starting at the three-foot mark, the first player in each line makes three throws and catches of the ball off the wall. Upon successful completion of the three catches, he may move back to the next mark. At any time that he misses he must go to the end of the line, and the next player in line takes his turn, beginning at the three-foot mark. Each player in the line does likewise. When the first player has his turn again, he begins at the mark where he previously missed. When he successfully completes the catches at each mark, he is through. The team with all of its players completing their catches first is the winner.

BULL IN THE RING (Grades 3–5).   Ten to twelve players form a circle with hands joined. One player, the *Bull,* is inside this circle. The *Bull* tries to break through the circle or slip under the hands. If he gets out, all players chase him. The player who did the tagging becomes the new *Bull*. The *Bull* is allowed three tries to break through. If he fails, he chooses a new *Bull*.

BEAT BALL (Grades 4–5).   Five to ten players on each of two teams. Indian clubs or bowling pins used as bases are set up in a softball or kick-ball formation. One team is at "bat," the other in the field. The pitcher rolls a soccer ball to the batter, who kicks it and runs to first, second, third, and home. The fielding team catches the ball and throws it to the first baseman, who knocks over the pin, throws the ball to the second baseman, who knocks over the pin, and so on. If the batter gets home before all the pins are knocked down, he scores one run—otherwise, he's out.

Outs: ball at home plate before runner; fly ball caught; batter misses kick and ball knocks over pin at home; runner knocks over any pin while running bases; or kicked ball knocks over any pin not touched by fielder first.

Runs: ball not thrown in correct order of bases; or baseman does not knock over pin with ball before throwing to next base.

BAT BALL (Grades 4–5).   Players divide into two teams, one at bat and one in the field. A volleyball or soccer ball is used. The first player at bat hits the ball into the field and runs to a base and home. If the player makes the complete trip without the fielder catching the fly or hitting him below the waist with the ball, one run is scored. Three outs and teams change. The team with the most runs wins.

CIRCLE KICK BALL (Grades 4–5).   Divide the players into two teams. One team stands in one half of a 25-foot circle, the other team in the remaining half. The leader rolls a ball to one team, which kicks the ball toward the opposite team, which kicks it back. One point is scored for each ball kicked out of the circle past the opponents at waist height or below. A ball kicked out above the waist scores for the opposite team. The team having the largest number of points at the end of the playing time wins.

LINE SOCCER (Grades 4–5).   Two even-numbered teams form lines facing each other. Players stand side by side in each line. Teams count off from diagonal ends so that number one of one line faces the last number in the opposite line. A leader places the ball between the lines and calls out a number. The two players with that number rush into the center and attempt to kick the ball through the opposite line. Players in line may stop the ball from going through. A ball kicked through the line scores a point.

LEAP FROG (Grades 4–6).   Players take squat positions four to five apart in a line. One player runs toward the end of the line and leaps over each player in succession by placing his hands, fingers forward, on the player's shoulders and pushing off as he jumps. When he reaches the front of the line, he squats down. The last person in the line rises and follows the same procedure until everyone has had an opportunity to leap the entire line.

HOT POTATOES (Grades 4–6).   Players form a circle with six to twenty players in each circle. Players all sit crosslegged and roll or punch balls across the circle. Three or four balls are kept going at once. Players try to knock the ball past other players through the circle. The player permitting the least number of balls to go through the circle wins. An extra player retrieves all the balls going out of the circle. No ball higher than the shoulders counts. Balls may not be bounced or thrown.

CROWS AND CRANES (Grades 4–6).   Players divide into two groups of eight to twenty players. One group is called *Crows* and the other *Cranes*. The playing area is divided with a line in the center and a goal line at each end of the area. *Crows* and *Cranes* stand facing each other at the center. The leader calls "Crows" or "Cranes." The group called runs to the goal line behind them with the other group chasing. Players tagged go to the other group. *Crows* and *Cranes* return to the center line. The leader gives the call again. The group with the larger number of players at the end of the playing time wins.

FROG TIP-UP (Grades 4–8).   Child takes a squat position with the knees apart and arms between the knees. The hands are placed on the floor with the fingers extended toward the sides and about shoulder distance apart. The knees are braced against the elbows. The child leans forward with his weight on the arms and lifts his feet off the floor. He holds this position until balance is achieved.

SEAL WALK (Grades 4–8).   Each person puts his weight on his hands on the floor and extends legs backward. He walks forward on his hands, dragging his legs behind.

ROCKER (Grades 4–8).   Children lie on their stomachs and arch their backs to grasp the raised legs at the ankles with their hands. In this position, they rock forward and backward.

WALKING CHAIRS (Grades 4–8).   Children form a line standing behind each other with their hands on the waist of the one in front. All bend knees to sit on the knees of the one behind. Last person must balance himself in the sitting position. Beginning with the left foot, the line walks forward in rhythm.

SQUAT THRUST (Grades 4–8).   From a standing position, the participant squats and places his hands on the floor. Body weight is momentarily taken on the hands as the feet are thrown back and the participant assumes a front leaning position. He then returns to a squat position and stands.

SNAIL (Grades 4–8).   Children lie on their backs and raise the legs to touch the floor back of their heads with their toes. The arms are raised and the elbows bent to place the hands palms down near the shoulders.

ROCKER (DUAL) (Grades 4–8).   Partners take sitting positions and sit on each other's feet. One partner must bring his legs to the outside of the other's to do this. The knees must be kept bent. The partners place their hands on each other's shoulders. To create the rocking motion they alternate pulling forward on the partner's shoulders and lifting him off the floor with the feet.

TURK STAND (Grades 4–8).   Children cross feet and fold arms while standing. Keeping the arms and legs crossed, they sit. To raise themselves to the standing position, they move forward, place weight over their feet, and lift.

CRAB WALK (Grades 4–8).   Child takes a squat position. He reaches back and places his hands flat on the floor without sitting. Distributing his weight equally on all fours, he walks forward in this position.

CHINESE STAND-UP (Grades 4–8).   Partners stand back to back and lock elbows with each other. They push against each other's back and with small steps walk forward and sit on the floor. To stand up, the partners keep arms locked and bend the knees with the feet close to the body. They brace their feet, push against each other's back, extend legs, and come to a standing position.

INDIAN WRESTLE (Grades 4–8).   Partners stand facing opposite directions beside each other. The outsides of the right feet are placed together. Right hands are joined. The two players push and pull until one person's right foot is lifted from position. The person whose right foot remains in position wins.

LINE DODGE BALL (Grades 4–8).   Players standing side by side form two lines 20 feet apart with a four-foot square drawn in the middle. One person stands in this box, and the other players take turns trying to hit him below the waist with the ball. The player may dodge the ball but must keep one foot in the box. When hit, the player changes places with the one who hit him.

HAND WRESTLE (Grades 4–8).   Partners lie on their stomachs on the floor facing each other with their right hands grasped and right elbows together. They push on each other's hand, attempting to force the opponent's hand to the floor. The one forcing the other's hand down wins.

GRAPEVINE (Grades 4–8).   Child bends over and places hands from front to back through the legs. The hands are wound around the legs so that the fingers of both hands touch in front of the ankles.

WHEELBARROW (Grades 4–8).   Partners stand one behind the other facing the same way. The one in front places his hands on floor while the one behind lifts his legs at the knees. The first child walks forward on his hands with his partner holding his legs in wheelbarrow fashion.

TUG PICK-UP (Grades 4–8).   Two people hold a six-foot rope at opposite ends. A block is placed six inches behind each person. On a signal, each player tries to pick up the block behind him. Releasing the rope or permitting the other player to reach the block gives one point to the winner. One match consists of three points.

INDIAN LEG WRESTLE (Grades 4–8).   Partners lie side by side on their backs facing opposite directions. The right arms are locked together. On signal, the partners raise right legs and lock knees. They attempt to throw each other over by pushing, pulling, etc. Two out of three victories constitute a match.

DODGE BALL (Grades 5–8).   Players form teams. One team forms a circle; the other team stands inside the circle. The players outside try to hit the players inside below the waist with the ball. Inside players may dodge the ball. Players who are hit join the circle. When all players inside have been hit by the ball, teams change places.

ADAPTATIONS

The basic skill games are readily modified for one youngster in the group or for an entire group. Generally, the games may be modified in one of more of the following ways:

(1) substituting walking for skipping and running;
(2) replacing throwing with underhand tossing;
(3) sitting or lying in place of standing;
(4) decreasing distances;
(5) slowing the tempo;
(6) providing more rest periods;
(7) simplifying the patterns of movement;
(8) supplying oral and kinesthetic cues to the players.

Which of these suggested adaptations is used depends, of course, upon the conditions of the children involved. In cases of limited use of the arms and legs, the adaptation may have to be made in the type of movement required by the game or in the amount of movement required. For children who lack endurance or must not exert themselves, the games will probably need to be adapted to provide more frequent rest periods and to decrease the work involved in playing the game by slowing the tempo, reducing the distances, etc. Games involving more complex patterns of movement may need to be simplified for mentally retarded youngsters. For these youngsters and for those who are blind and deaf, kinesthetic cues are very helpful; modifying the game to permit those who cannot perform the skills to be led through the movements kinesthetically often spells the difference between success and failure in teaching games to these youngsters.

QUESTIONS

1. Discuss the reasons for including basic skill games in the physical education program for elementary school children regardless of their mental and physical capacities.

2. Under what circumstances should handicapped children be placed in a regular physical education program? When should a special class be made for them?

3. Develop criteria for the selection of basic skill games for any given group of children.

4. Select a group of basic skill games from the text and show how each could be adapted for the blind, the mentally retarded, and those with lower limb involvement.

5. What basic adaptations would be necessary in the basic skill games for a boy who is hard of hearing in a class of normal youngsters?

6. Discuss the ways in which the student with a heart disorder could participate in some of the more strenuous running games of the basic skill games. Identify the games you are discussing.

SELECTED READINGS

Andrews, Gladys, *et al.: Physical Education for Today's Boys and Girls.* Boston, Allyn & Bacon, 1960.

Bucher, Charles A., and Reade, Evelyn M.: *Physical Education and Health in the Elementary School,* ed. 2. New York, The Macmillan Co., 1964.

Evans, Ruth, *et al.: Physical Education for Elementary Schools.* New York, McGraw-Hill Book Co., Inc., 1958.

Fait, Hollis F.: *Physical Education for the Elementary School Child.* Philadelphia, W. B. Saunders Co., 1964.

Halsey, Elizabeth, and Porter, Lorena: *Physical Education for Children: A Developmental Program.* New York, Holt, Rinehart & Winston, Inc., 1963.

Humphrey, James H.: *Elementary School Physical Education.* New York, Harper & Brothers, 1958.

Salt, Ellis B., *et al.: Teaching Physical Education in the Elementary School,* ed. 2. New York, The Ronald Press Company, 1960.

Vannier, Maryhelen, and Foster, Mildred: *Teaching Physical Education in Elementary Schools,* ed. 3. Philadelphia, W. B. Saunders Co., 1963.

17
RHYTHMS AND DANCE

Rhythm permeates the universe, and all children are capable of responding to rhythmic activity provided the stimulation exists. Basic rhythm yields simple movement patterns. Dance itself is an accumulation of various forms of movement and may be thought of as a formal composition or as a vehicle of emotional expression. Dance contains elements that can satisfy the individual's need for recognition, satisfaction, and creativity and can provide opportunities to develop a sense of belonging and of adequacy.

Rhythms and dance play an essential role in the physical education program for the exceptional child. Many handicapped children have a basic need to develop freedom of self-expression, skill in social interaction, and fundamental movement patterns. Dance provides a medium through which these may be realized.

It is frequently observed that the exceptional child must adjust not only to problems which he has in common with other students but also to individual difficulties that stem more directly from his own disability. The teacher must continually keep in mind that these youngsters are, first, children in the dance class and, secondly, individuals who are handicapped. Given the opportunity, each will benefit as well as contribute to the school dance program.

EQUIPMENT

Elaborate equipment is not necessary to provide dance activities for the exceptional child; the materials available for regular dance classes are

FIGURE 24.   A blind youngster beats out the tempo for a
rhythmic activity. (The Light-
house of the New York Association for the Blind.)

more than adequate. Musical accompaniment is essential. If a well-tuned
piano is not at the disposal of the dance instructor, a three-speed record
player is an excellent substitute.

Specially prepared records ranging from pieces with simple and
definite tempos to intricate folk and square dance melodies are available
through special firms.[1] Permitting the children to make personal selections
from the records may reinforce self-expression in a new situation. Marking
each record alphabetically and keeping a small index-card file of the
records eliminates needless disorganization.

In a secondary program, if at all possible, the dance area should be
open to the students during free periods. The blind or partially sighted
child will become accustomed to the records and other equipment by
familiar sensory cues. The emotionally disturbed child when accompanied
by a teacher, may find the permissiveness of the empty dance area a
rewarding atmosphere for self-expression.

To obtain satisfying results in various dance activities, use individual
pieces of equipment. The drum, in particular, accentuates basic accents
in rhythmic patterns and is a valuable dance instrument for the student
who is hard of hearing. Rhythm is recognizable in terms of what it does,
and its real significance on an elementary level can only be grasped by
actually experiencing it.[2] Maracas, tambourines, rhythm sticks, triangles,

[1]Record sources are given in the Appendix.
[2]Margaret H'Doubler: *Movement and Its Rhythmic Structure.* Kramer Business Service,
1946, p. 6.

and homemade musical instruments are helpful. The mentally retarded child responds to the "feel" of the muscle sensations and activity aroused within his body through the use of this equipment. Movements are often awkward efforts at first, but, after timing and values of intensity are understood, efficient and more skilled movement results.

The physically handicapped child, when not involved in group-oriented activity, finds great pleasure in rhythmic muscle exercises at the dance bar. Mirrors help in stimulating self-awareness in emotionally disturbed children as well as in aiding the growth of poise and unison of dance movement in other handicapped children. Heavy equipment such as the piano should be located where it will not have to be moved often; smaller instruments and dance materials should be put away after use. This allows the blind or partially sighted student full freedom of the dance area.

Equipment that provides additional expression and interpretative movement plays a vital role in rhythmic activity for the exceptional child. However, it will not take the place of the structuring and dynamic role of the dance instructor. The teacher must use these materials as tools toward a better understanding of rhythm and basic movement.

SCHEDULING THE DANCE CLASS

The exceptional child should be included whenever possible, in the regular dance class as well as in extracurricular dance activities. If these children are to function in a normal society, experiences should be provided to develop skills in an integrated atmosphere.

Each child should be placed in a dance group with others of his own chronological age and skill ability. With proper scheduling, the exceptional child finds cumulative success and a minimal amount of failure in various dance activities. Frequent rest periods of a short duration are beneficial. Medical records and interest inventories should be periodically examined in order that the teacher have a better understanding of each child and his deficiency.

ORGANIZATION FOR INSTRUCTION

The development and application of teaching methods in dance for the handicapped are similar to those methods used with children of normal capacity, because the learning process is basically the same for all individuals. However, in teaching the handicapped, the rate at which they learn and the extent to which they must adapt are more important considerations than they are with normal children.

Specific disabilities have been discussed in previous chapters. An understanding of the capabilities and limitations of each handicapped child is most valuable when considering various teaching techniques. The instructor cannot safely assume that dance fundamentals will have been previously acquired. The type and extent of the disability provides an individual guide to instruction.

MENTALLY RETARDED CHILDREN.   With an increasing number of mentally retarded children involved in the school program, the dance teacher must try to meet the needs of these "special class" children.

In many instances, educable mentally retarded children may be included in the regular dance class; they are much more like their chronological age peers than they are different from them. Naturally, particular attention must be given to appropriate placement. Motor ability and chronological age are excellent criteria.

The dance teacher is in a position to help the elementary school "special class" instructor by working directly with the class in rhythms and basic dance technique. The trainable mentally retarded child should receive his basic instruction within the "special class." Progress will be slow, and stress should be placed on fundamental skills rather than complex activity. Often the teacher serves as a consultant to the "special class" teacher only when new skills are introduced. After the trainable child has successfully developed skills in following directions and rhythmic movement, he, too, should be allowed to participate in a regular dance class.

A short attention span is a known characteristic of the retarded. Dance periods, therefore, should be short and repetitive to allow for reinforcement. Techniques in teaching should be widely diversified, using such methods as mirror image, kinesthesis, and specific learning cues. Finally, little time should be given to verbal explanations of dance techniques, as these are too abstract. Action is more meaningful: the key to effectiveness with the retarded child lies in the rate at which the rhythm and dance techniques are introduced.

EMOTIONALLY DISTURBED CHILDREN.   Emotionally disturbed children often have good mental ability but are unable to integrate their intellectual efforts and direct them toward realistic goals. Erratic behavior, insecurity, hostility, and withdrawal are characteristic. Rigidity of thought and insecurity of self-expression severely constrict the emotional growth of many of these children. Dance may prove most helpful in developing appropriate social adjustment.

Under the supervision of trained personnel, the dance instructor should focus the program on stimulating interaction with the environment. The disturbed child may find satisfactory emotional experiences through the medium of dance. By identifying with objects, the child finds gratification in rhythmic movement. Later, the learning process will involve interaction with an authority figure, such as the dance instructor. Dance is then introduced in formal step sequences under conditions of enforced reality.[3] Once the disturbed child has successfully mastered organized

---

[3]Laurence Weiner: "Educating the Emotionally Disturbed Blind Child." International Journal of Education of the Blind, xi, 1962, pp. 77–79.

dance patterns, inclusion in the regular dance class may be considered, but it is important that care be taken to minimize frustration during this initial period.

BLIND AND PARTIALLY SIGHTED CHILDREN.   Today many blind and partially sighted youngsters are attending regular public school classes. Their acute auditory skill as well as their ability to follow directions prove extremely helpful in various dance experiences.

Blind children often develop an early awareness of music and rhythmic movement because they must use auditory cues. "Blindisms" or unique mannerisms, which may take the form of rocking, twisting, or waving of the arms or fingers, are characteristic of many young blind children entering elementary school. These habits, not particularly socially acceptable, are often best controlled by calling them to the attention of the child. Interestingly enough, these very characteristics are self-expressive and almost always have a rhythmic pattern. Thus, the next obvious means of control is to utilize these forms of expression into acceptable patterns of movement. Tap dancing has always been an enjoyable experience for these children.

Precise verbal instruction and kinesthesis are good teaching techniques. After a basic understanding of position and formation, the blind or partially sighted student can successfully be included as an active and enthusiastic member of many folk and square dance groups.

DEAF AND HARD-OF-HEARING CHILDREN.   Many children in the public school program have auditory deficiencies. A prime objective for these exceptional children is the utilization of residual hearing. Speech may be stimulated through the use of auditory as well as visual training. The dance teacher is in an excellent position to provide experiences in gross discrimination through rhythm instruments and dance recordings. The child may be taught to feel vibrations from instruments and to use rhythm to develop inflection and timing in dance quality. Rhythm may be channeled in clapping activities as well as visually in an integrated group dance situation. It may first be necessary for the child who is hard of hearing to be conditioned by the beat of a drum or to sit close to a record player and familiarize himself with the basic rhythm being introduced. Sound instruments such as drums, whistles, or maracas may be calibrated by an audiometer if necessary.

With amplification, the hard of hearing may function in a normal society. Whenever possible, these children should be placed in a regular dance class. The teacher should position herself in such a manner that the hard-of-hearing student can see her face during the learning experience. Sound instruments that can be discriminated provide self-expression and rhythmic movement. Group dancing will prove beneficial and enjoyable if the child is appropriately placed nearest the music and possibly accompanied by a child with normal auditory skills.

PHYSICALLY HANDICAPPED CHILDREN.   Many handicaps have been found to be relative to cultural expectations. Through dance activities, the child with a physical disability can successfully fulfill various basic needs that might not be met in other areas of motor activity. Each handicapped student formulates his own response to his disability. The dance instructor may stimulate proper adjustment by providing avenues of self-expression and group interaction.

Basic rhythmic activity acts as a stimulus to control otherwise involuntary movement; however, this stimulus may also release emotional expression in free activity.

The physically handicapped child participating in an integrated dance will undoubtedly benefit more than he would if excused from such activity. Frustration can be minimized by adapting dance activities to meet the needs and capacities of these students. The teacher must use ingenuity to determine the benefits the physically handicapped may gain from dance experiences. Children in wheelchairs enjoy folk and square dances and can easily be propelled by other members of the class. Creative exploration utilizing upper trunk and arm movement instills physical poise and reassurance. Children with hand deficiencies can be frustrated unnecessarily when working with rhythm toys. By manipulating instruments with the knees and upper arm, these children can play successfully.

TYPES OF DANCES AND RHYTHMS

With modification, rhythmics and dancing may prove to be an enjoyable experience for the handicapped. The major objective in the adaption of dance for the exceptional child is to provide experiences which allow these children to perform on a common ground with their peers. The dance instructor must select those activities that remain within the intellectual comprehension and work tolerance level of the child. The aim of instruction is to enable the child to find pleasurable and rewarding activity rather than master intricate dance techniques. The following items concerning procedure should be considered:[4]

1. Demonstration by teacher or pupil provides the visual picture of rhythmic movement. Demonstration sets the pattern when predetermined steps are to be learned; it illustrates and stimulates the imagination when creative expression is the goal.

2. Explanations should be brief and precise. Motivation may be increased by stating a brief history of the activity. Performance should immediately follow demonstration and explanation.

3. The instructor should analyze performance and vary the method of explanation when necessary.

4. Each child should experience success. All must feel that they are dancing rather than preparing for a later performance.

[4]Clyde G. Knapp and E. Patricia Hagman: *Teaching Methods for Physical Education*, Mc-Graw-Hill Book Co., Inc., 1953, pp. 301–302.

5. Ample opportunity for individual practice should be provided.

6. Listening, clapping, stamping, and beating to music stimulate an understanding of tempo, accent, and phrasing.

7. For beginners in partner dancing, frequent partner change in mixer-type activities is advisable.

8. Integrating the dance program with academic and extracurricular opportunities enriches the school experience of the child.

Special methods of instruction are made necessary by the limitations imposed by specific handicaps. As pointed out in Chapter 4, verbal and visual cues and kinesthesis are vital teaching techniques in any adapted program.

Brief and precise verbal explanations are beneficial to all handicapped individuals and are essential for the blind or partially sighted.

Demonstrations and "do-as-I-do" activities are invaluable when working with the mentally retarded, and the child who is deaf or hard of hearing must also be given opportunities to watch the skill being performed.

By leading a student's arm or part of the body involved in the activity through the movement, wide avenues of understanding are opened to the exceptional child. Directing the student in this manner permits skills to be mastered and difficulties to be overcome in a pleasant and non-threatening atmosphere. Only when the child associates the desired result with the appropriate form will he begin to "feel right" about his performance.

RHYTHMIC ACTIVITY.   Rhythms are the basic skills of the dance. They should be an essential part of the elementary school program and occur repeatedly throughout subsequent dance activity. The study of rhythmic movement will better equip the exceptional child to express himself in social activities.

With fundamental rhythms to an accompaniment, children walk, run, jump, hop, skip, slide, and leap.

In informal rhythmic "do-as-I-do and-say" games, children experiment with space, focus, direction of movement, levels, varying tempo, different qualities of movement.

With interpretive rhythms, children can express themselves as animals, sounds, paintings, fairy tales.

Adapted teaching hints: Activities may be stimulated by listening to the basic beat and clapping to the rhythm. The handicapped child learns best by doing, and each student must make an effort to perform the movement to his utmost capacity. A high degree of motivation produced and maintained by the teacher is essential. If the child is confined to a wheelchair, he can clap the basic rhythm with the class while being pushed in his chair during locomotor activity. The hard-of-hearing child must use visual cues and experience the vibration of the instruments. The blind child may find great joy in marking the rhythmic beat through sound and touch.

Most children, normal or handicapped, particularly enjoy creative activity and spend much of their leisure time in imaginative play. The mentally retarded child is sometimes the exception. For him, various stimuli such as musical instruments and other toys that are easily manipulated reinforce his concentration and lead to self-expressive motor activity.

TRADITIONAL DANCE STEPS.   Traditional dance steps have their foundation in fundamental rhythms. Folk dancing and much social dancing involve one or more traditional dance steps.

"Step Point." The step point is a step on the left foot, pointing the right foot in front. This action is repeated stepping on the right foot.

count 1	count 2	count 3	count 4
step left	point right	step right	point left

Adapted teaching hints: Floor markings prove beneficial. Teach the step first in a stationary position without the music. Do the step in a circle formation later, alone or with partners.

"Step Hop." The step hop is a step on the left foot and a hop on the same foot. This action is repeated using the right foot.

count 1	count 2	count 3	count 4
step left	hop left	step right	hop right

Adapted teaching hints: Practice entirely with one foot at first, and later alternate feet. Students in wheelchairs can enjoy the activity by moving arms on count, one and three and clapping on counts two and four.

"Step Swing." The step swing is a step on the left foot followed by a swing of the right foot across in front of the left. This action is repeated, stepping on the right foot.

count 1	count 2	count 3	count 4
step left	swing right	step right	swing left

Adapted teaching hints: This step is an excellent follow-the-leader activity. The use of the dance bar as well as kinesthesis should be considered when introducing the "swing" technique to the blind.

"Balance Step." The balance step can be done in any direction. The dancer steps left and closes right foot to left, rising on the balls of both feet.

count 1	count 2	count 3
step left	close right	rise on toes, lower

count 1	count 2	count 3
step right	close left	rise on toes, lower

Adapted teaching hint: A child who is handicapped by brain damage will have considerable difficulty coordinating this movement. The teacher should suggest that the student gaze at a distant object at eye level to attain balance initially.

"*Polka.*" The simple polka is a step on the right, close left to right, step on right, hold. The action is repeated, using the opposite foot.

count 1	and	count 2	and
heel		toe	

count 1	and	count 2	and
step	close	step	hold

Adapted teaching hints: After listening to the music and viewing the demonstration, all children should verbally recite the action words, "heel and toe," etc. The steps should be practiced informally in front of the mirror to a familiar recording. The teacher can then give individual attention to each student by taking him in hand and walking through the dance pattern.

"*Waltz.*" The waltz step is a step forward left, step sideward right, and close left to right; then a step backward right, step sideward left, and close right to left.

count 1	count 2	count 3
step left (forward)	side right	close left

count 1	count 2	count 3
step right (backward)	side left	close right

Adapted teaching hints: The step should be first introduced in a line formation. Marking individual "boxes" on the floor with tape gives the students an outline to follow for a better understanding of the waltz pattern. Blind students may pass their hands over the markings on the floor to gain tactual cues.

"*Two Step.*" The two step is a step forward on the left, close right to left, step left and hold. The action is repeated, beginning right.

count 1	count 2	count 3
step left	close right	step left

count 1	count 2	count 3
step right	close left	step right

Adapted teaching hints: The two step is the foundation of social dancing and can be introduced in partner formation. The tempo should first start out slowly. Practice in parallel lines leads to a better understanding of the step sequence.

FOLK DANCES. Folk dancing has a fascinating history that belongs to the handicapped as well as the normal child. Many of the dances done today originally stemmed from various rites that celebrated important

FIGURE 25. Adapted square dance uses one couple performing a simple pattern. (Journal of Health, Physical Education and Recreation.)

events in men's lives—the planting of crops, weddings, and even religious sacrifices. Our heritage is rich in its variety of movement qualities, styles, and patterns. Yet with all these differences, there is a lasting universality in the social satisfaction that people derive when they move together in rhythmic harmony.

Folk and square dancing afford excellent opportunities for the handicapped to learn desirable social skills and attitudes. Much of the vigorous activity provided in this type of social dancing may be modified for the exceptional student without losing its authenticity or original sequence.

A firm understanding of basic formation and specific skills involved in various patterns are foundations for enjoyable dance experiences. Repetition and enthusiasm are tools for success. The hard-of-hearing child will learn by listening to the accompaniment and by seeing the formation in movement. The blind student may be placed with a seeing partner. With a group of partially sighted students, in dances calling for "crossing over," arch formations, or grand right and left, steps can be worked out going forward and backward instead.

The following dances are but a few examples that are easily adaptable.

"Tinikling" (Philippines). Victor Record 1619. By taking only some of the figures and steps from the dance, it becomes appropriate for almost

any age group. The dance depicts the movements of the long-legged and long-necked bird tinikling. As it supposedly prances around, two dancers sitting on the floor manipulate two long bamboo poles, trying to trap its legs. This is an excellent exhibition dance.

Adapted teaching hints: Enthusiasm can be stimulated by beginning the activity with the background of the dance. A blind or physically disabled child can join in the activity by manipulating the poles. The steps should be taught with the poles in a stationary position. Timing and creative activity are goals to be sought after the basic step is understood.

"Troika" (Russian). Folk Dance Record MH1059. Troika means three horses. The dance symbolizes the three horses which traditionally drew sleighs for noble Russian families.

Adapted teaching hints: This dance makes use of fundamental rhythms. In a formation of three, a student with a disabled arm can choose the side on which he wishes to dance. The emotionally disturbed child may, for example, find security in the middle position of the formation.

"Chimes of Dunkirk" (French). Victor Record 21618. Here is a folk dance that sparkles with spontaneity. It was brought to this country by the French masters many years ago.

Adapted teaching hints: This simple activity is an enjoyable experience for the mentally retarded child. The Danish Dance of Greeting, Lazy Mary, and London Bridge should all be included in their dance program. If the group is small, each handicapped student should be given the opportunity to dance with the teacher. This may stimulate the slow repetitive learning process.

"Mexican Hat Dance" (Spanish). Folkcraft Record 1119. Many Mexican dances were originally Spanish folk dances and were extremely popular during the period when Maximilian was Emperor of Mexico. The dance was previously known as Baile de España.

Adapted teaching hint: This folk dance is a community favorite and should be introduced to the handicapped. Simple costumes have great appeal to these children, and many of them enjoy organizing and carrying on folk dance clubs.

SQUARE DANCES.   Folk, in the literal sense, means people. Folk dancing, therefore, is the "dance of the people." With the steady influx of people from many lands to the United States, there slowly emerged an array of international dance figures. The basic formation was the "drill of four" or the quadrille, thus leading to the name *square dance*.[5] The following square dances are examples of easily adapted activity:

"Head Two Ladies Cross Over." Square Dance Associates, Inc., Honor Your Partner Series, Album 1. The four ladies are active in this exchange

[5]Jane A. Harris, *et al., Dance A While*, Minneapolis, Burgess Publishing Co., 1964, p. 3.

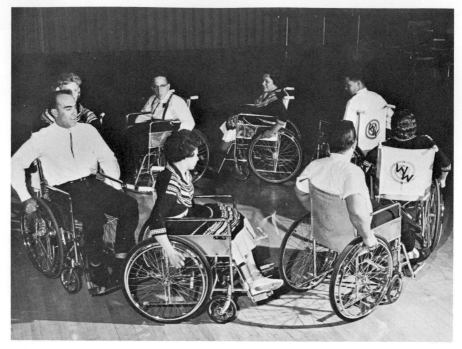

FIGURE 26. Dancers in wheelchairs "Circle all." (The National Society for Crippled Children and Adults.)

partner dance. A child in a wheelchair could easily be the stationary partner.

"*Duck for the Oyster.*" Victor Record 20592. Duck for the Oyster is one of the oldest and most popular square dances in this country. While the square performs allemande left, grand right and left, the handicapped child with limited locomotion can circle or stamp in the center.

"*Virginia Reel.*" Victor Record 35771. This contradance is an old favorite. Extensive right- and left-hand instruction may be necessary for the mentally retarded. When blind or partially sighted children are participating, clapping should be restricted to the child in the contra line who is waiting to be swung. This will enable the visually handicapped child to find the one he is to swing more easily.

Adapted teaching hints for square dances: Because of the frequent partner changes, square dancing provides unique opportunities in the school program for developing an appreciation and respect for others. It is an activity the handicapped can participate in throughout their adult years.

When a child who is hard of hearing is included, dancers should refrain from loud clapping when the dance is in progress, so that he may better follow instruction and tempo.

The walk-through method of teaching is the most profitable. Frequent repetition and an overexaggeration of directional cues are necessary. Allow the children to listen to the music at first; then demonstrate, using one couple or square; complete the entire pattern with music. The blind are more successful when taught in musical phrases rather than count. The mentally retarded achieve success when the continuity of the dance has been preserved.

SOCIAL DANCE.   Social dance is an activity that can be engaged in with pleasure throughout life. It is one of the most popular of all recreational activities among normal as well as handicapped teenagers. The courtesies and standards of social dancing can best be taught under wholesome supervision in school. Mastering these social graces will provide the handicapped student with the poise that is so important to adjustment. Self-confidence is also encouraged by the use of familiar, currently popular songs with a definite rhythm.

MODERN DANCE.   Modern dance teaches the handicapped expression. This type of dance derives its name from its effort to portray through movement significant ideas of current life. It represents ideas or emotion rather than some standard and traditional dance form. Modern dance is an area of dynamic movement that releases anxieties and frustrations in a socially acceptable fashion. It is founded on techniques that develop maximum muscular strength, joint flexibility, and body coordination.

The exceptional child has a pervasive need for self-expression and harmonious utilization of the entire body. The blind child dances to abstract impressions and learns to express himself through movement of his arms and hands as well as his entire body. The child with cerebral palsy can release frustrations by freely engaging in gross rhythmic movement and can actually benefit from concentrated movement, which leads to greater control of disabled limbs. The deaf or hard-of-hearing child seeks continuity in muscular activity. The emotionally disturbed student finds self-expressive movement a relaxing adventure. Creativity and self-awareness are developed in the mentally retarded child with the use of modern dance activities.

The program may be structured or nonstructured; the teacher must have a purpose for all activities. Scarves, pieces of rope, costumes, chairs, or other accessible materials can stimulate activity. Musical accompaniment should clearly represent various tempos or moods; many popular recordings can accomplish this goal. Narrative stories and recent happenings also provide interesting stimuli for movement.

Children should be introduced to interpretive dance first as a group and later in couples or alone. Stress should be placed on the concept that the entire body acts as a unit and not as separate entities.

QUESTIONS

1. What are the values of a rhythms and dance program for the handicapped?
2. In what ways may self-expression be encouraged through the dance?

3. Discuss the use of verbalization, visualization, and kinesthesis in teaching any given dance form to the handicapped.

4. Select a dance not described in the text and plan the adaptations of it that would be necessary to teach it effectively to the blind, deaf, and those in wheelchairs.

5. How may dance be used to promote better movement patterns?

6. Add to the list of teaching hints in the chapter, drawing on the information you have gained about the nature of various types of handicaps in earlier chapters.

SELECTED READINGS

Cruickshank, William (ed.): *Psychology of Exceptional Children and Youth,* ed. 2. Englewood Cliffs, N.J., Prentice-Hall, Inc., 1963.

Fait, Hollis: *Physical Education for the Elementary School Child.* Philadelphia, W. B. Saunders Co., 1964.

Harris, Jane A., *et al.: Dance A While.* Minneapolis, Burgess Publishing Co., 1964.

H'Doubler, Margaret: *Movement and Its Rhythmic Structure.* Madison, Wis. Kramer Business Service, 1946.

Knapp, Clyde G., and Hagman, E. Patricia: *Teaching Methods for Physical Education.* New York, McGraw-Hill Book Co., Inc., 1953.

Robins, Ferris and Jennet: *Educational Rhythmics for Mentally Handicapped Children.* Rapperswilz, Switzerland, Ra-Verlag, 1963.

18
INDIVIDUAL SPORTS

Individual sports is a term used to identify those sports in which one person may participate alone or with a single opponent. Among the most widely played individual sports are archery, bowling, and golf.

Because these activities are designed for individual participation, they are readily adapted to individual restrictions and capacities. For this reason alone, they are excellent choices for the adapted physical education curriculum. However, there are other important reasons for including them in the program for the handicapped. One of the most obvious of these reasons is their contribution to the physical fitness of the participants. While individual sports are not considered vigorous, they do place sufficient demands upon the body to insure desirable development for handicapped players in such fitness factors as strength, coordination, and cardiorespiratory endurance. Then, too, individual sports have high carry-over value. Because they require less organization than most other active games, they are among our most popular leisure-time activities. Consequently, participation in these sports virtually insures the handicapped opportunities for good fellowship with nonhandicapped players who enjoy these sports as leisure-time recreation.

ORGANIZING THE INSTRUCTION

Instruction in the individual sports requires considerable planning and organization on the part of the teacher. Because these are individual activities, each student requires considerable individual instruction, and the planning of class time must provide for this. Moreover, equipment is required by each participant, and there may not be sufficient equipment for all members of the class to practice simultaneously.

Fortunately, in most school situations the handicapped can be accommodated in the regular physical education classes. The nature of the activities is such that each participant can move at his own pace. Students who are extremely skilled and have mastered the techniques may be used by the teacher to assist in the instruction of the handicapped. If the class must be paired because of lack of equipment, it is wise to have a more skilled student with a less skilled one in the early practice sessions. Later it will prove more stimulating to the participants if they are more evenly matched.

Nearly all handicapped students will require considerable experimentation to determine the best method of performing the skills of the various individual sports. It is important for the handicapped learner to understand the mechanics of each skill in the activity. Toward this end, audiovisual aids, and textbooks which describe the performance of the skills in detail are extremely useful, for, although in many instances the descriptions are not directly applicable, they do help the students to gain insight into the mechanics of performing the skills and thereby make possible a better understanding of how an adaptation may be made successfully.

Few schools will have their own golf courses and bowling alleys. Many aspects of these games can be taught, however, without actual use of these facilities. By utilizing plastic golf balls, golf cages, and indoor and outdoor putting areas, most of the skills of golf can be introduced to the students. Bowling skills can be taught very successfully with sets of polyethylene bowling balls and pins now on the market. If necessary, Indian clubs and a soccer ball can be used satisfactorily as substitutes for pins and ball in teaching the fundamental skills of bowling. It is, of course, desirable to give students opportunities to play in actual game situations if at all possible. Frequently, arrangements can be made with commercial bowling alleys and golf courses to use their facilities at certain slack hours for a nominal fee. If such arrangements are to be made, they should be worked out well in advance of the teaching unit in these sports and should, of course, have administrative approval.

ARCHERY

There are several forms of archery activity, the most common being that of shooting arrows at an upright target in an attempt to score points by hitting the center or near the center of the target. In official target-shooting competition, each archer must shoot a round—that is, a specific number of arrows from each of several specified distances. For example, in the Columbia Round, which is one of several possible kinds of rounds, the archer shoots 24 arrows from each of three distances: 50 yards, 40 yards, and 30 yards.

FIGURE 27. Archer maintains balance on crutches, releasing both arms to draw the bow.

SHOOTING AREA AND EQUIPMENT.   The shooting area and the area behind the targets should be free from buildings, trees, shrubs, and pedestrian and auto traffic. A regulation target is 48 inches in diameter and from 4 to 5 inches thick. It is highly desirable to place the target so that there will be a rise of land behind it to stop the arrows which overshoot the target.

The two types of bows used most commonly for recreational archery are the long bow and the recurve bow. The length of the bow to be used depends upon the length of the arms. Archers with short arms will use bows between 5 feet and 5 feet 3 inches in length. The students with longer arms will require bows of from 5 feet 4 inches to 5 feet 6 inches in length. The length of the arrow to be used is determined by the length of the bow. The shorter bows require 26-inch arrows, while the longer ones require 27- or 28-inch arrows.

The weight of the bow is the number of pounds required to pull the bow the length of the arrow. The weight of the bow used by an archer will depend upon his experience and the strength of his arm. A bow should be light enough so that the archer can concentrate on form and not have to struggle to draw the bow.

Finger tabs are used to cover three fingers of the shooting hand. Arm braces are worn to protect the inner forearm against the snapping bow string.

Adaptations: For wheelchair archers and those on crutches the target should be located where there is no rise behind it to stop the arrows, because these students will have too much difficulty retrieving arrows from an elevated area.

To assist blind students in moving from the shooting area to the target, a wire may be strung from one area to the other. At the shooting area, a stick 8 to 12 inches long should be placed on the ground, pointing in the direction of the target, to orient the blind archer. To help him determine the correct amount of pull on the bow, two poles are placed in the ground and aligned with the target; one pole indicates the place at which the hand of the extended arm should be, and the other the place where the back of the wrist of the hand drawing the string should be.

STRINGING THE BOW.   Because it is easier to develop adaptations for stringing the long bow than the recurve bow, only the techniques for the former will be discussed. To string the long bow, the lower end of the bow is placed against the inside of the arch of the left foot with the back of the bow facing left. The heel of the right hand is placed on the back of the bow near the top with the loop of the string held by the thumb and forefinger. With the left hand, the bow is grasped at its handle and is pulled back; at the same time, the right hand presses down and the loop of string is slipped up the bow and into the nock.

Adaptations: The handicapped student with a leg involvement may place the lower end of the bow against a low stationary object instead of placing it against his foot. If the archer is in a wheelchair, the side of the wheelchair may be used for this purpose.

Students with arm involvements may have so much difficulty achieving an adaptation of the stringing techniques that their bows will need to be strung for them by the teacher or student helper.

STANCE, NOCKING, AND DRAWING THE BOW.   In taking the stance, the feet are comfortably spread, with the left side of the body facing the target if the archer is right-handed. The head is turned toward the target. The bow is grasped in the left hand at the handle. It is held parallel to the ground and the target with the string toward the body and the back of the hand up. The arrow is picked up at the nock between the forefinger and thumb and placed across the bow at the arrow plate at right angles to the string. The cock feather is up. The thumb and forefinger encircle the string to hold the end of the arrow and to place the nock over the bowstring.

To assume the position for shooting, the fingers of the right hand are placed under the bowstring to grasp the string with the tips of the first three fingers. The arrow is held between the first and second fingers. The bow is raised and extended toward the target.

The elbow is straight but not locked. The other arm, with fingers bent to hold the string, is raised so the arm is bent at the elbow and is parallel to the ground. The bowstring is pulled back with the right arm so that the arm, wrist, and arrow make a straight line toward the target. The bowstring is pulled back against the chin. The hand is anchored under the jaw and against the neck with the forefinger up against the chin.

Adaptations: An archer in a wheelchair will turn the chair to the side and reach over the side of the chair to draw the bow.

Those on crutches will need to prop themselves with the crutches so as to free their arms. This can be accomplished by tilting the body toward the target and putting most of the weight on the front crutch. This will hold the crutch in place, and the arm can be used to hold the bow. The other arm will have to squeeze slightly on the rear crutch to hold it in place, but the arm is freed sufficiently to draw the bowstring parallel to the ground. Another method is to maintain equal weight on both crutches and bend the extended arm at the elbow so the front crutch can be cradled in the arm pit. The back crutch is cradled in the armpit by lowering the bowstring arm.

SIGHTING AND RELEASING.   For any given bow there is a certain distance from each target at which the center can be hit by sighting over the point of the arrow to the center of the target. If the archer is closer to or farther back from the target, he must aim above or below the target to hit it.

When the bow is sighted correctly, the arrow is released by straighening the fingers quickly. No other movement of the body should occur.

Adaptations: For the blind the two poles, already described as an aid in drawing the bow, may be wound with tape at the places where the hands should be for sighting accurately. The correct location of the tape is determined by trial and error. In shooting, the blind archer knows he is sighting correctly when the backs of his hands touch the taped areas.

For those who have the use of only one arm, the bow may be anchored to a standard of the type used for supporting a volleyball net. The bow is attached in the correct position for the correct range. If the standard is portable rather than permanently fixed, it must have a sufficiently large base to enable the archer to place his foot on it to help hold it securely. Sturdy poles might be substituted for standards. If the one-armed archer is confined to a wheelchair, the bow may be strapped to the chair.

There will be little need for adaptation for those with finger amputations if at least two functional fingers remain. These fingers can then be made to perform the work ordinarily performed by the missing fingers.

BOWLING

Bowling is an extremely popular American sport, played for the most part on indoor alleys. The object of the game is to knock down the ten pins located at the end of the alley with the bowling ball. Speed and control of the ball in the delivery are the essential factors in success in knocking down the pins.

PLAYING AREA AND EQUIPMENT.   The bowling alley is 41 to 42 inches

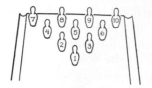

FIGURE 28.   Pin setting.

wide and 60 feet long. The ten pins are set in a triangle as shown in Figure 28. The ball is not more than 27 inches in circumference and must weigh not more than 16 pounds. The ball has three holes in which to place two fingers and the thumb. To determine if the ball fits the hands of the bowler well, the fingers and thumb are slipped into the holes. The fingers should fit snugly, while the thumb fits loosely but tightly enough so that the ball will not have to be squeezed to hold it in the hand. When the fingers are inserted to the second joint and the thumb is in the thumb hole, there should be barely enough space between the ball and the hand to place a pencil.

Adaptations: In addition to providing equipment for bowling instruction when regular alleys are not available, the polyethylene pins and balls discussed in the introduction are excellent for those students who, because of their handicaps, lack the strength and coordination to use the heavier regulation bowling balls. The grip on the ball is taken at the first joints of the fingers rather than the second joints, as in gripping a regulation bowling ball.

A recent innovation in equipment for the wheelchair bowler with limited arm movement is a light metal rack which provides a track for the ball to travel down from the lap of the holder to the floor of the alley. A polyethylene ball is used because of its light weight. The ball is placed on the track and the track is aimed toward the pins. The ball is released, and it rolls down the track and onto the alley to the pins.

PLAYING THE GAME.   A game consists of ten frames. Each time the bowler rolls two balls this constitutes a frame. The number of pins knocked down with both balls is recorded for each frame. If a strike is made (all the pins knocked down with the first ball), the score for that frame is 10 plus the number of pins knocked down in the next frame. If a spare is made (all the pins knocked down with the second ball), the score for that frame is 10 plus the number of pins knocked down on the next ball.

APPROACH AND DELIVERY.   The four-step approach is generally preferred. The ball is held chest high with both hands. Then, as the approach begins, the left hand (for a right-handed bowler) is withdrawn and the hand with the ball starts downward and into the backswing. The backward swing should be straight back. As the left hand is withdrawn, the first step in the approach is taken with the right foot. The second step is taken as the ball swings down. As the ball reaches the height of the back-swing, the third step is taken. With the final step, the arm swings forward. The last step is a longer stride than the other. After planting the foot, the

FIGURE 29.   Wheelchair patients can enjoy bowling with little modification of the game.
(National Recreation Association.)

feet are allowed to slide forward just back of the foul line. On the last
step, the body is crouched over the lead leg to enable the bowler to deliver
the ball on the floor smoothly so it will not bounce.

The two most common deliveries are the straight ball and the hook
ball. The former is the more simple to learn. For this delivery, the thumb
is on top of the ball and pointing directly at the head pin. As the ball is
released, the thumb leaves the hold first, and the ball rolls off the fingers
smoothly onto the alley. The ball is directed to the 1–3 pin pocket (halfway
between the first and third pins).

In a hook-ball delivery, the thumb is twisted toward the left and the
V formed by the thumb and forefinger is on top of the ball when it is
released. The ball should travel in a straight line toward the 3 or 6 pin,
depending upon the sharpness of the hook. Just before contact with the
pin, the ball should hook into the 1–3 pocket.

Adaptations: To bowl from a wheelchair when the metal rack need not
be used, the bowler must place the chair to face the pins. The body is
leaned over the side of the chair to permit the arm to swing freely in
delivering the ball. To compensate for the lack of approach in the delivery,
a preliminary swing may be taken. The ball swings back, then forward
without touching the floor, back again, and in the forward swing the body
is leaned farther to the side so that the ball can be released smoothly on the
floor.

If the wheelchair is too high for the bowler, a chair without arms may be used. A chair might also be used by bowlers on crutches or others with limited locomotion. An adaptation for those able to stand but unable to make the necessary steps in the approach is to permit them to stand at the foul line to make the delivery.

All bowlers who lack strength in the arm and shoulder should use the lighter polyethylene ball. In using this ball, only the straight ball may be thrown, because the ball is not easily controlled in a spin; otherwise the ball responds similarly to the regulation bowling ball.

Blind bowlers orient themselves by feeling the sides of the alley. The accuracy of the aim may be determined by the number of pins knocked down, which is told them by a sighted person.

GOLF

The game of golf is played on a course on which are located nine or eighteen holes. The object of the game is to hit a small hard ball with the appropriate club from one hole to the next in the fewest possible number of strokes.

PLAYING AREA AND EQUIPMENT.   The golf course, which is laid out on the natural terrain, has no specific dimensions, but its boundaries must be clearly marked for the players. The distance between the holes may vary from under 100 yards to over 500 yards. Each hole is made up of the tee areas, fairway, and green. The ball is put into play from the tee and is hit down the fairway to the green where the hole or cup is located. Hazards to play consist of natural obstacles such as trees and water or artificial obstacles such as bunkers and sand traps.

Equipment for playing golf consists of a set of clubs, golf balls, and tees. The clubs in a set are designed to accomplish all the various types of shots required by the conditions of the course. Clubs are classified as woods and irons. There are four woods, the lofts of which are graduated to produce different trajectories of the ball, which in turn affect the distance the ball travels. The clubs are numbered according to the amount of loft; the highest loft is the number 4 wood, and the flattest, the number 1 wood. All the woods are used for long distances.

The irons are also designed with increasing loft, equally graduated. The irons (except the putter) are numbered according to the amount of loft from 1 to 9, with higher numbers indicating greater loft. The iron clubs are grouped as long, middle, and short irons. This classification refers to both the length of the shaft and the distance the ball will travel. The long irons include numbers 1, 2, and 3 and are used for long shots from good lies. The middle irons are numbers 4, 5, and 6 and are used from the fairway and the rough for medium distances. The 7, 8, and 9 clubs make up the short irons and are employed for quick-rising shots from the fairway and traps. The putter, which has a flat face, is the only club used on the greens to drive the ball into the cup.

It is not necessary to have a full set of clubs in order to play the game. A short set composed of the number 1 and 3 woods and the 3, 5, 7, and 9 irons plus the putter will serve adequately.

Adaptations: Some handicapped players, while able to execute the strokes, are unable to do the amount of walking required by the game. The use of motor-powered carts, which are now on the market, can solve this problem if the cost of their purchase is not prohibitive. When carts cannot be provided for them, these players will need to restrict their playing to putting or shooting plastic golf balls on an available grassed area or shooting into a golf cage.

PLAYING THE GAME.   There are two basic types of play: *match play*, in which the player winning the most holes wins the match (strokes are counted for each hole, and the player with the fewest number of strokes wins the hole); and *stroke play*, in which the player having the least number of strokes per round is declared the winner. Essential basic rules for the beginning player are:

1. The ball is teed up in the tee area. After the tee shots, the player whose ball lies farthest from the green plays first.

2. Each swing at the ball counts as one stroke. In "summer rules" the ball is played where it lies. In "winter rules" improving the lie is permitted within six inches of the original lie but not nearer the cup.

3. In cases of an unplayable lie, lost ball, or out-of-bounds ball, the penalty is one stroke or one stroke and loss of distance, depending upon why the ball was moved or why a new ball was played.

Adaptations: Golf can be played by many handicapped players without modifications if they have sufficient stamina. Since the weather conditions and the hilliness of the course are related to the physical demands of the game, special consideration must be given to these factors if the players are convalescents, have arrested tuberculosis, or have cardiac, asthmatic, or anemic conditions.

Blind players are able to play golf without modifications if accompanied by a seeing player who will help locate the ball.

GRIP.   The most commonly used grip on the golf club is the overlapping grip. To take this grip, the handle of the club is placed across the fingers of the left hand (for a right-handed player) so that the shaft is angled. It should cross the index finger at the second joint and extend up to the lower part of the palm. The hand is then closed over the handle with the thumb on the top of the shaft. The right hand is placed under the shaft, with the little finger overlapping the first finger of the left hand and the left thumb fitting into the palm of the right hand. The thumb of the right hand is slightly on the left side of the shaft.

Adaptations: Students with hand or arm disabilities may require considerable adaptation of the grip on the golf club. Those with finger amputations or hand deformities may need to do extensive experimentation with gripping the club to find the grip that provides the greatest stability. For example, if the thumb is missing on the left hand of a right-handed player, instead of taking a regular grip where the palm of the right hand covers the left thumb, the right-hand grip may be taken so that the palm will come in firm contact with the base of the thumb. The interlocking grip, in which the little finger of the right hand interlocks with the forefinger of the left hand, will bring the fists closer together to make a better contact with the base of the thumb and palm.

Missing fingers other than the little finger on the right hand and forefinger on the left hand require little, if any, adjustment in the grip for a right-handed player. If the little finger of the right hand or the forefinger of the left hand is missing, the next finger may be used to make contact with the opposite hand. In this case the overlapping grip is likely to give greater stability.

A player whose left arm is missing or incapacitated must use golf clubs designed for use by left-handed players; in the case of a missing or disabled right arm, regular clubs will be used in the left hand.

With a missing hand, the stump is utilized to stabilize the club during the swing by placing it against the shaft of the club or against the arm of the hand that is grasping the club.

Players with one arm of limited function may find that the disabled arm can be used in some manner of grip to stabilize the club in the swing. Experimentation will determine if the disabled arm has a functional use in holding and swinging the club or if it will be necessary to rely entirely on one arm.

STANCE, ADDRESS, AND SWING.   In all strokes, the weight is distributed equally on the feet, which are spread about shoulders' width apart. The body is held partially bent at the hips with the knees flexed. There are three general types of stances used when addressing the ball preparatory to stroking it: the open stance, the closed stance, and the square stance. Each type of stance will affect the flight of the ball. In the square stance, both feet are perpendicular to the line of flight of the ball. In the open stance, the front foot is placed farther back from the intended flight; this will normally cause the ball to curve to the right. In the closed stance, the rear foot is dropped back, which causes the ball to curve to the left. The square stance is the one most frequently used.

In most shots the ball is placed in position in front of the body in line with the heel of the forward foot. The body is positioned so that the head of the golf club rests behind the ball. The swing begins by a preliminary waggle of the club head to emphasize the point of contact followed by moving the club head, hands, and arms backward in unison. The arms swing close to the body. The left arm is held straight but not rigid. The club head is carried back by rotating the body and shifting the weight to the right foot. The wrists are allowed to cock as the club reaches the waistline. The club is brought over the shoulder to a horizontal position. The head is held still throughout the swing, and the eyes are kept on the ball.

The forward swing starts with a rotation of the left hip; simultaneously the weight is transferred from the right to the left foot. This is followed immediately by a rotation of the body back to its original position. The arms are kept close to the body, and the wrists are held in the cocked position until the hands reach the level of the waist. Then the wrists uncock as the club follows its arc to and through the ball. The club head should swing out along the intended line of flight, while the body rotates to permit a complete follow-through of the hands and arms.

Adaptations: For those with limitations in movement, the stance must be adjusted to create the balance necessary for swinging correctly. The distance of the feet from the ball will generally depend upon body structure (length of arms, trunk, and legs). However, players who, because of hip disabilities, cannot bend forward easily at the hips will need to stand closer to the ball or use extra long clubs.

In the case of leg impairment, the stance may need to be modified. The leg spread may be lengthened to provide a wider base for balance in the case of unilateral weight distribution caused by wearing a brace or by unequal leg lengths.

Players with crutches who cannot stand and swing a club without support can brace themselves on their left crutch, disposing of the right crutch; then, using a left-handed club in the right hand, they execute the swing with one arm. A little experimentation will determine where the left crutch should be placed on the ground to maintain the best balance for swinging; usually this will be achieved by placing the crutch slightly behind and out from the left leg.

Players who cannot maintain their balance on one crutch or are unable to stand may sit in a sturdy straight chair with a wide base to prevent tipping for such activities as driving balls into a golf cage or putting on a practice green. Those playing from a chair, as well as those in wheelchairs, must have the chair turned so they are facing the ball, with the left side (for right-handed players) in the direction of intended flight. Extra long clubs may be needed by some wheelchair players in order to reach over the foot of the chair. The wheels of the chair should be locked or blocked to prevent rolling during the swing.

Contrary to what would appear to be the case, a player with only a right arm should use left-handed clubs and one with only a left arm should use right-handed clubs. The arm that holds the club starts back as in the regular swing. As the club is brought parallel with the ground, the wrist is adducted or cocked and the arm remains straight. At the top of the backswing the arm continues to be held straight and the grip on the shaft is firm. In the downswing the arm follows exactly the same path made in swinging back. The left arm leads the head of the club until impact with the ball.

Those with leg disabilities who cannot shift the weight readily from one foot to the other will need to cut down on the length of the backswing and secure force more from the rotation of the hips than from the total body, as would normally be the case.

Those seated in chairs or wheelchairs will shift their weight to the right side of the buttocks on the backswing if they are right-handed players. The trunk will twist to the right. The head will be over the left shoulder with eyes upon the ball at the end of the backswing, as in the regular stance. The head remains stationary in the swing until after contact with the ball. As the swing is brought down, the weight is shifted to the left side and the trunk is twisted back. A follow-through is made, the trunk is twisted to the left, and the weight comes to rest on the left side.

The blind player need make no adaptation of grip, stance, or swing; but before taking the stance he may place the ball on the ground with one hand and with the other place the head of the club beside it. He then stands up and takes his stance without moving the head of his club. The preliminary waggle before stroking is eliminated because this may throw off the alignment of the club with the ball.

ERROR IN STROKING.   The chart in Table 2 discusses some of the errors most frequently made by normal players in stroking the ball. The possible cause of the error and its means of correction are given. In some cases the suggested corrections cannot be made by the atypical player because of his particular physical limitations; then some substitution or adaptation will need to be made to overcome the error.

Most errors are the result of improper movement which causes a change in the radius of the swing. If, then, a handicapped golfer cannot make the necessary correction of his swing, he will need to make some compensation in the swing to overcome the difficulty. If, because of his disability, the player must keep his weight on the left leg in the backswing, he will need to exert conscious effort to control the arms so that, at the bottom arc of the swing, the head of the club will come where the ball is resting. A shift of the hips to the right may help to compensate for the inability to shift the weight to the right leg. In cases of an abnormal alignment of the legs, hips, or trunk, the position of the left foot cannot perhaps be moved as suggested in the chart. Consequently, the angle of the foot will have to be adjusted to that it will allow the trunk to be parallel to the ball when addressing it.

PUTTING.   The grip for putting differs from the grip used in other strokes. In the most commonly used grip, the whole right hand (for right-handed players) is placed on the handle and the index finger of the left hand covers the little finger of the right hand. The thumbs of both hands run straight down the top of the shaft. The left thumb is in the palm of the right hand, as in the regular grip. After the grip is taken, the head of the club is placed directly behind the ball and the stance is adjusted to center the weight opposite the ball with the eyes directly above the ball. The ball is stroked by keeping the face of the club perpendicular to the line of the putt throughout the swing. The distance of a putt is governed by the amount of backswing. The club is swung toward the cup, imparting an overspin or roll. The club should follow through for a distance greater than the backswing.

Adaptations: In cases where the thumb on either hand is missing, the forefinger may be substituted for the thumb in taking the proper grip to give stability to the club in the swing.

Wheelchair players may find the use of one arm more effective than both arms in putting. Because the wheels may cut into the greens, wide-wheeled chairs should be used; if these are not available, wide boards may be placed under the wheels while on the greens. Precautions against cutting are not necessary on the fairways or grassed playing fields on which wheelchair players may wish to practice.

TABLE 2. *Error Chart for Golf**

ERRORS	CAUSES	CORRECTIONS
Topped ball (hitting too near top of ball)	(1) Head is lifted, raising the shoulders and arms and lifting the club head.	Eyes are focused on ball at all times until ball is hit. Special care must be taken that head and shoulders are not lifted in backswing.
	(2) Body is swayed forward or backward, causing the lowest point of arc in the downswing to fall in front or back of the ball depending on the direction of the lean.	Head is held stationary and the body kept vertical.
	(3) Weight is kept on left leg on backswing.	As backswing is made, weight is shifted to the right leg.
	(4) Right knee is straightened and locked.	Weight is placed on inside of right foot and leg is not straightened as weight is shifted to that leg.
	(5) Left arm is bent, causing lifting of club head.	Left arm is held straight in backswing as well as in downswing.
Sclaffed ball (hitting behind ball)	(1) Weight is not transferred from left to right on backswing.	As backswing is made, weight is shifted from left side to right side.
	(2) Left knee is dipped or bent on backswing.	Left knee sways in on backswing but is not allowed to dip.
	(3) Right shoulder is dropped either at the address or downswing.	Shoulders remain level throughout stroke.

*Description is for right-handed players

ERRORS	CAUSES	CORRECTIONS
Smothered ball (ball is hit on top and driven down)	(1) Hands are too far to the right on the shaft.	Correct grip is taken.
	(2) Weight is not shifted from left leg to right on backswing.	As backswing is made, weight is shifted from left leg to right.
	(3) Left hand is twisted under right hand.	At top of backswing club face is half closed, not closed.
Sliced ball (flight of ball curves outward	(1) Right hand may be too far under shaft or left hand is not directly on top.	Correct grip is taken.
	(2) Left foot is slanting too much toward path of ball.	Straighten foot to close stance.
	(3) Hands are thrown forward or away from body at start of downswing.	Hands, arms, and trunk start together in downswing.
	(4) Overswinging in backswing, which causes bending of left arm and makes hips lead too much on downswing.	Left arm is held straight in backswing.
	(5) Weight is transferred back to right foot as head of golf club comes near ball.	Left foot is straightened in the stance
	(6) Left hip moves too fast for arms and shoulders.	Left foot is straightened and weight is kept on balls of the feet.
Pushed ball (flight of ball angles to right)	(1) Left foot pointing too straight ahead.	Left foot is pointed more toward path of flight.
	(2) Hands are too far ahead of head of club on impact with the ball.	Wrists are uncocked near waist on downswing and just slightly lead the head of club at impact.
	(3) Body is too far ahead at impact.	Hips and arms start together in downswing.
	(4) Ball is played too far back.	Ball is placed even with left heel.
Hook ball (flight of ball curves inward)	(1) Left foot is pointing too straight ahead.	Left foot is slanted more toward path of flight of ball to open stance.
	(2) Right hand is rolled over, which may be caused by right working independently of left.	Little finger of right hand and forefinger of left hand are interlocked or overlapped (depending on grip), forcing both hands to work together.

ERRORS	CAUSES	CORRECTIONS
	(3) Right hand is placed too far under shaft in the grip.	Correct grip is taken.
	(4) Hands break at top swing.	Firm grip is taken and kept throughout swing.
Pulled ball (flight of ball angles to the left)	(1) Right hand is too far over in grip.	Correct grip is taken.
	(2) Left foot points inward.	Left foot is pointed slightly toward path of ball to open stance.

QUESTIONS

1. What contributions to the total education of the handicapped do the individual sports make?

2. Discuss how bowling and golf may be taught in the adapted physical education program without an alley or course.

3. Select a specific handicap not discussed in the chapter and plan the adaptations that would be necessary to teach each of the individual sports to someone with this particular disability.

4. Develop an error chart for archery similar to the one for golf on page 221.

5. Using the chart you have made for question 4, suggest ways in which errors made by students with various kinds of handicaps would be corrected.

SELECTED READINGS

AAHPER: *Physical Education for High School Students*, ed. 3. Washington, D.C., American Association for Health, Physical Education, and Recreation, 1963.

Ainsworth, Dorothy S., *et al.: Individual Sports for Women*, ed. 4. Philadelphia, W. B. Saunders Co., 1963.

Fait, Hollis F., *et al.: A Manual of Physical Education Activities*, ed. 2. Philadelphia, W. B. Saunders Co., 1961.

Falcaro, Joe, and Goodman, Murray: *Bowling for All*, ed. 3. New York, The Ronald Press Company, 1957.

Hodgkin, Adrian E.: *The Archer's Craft*. New York, The Ronald Press Company, 1954.

Reichart, Natalie, and Keasey, Gilman: *Archery*, ed. 3. New York, The Ronald Press Company, 1961.

Shaw, John H., *et al.: Individual Sports for Men*, ed. 2. Philadelphia, W. B. Saunders Co., 1955.

Vannier, Maryhelen, and Fait, Hollis F.: *Teaching Physical Education in Secondary Schools*, ed. 2. Philadelphia, W. B. Saunders Co., 1964.

Vannier, Maryhelen, and Poindexter, Hally Beth: *Individual and Team Sports for Girls and Women*. Philadelphia, W. B. Saunders Co., 1960.

19
DUAL GAMES

Dual games are all those games in which one player engages in play with a single opponent or two players engage in play with a pair of opponents. Among the better known and most widely played dual games are tennis, badminton, and table tennis. Suitably large playing areas are required for tennis and badminton, and a special table is needed for playing table tennis. There are other dual games, however, which require much less space or special equipment; among these are loop badminton, corner ping pong, and shuffleboard.

Some proficiency in playing all of these games can be acquired by most handicapped students, even those with severe limitations. The more simple games can, of course, be learned more easily and require less adaptation. Tennis, badminton, and table tennis require greater physical effort on the part of the learner and, consequently, usually necessitate extensive adaptations; but the rewards to the handicapped participants are so great that the games should be included in the adapted program if at all possible.

The most obvious reward is the physiological benefit to the body resulting from the vigorous workout afforded by playing the dual games. There are other important but less tangible rewards. Because a certain amount of prestige is attached to participation in such games as tennis, playing them gives the handicapped person a real sense of achievement and the feeling of being like others. Then, too, the playing of these games opens up opportunities for social contacts with both sexes, an important consideration in selecting activities for the adapted program.

ORGANIZING THE INSTRUCTION

Those dual games played on large courts can become strenuous, and because of this they are sometimes overlooked as possibilities for adaption for play by those whose handicaps limit the area through which they are able to move when playing. It is possible, however, to modify these games to decrease the amount of locomotion that is necessary. Most of the other games can be played with few or no adaptations by those with limited movement or by those confined to wheelchairs. All of the games discussed in this chapter are readily modified for those with malfunction of one arm and for single-arm amputees; adaptation for these, as well as for those who have a weak shoulder on the side of the dominant arm which is subject to dislocation, consists of learning to play with the other arm.

Double-arm amputees can play all the games presented here if a functional stump remains on one arm to which the racquet or cue may be taped. In taping, padding should be placed between the handle of the equipment and the arm to prevent chafing and to insure comfort. Enough of the handle should extend up the arm to allow two straps to encircle the arm and handle. The handle may be placed on the inside or outside of the arm, but usually the inside is preferable. The position in which the piece of equipment is taped should simulate that in which it would be held by a normal player. Two leather or cloth straps may be used to hold the handle in place. Taping makes the equipment more secure but, since this cannot be done by double-arm amputees, they may prefer to use straps which they can learn to put on themselves, using the stumps and mouth.

When the disability of the student is such that considerable adaptation of the playing skills is required, as in the case of the double-arm amputee, extensive experimentation is usually necessary to discover the most effective way to perform the skills. Since the process of experimenting is likely to be emotionally frustrating and physically uncomfortable, the teacher should be particularly generous with praise and encouragement during this phase of instruction.

Like the individual sports, the dual sports require careful organization of the class time to permit as much individual instruction as possible. Equally important is planning the use of the facilities to insure as much actual playing of the game as possible. This is particularly applicable in games such as tennis and table tennis, where only a limited number of players can be accommodated at any one time.

TENNIS

Tennis is a game played with racquets and ball on a court which is divided into two playing areas by a net. The game may be played as singles with one player on each side of the net or as doubles with two players, who are partners, on each side. The ball is put into play by one of the players and is played back and forth across the net until one of the players fails to return it legally.

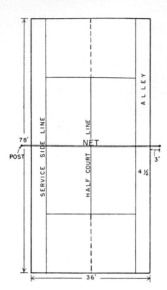

FIGURE 30.   Doubles tennis court. Dotted lines show one way to reduce the size of the singles court for modified play.

PLAYING COURT AND EQUIPMENT.   The singles and doubles courts are identical except that for doubles a 4½-foot alley, located on each side of the single court playing area, is included as part of the court for all shots after the service. The net is 3 feet in height. Court markings and dimensions are shown in Figure 30.

The choice of the tennis racquet is important. The weight of the racquet should be such that it can be controlled easily in play. The size of the grip should permit easy control; if it is too large, holding and controlling the racquet becomes difficult.

PLAYING THE GAME.   A point is scored whenever a fault is committed. The units of scoring are point, game, set, and match.

When a player has no points, his score is called love. The first score is called 15; the second, 30, the third, 40; and the fourth, game, unless the game is tied at 40 to 40. When this happens, the score is called deuce. If the next score is made by the server, it is called advantage in or ad in. If the score is made by the receiver, it is called advantage out or ad out. If the player who made the point wins the next point, he wins the game. If he doesn't, the score is again deuce. Before a game can be won, the winner must be ahead by two points.

A set is won when a player wins six or more games and is two games ahead of his opponent. Participants change ends after each game. A match consists of three sets.

Adaptation: For individuals whose skills are inadequate to keep the ball in play for any length of time, regulation scoring may be dispensed with. As a substitution the score may be counted as the number of times the ball is successfully returned during a given period of time. The objective in this case is playing the ball so that the opponent is able to return it rather than playing it so that the opponent cannot return it, as in regulation tennis.

GRIP. The most commonly used forehand grip in tennis is the Eastern grip. To take this grip for the forehand stroke, the racquet is held in the left hand (if the player is right-handed) with the racquet head vertical to the ground and the handle toward the body. A grip is taken on the handle as if shaking hands with it. The heel of the hand comes to rest on the end of the handle. The **V** angle formed by the thumb and forefinger should be in the center of the handle.

The backhand grip can be taken from the position of the hand in the forehand grip by moving the hand about a quarter of a turn around the racquet handle toward the thumb side.

Adaptation: Those who have insufficient strength to hold the racquet at arm's length with a proper grip may choke up on the handle — that is, move the hand up the handle toward the head of the racquet a few inches.

FOREHAND AND BACKHAND STROKES. Basic to both forehand and backhand strokes is footwork. The player must be ready to move in any direction as the ball is returned to him by his opponent. In returning the ball, the player must place his body to the side of the ball so that he may swing freely at it. The racquet is swung back while the player is moving into position, with the side of the body turned toward the net while stroking the ball.

In the forehand stroke, the left foot and shoulder are forward. When the racquet head is swung back in the backswing, the elbow is lightly bent. The weight of the body is carried well on the rear foot. A slight hesitation occurs at the end of the back swing. As the swing starts forward, the weight is shifted to the forward foot. The ball should be stroked at about waist height. The wrist is held firm as the ball is hit. After the ball is hit, the racquet continues to follow through, first following the path of the ball and then swinging in a wide arc in front of the body.

The flight of the ball is determined by how the ball is stroked and the direction the face of the racquet (the part that comes in contact with the ball) is at the moment of impact. With the face tilted upward the ball bounces higher into the air than if it is tilted downward. A ball going to the right or left of the intended flight may be caused by the direction the face was pointing on contact with the ball.

The backhand stroke is similar to the forehand and is used to return balls that are on the opposite side of the body from the arm that holds the racquet. For a right-handed player the right foot and the right shoulder are facing the net. The backswing is brought across the body as the weight shifts to the rear foot. Before the backswing is made, the backhand grip is taken. There is a slight pause at the end of the backswing before the racquet is brought forward in a wide arc to meet the ball at hip level just opposite the forward foot. The racquet follows through in the direction of the ball's flight and then swings wide in front of the body.

FIGURE 31.   A modified court allows those with restricted locomotion to play tennis. (The National Society for Crippled Children and Adults.)

Adaptations: For those with some limitations in locomotion who are playing on one-half of the singles court, the movement to place the body in the proper position for stroking may be limited to one step.

A player who has the racquet strapped to his arm cannot change the position of the racquet for the backhand stroke. Therefore, he will stroke the ball in the same way as in making the forehand stroke.

SERVE.   The game commences with the serve. The server stands behind his base line to the right of the center mark. The body is turned with its side to the net as in the forehand stroke. The ball is carried in the opposite hand of that which holds the racquet. The ball is tossed at arm's length from the body high enough in the air so the racquet arm is fully extended when the ball is hit. The weight is shifted to the rear foot as the ball is tossed into the air. As the toss is begun, the racquet is swung back behind the head. As the ball drops to the correct height, the weight shifts to the forward leg and the racquet is brought up with the wrist super-extended. The racquet is brought down upon the ball, driving it over the net into the opponent's right service court. The follow-through is made with a complete swing, the racquet coming to rest near the opposite knee. The server has two attempts to get the ball within the service area.

After failure by the opponent or server to return the ball, the server moves to the left court to serve. The service is alternated with the same server serving until the game is won. The serve then passes to the receiver for the next game.

Adaptations: Individuals who lack coordination and the ability to learn the regulation serve may perform the service by bringing the racquet up in front of the body as the ball is tossed into the air. The ball is stroked as it falls within reach of the racquet head. Served in this way the ball will lack speed and will make a higher arc over the net, but many players are able to learn to serve in this way who may never develop skill in serving it in the usual way.

Double-arm amputees who have the racquet taped to their arms may serve by balancing the ball on the face of the racquet. The ball is tossed into the air by a short quick upward movement of the racquet and stroked as it bounces. A loose rolling ball is brought under control by placing the racquet over the ball and pressing it to the ground. It is picked up by placing the racquet under the rolling ball and gradually brought under control by bouncing it on the face of the racquet. A stationary ball may be picked up on the racquet by placing the face of the racquet (near the handle) on the ball, drawing the racquet quickly toward the body to start the ball rolling, and slipping the head of the racquet under the rolling ball, which is brought to balance on the racquet face. A loose bouncing ball is brought under control by catching it on the racquet face and bouncing it up and down on the face until it is under control.

Players with only **one** arm serve by carrying the ball in the racquet hand. A regular grip is taken, and the thumb and forefinger are extended beyond the handle. The ball is grasped between these extended fingers and rests against the handle. The ball may be tossed into the air and stroked as described for players who lack coordination, or it may be tossed into the air and stroked as it bounces.

BASIC STROKES AND STRATEGY. Volley is the term used for the act of hitting the ball after it comes over the net but before it bounces on the court. A volley is made chiefly in the forecourt position. The smash or kill is a stroke used on a high bouncing ball or a short lob. The ball is hit hard and at a sharp angle so that it will bounce above the opponent's reach. It can be made effectively between the serving line and the net. The lob is a stroke in which the ball is hit so that it is lifted above the opponent's head and falls near his base line. It is used as a defensive shot to force the opponent back to the rear court.

In singles, as soon as the ball has been stroked, the player should move to one of two places: the center of the court, three or four feet from the net, or about two feet behind the base line in the center of the court. The net position is taken when it appears that the opponent will have a difficult time returning the shot. The back court position is safer but does not allow the advantage that can be had from handling balls at the net.

The doubles game requires less speed and endurance than singles. The lob becomes one of the most important strokes to keep the opponent away from the net. It is desirable to force one of the opponents far back into the back court so that a net position can be taken by the other two players. Players should always come to the net on each serve to gain the attack. The return of the service should usually be to the deep middle court. In rallying, partners should play parallel positions. The volley and smash are used whenever possible. All lobs should be hit before they bounce, if possible, in order to keep the offensive.

Adaptations: In using one half of a singles court with chops and drop shots eliminated, the player stands in the middle of the court about two feet behind the base line. The body can be positioned properly by taking one or two steps in either direction.

In the doubles game three or four players may be used on each side to decrease the amount of movement necessary to get into the proper position to stroke the ball. If three people are playing on a side, one plays at the net, the other two near the base line on each side of the court. Two players are placed on the net if four people are playing on a side.

BADMINTON

Badminton is a popular racquet game that is being used increasingly for family recreation in back yards. The object of the game is to hit the shuttlecock (also called the cock or bird) legally with the racquet back and forth over the net without permitting it to hit the ground or the floor. Badminton may be played as a singles or doubles game.

PLAYING COURT AND EQUIPMENT.   The badminton courts are marked for play as shown in Figure 32. The doubles court is 3 feet wider than the singles court. The net in the middle of the court is 5 feet high.

The badminton racquet is smaller and lighter than a tennis racquet and easily controlled. The shuttlecock is made from a piece of semi-spherical cork covered with thin leather or plastic into which feathers are inserted around the base. Light plastic feathers are frequently used in place of actual feathers. Shuttlecocks are constructed for both indoor and outdoor use. The latter are heavier and so are less easily affected by the wind.

Adaptations: To decrease the amount of movement required by the game, play may be limited to half the singles court or to half the doubles court, using the back serving line of the doubles court as the back line in either case. If half the singles court is used, the players will not have to move to either right or left to return the bird. Only one or two steps will be required to return all possible placements of the bird when half a doubles court is used. To avoid the necessity of movements to and back from the net, the drop shot may be made an illegal shot.

If a double-arm amputee is using a strapped-on racquet, the handle should be placed up the arm six to eight inches where it is taped or

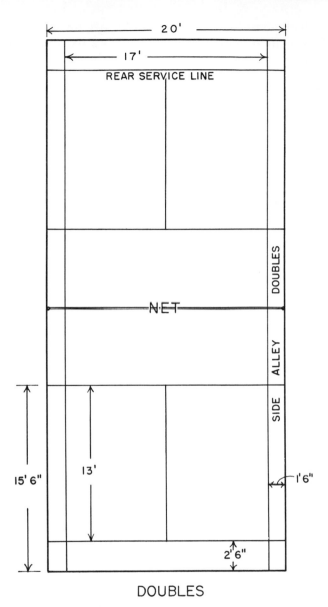

DOUBLES

FIGURE 32.   Badminton court.

strapped to the stump. The best location must be determined for each individual through trial and error. Even though a large portion of the badminton stroke is made by the wrist, those with strapped-on racquets can achieve considerable success in playing the game because the racquet is relatively light. Furthermore, a good defensive game can be built around drop shots that are made effectively without wrist action.

Outdoor badminton is never very satisfactory for class work because breezes even of light velocity blow the shuttlecock off course. However, if badminton is scheduled for an outdoor court, the bird to be used can be made more stable in slight breezes by weaving copper wire between the feathers at their base.

PLAYING THE GAME.   Scoring is possible in badminton only while serving. The server scores if the receiver fails to return the bird legally. When the server fails to return the bird or fails to make a legal serve, he loses the serve.

Although all other rules for badminton are the same for both boys and girls, the scoring differs in the singles game. For boys in doubles and singles, a game consists of 15 points. When the score has reached 13 all, the first side to reach 13 has the option of setting the game to five more points or permitting it to remain at two more points. When the score is 14 all, the first side to reach that score has the option of setting the game to three more points.

In girls' singles, the game consists of 11 points. In girls' doubles, it is 15 points. In singles, when the players are tied at 9 points, the first player to reach this number has the option of setting the game to three more points. When the score is 10 all, the one who first reaches 10 has the option of setting the game to two more points.

Adaptation: Beginners may work as a team to keep the bird aloft as long as possible. Consequently, instead of attempting to make the opponent miss the shot, they must attempt to place the bird so it can be stroked.

GRIP.   The racquet handle is grasped as if one were shaking hands with the racquet. The fingers are spread slightly. When the racquet handle is held toward the body and the racquet head is vertical to the floor, the **V** formed between the thumb and forefinger is on top of the handle. The grip is taken so that the heel of the hand is flush with the end of the handle.

Adaptations: Because of the lightness of the racquet, very few players will be unable to control the racquet with the regular grip. However, in extreme cases of grip weakness, the grip may be taken higher on the handle.

SERVE.   The serve is made from the short service line into the service area diagonally across the net from the server. The server starts in his right service court. When his score is an uneven number, he will serve from his left service court. When the server faults, the serve passes to his opponent. In doubles, if he is the first server in the game, the serve passes to his opponent. After the first service, both players on one side serve before it passes to the other side.

The right-handed server stands with the left foot forward. The bird is held low in front and to the right of the body by the feathers with the thumb and forefinger. The racquet is swung back with the wrist superextended. The racquet is brought forward and the wrist is flexed just before contact with the shuttlecock. The left hand releases the shuttlecock just before it is hit. In singles the safest serve is a long high serve to the back court, while in doubles the short serve is generally more effective.

Adaptation: Those individuals who cannot use wrist action in serving may be allowed to serve in front of the service line so that the high serve to the back court will be effective.

BASIC STROKES, FLIGHTS, AND STRATEGY.   The overhead, forehand, backhand, and underhand lift strokes are the basic strokes in badminton. When the bird is to be hit above the head, an overhead stroke is used. For this stroke the left side of the body is turned to the net (for right-handed players). The backswing is made by swinging the racquet back at waist height and bringing its handle up above the right shoulder while the racquet head is above and behind the left shoulder. The arm is slightly bent and the wrist is superextended. As the shuttlecock falls to the proper height, the arm is extended its full length and contact is made with the shuttlecock. Just before contact, the wrist is snapped forward. At the beginning of the stroke, the weight is on the back foot. As the stroke is made, the weight shifts forward. The arm follows through, describing a half circle.

The forehand stroke is used when the bird falls below the head on the right side (for right-handed player). The stance is taken as in the overhead stroke. With the wrist superextended, the arm is swung back on the level at which the bird will be hit. As it falls into hitting position, the arm is brought forward and the wrist is flexed as contact is made with the shuttlecock. The weight is shifted forward as in the overhead stroke. The racquet follows through in a natural arc.

In the backhand stroke (for right-handed players), the right foot is forward as the body is sideways to the net. The arm is brought in front of the body and most of the weight of the body is brought onto the back foot. The wrist is flexed. The arm is brought forward to meet the shuttlecock as the weight is shifted to the front foot. The wrist is superextended as the racquet hits the shuttlecock. Contact is made with the bird on the left side and slightly in front of the body. The arm follows through across the body with the arm extended and with the racquet head rolled over.

The underhand lift stroke is used when the bird is falling close to the net and below it. It can be used with the backhand or forehand. The appropriate foot is placed forward (right for backhand and left for forehand), and the racquet is extended face up to come under the bird. The bird is stroked upward with the wrist held rigid. It is raised just enough to clear the net and drop on the other side.

The common flights are the high clear, smash, and drop shot. The high clear is a shot that is driven high and deep into the opponent's back court. The smash is a "kill" shot executed from the overhead position.

The stroke is made so that the bird is driven down into the opponent's court. In the drop shot the bird is struck lightly so that it drops immediately after passing over the net.

The flight that is used will depend on the situation. The high clear is used most frequently. It is a defensive stroke used to force the opponent back. It can be used anywhere on the court. The drop shot is used when the opponent is not expecting it and is away from the net. The underhand lift is used only when the bird is falling too close to the net for any other shot. The shot is more effective if the bird is stroked so that it goes to the other side of the court as it goes over the net from where it was played. The smash is used whenever the bird is higher than the net and in the forecourt.

Adaptations: The ability to use different strokes will vary according to the nature of the handicap. Those players with limited wrist action will not be able to employ the smash as effectively as they do the drop shot. Strategy for these players will be to use chiefly the high clear and the drop shot. Those who are playing on half a singles court with the drop shot made illegal will necessarily have to rely upon the smash and high clear. Playing on the modified court, the player stands in the center of the court and merely moves the appropriate foot forward to get into position for a back-hand or forehand stroke.

LOOP BADMINTON

Loop badminton is an adaptation of badminton developed by the author which is played with a badminton shuttlecock, table tennis paddles, and an upright metal loop. It is an active game, requires considerably less space than badminton, and is more adaptable to play by those who are restricted in movement than is badminton. Two players engage in play with the objective of hitting the cock legally through the loop to score.

The playing area is 10 feet by 5 feet with a metal loop 24 inches in diameter placed in the center of the area. The loop is strapped on an upright pole such as a badminton or volleyball standard so that the pole bisects the loop. The bottom of the loop is 46 inches from the floor. A restraining line is drawn across the court 3 feet from each side of the loop (Figure 33).

Adaptations: The size of the loop may be increased to enable the less skilled to return the bird through the loop successfully. For those who have very poor skills, the loop may be placed to the side of the standard so that it projects from the side and is not bisected by the standard.

If a standard is not available, the loop may be hung from the ceiling with a cord. To keep it from swinging, another cord must anchor it to the floor. For those who are seated either in a chair or a wheelchair while playing, the loop may be placed lower than the recommended 46 inches.

The loops may be constructed from heavy wire or from small flexible

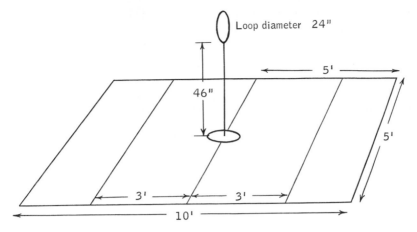

FIGURE 33.   Loop badminton court.

branches. The ends are brought together to form the loop and secured with wire or adhesive tape.

PLAYING THE GAME.   The game starts with an underhand service, as in badminton, behind the end line. The serve must pass through the loop without touching the loop or standard. If it touches the loop or standard, it is called a let serve and the server serves again. The bird must land beyond the opponent's restraining line and in his court. The receiver can stand anywhere behind his restraining line to receive the serve. The bird must be returned through the loop. After the serve the bird may be struck so that it lands anywhere in the opponent's court, including in front of the restraining line, as long as it passes through the loop. A bird that touches the loop or standard and goes through the loop is considered fair if it is not the serve. The bird must be struck sharply and cannot be carried momentarily on the paddle. If a player touches the loop or reaches through it or around it, he loses either a point or the serve. A player may not play the bird while standing in front of the restraining line, nor may he hold his paddle in front of the loop to prevent the bird from passing through.

Scoring is done as in badminton. Only the server can score a point. If the server makes a fault, he loses the serve. The winner of the game is the first player to get 15 points in a boy's game and 11 points in a girl's game. In boys' play, when the score has reached 13 all, the first person to reach 13 has the option of setting the game to five more points or allowing it to remain at two more. When the score is 14 all, the first player to reach the score has the option of setting the game to three more points. For girls, when the players are tied at 9 points, the first player to reach that score has the option of setting the game to three more points. At 10 all the first to reach that number has the option of setting the game to two more points.

Adaptations: If players are playing from wheelchairs or crutches, the serve is made from in front of the service line. If the player is playing from a chair that is not mobile, it is placed in the center of the court. The serve is made from this position. When the player's mobility is limited, any bird that does not land beyond the opponent's restraining line is considered a fault.

Those who are subject to chronic shoulder dislocation can usually play loop badminton using the involved arm without adverse effect, since all strokes can be made with the arm held lower than the shoulder.

TABLE TENNIS

Table tennis is a form of tennis played on a table with paddles and a small ball. It may be played as a singles or doubles game.

PLAYING AREA AND EQUIPMENT.   The regulation table top is 5 feet by 9 feet, divided in the center by a net 6 inches to 6¾ inches high. Markings on the table may be seen in Figure 34. For optimum playing conditions it is recommended that there be 6 feet on either side of the table and 12 feet at each end. A ceiling height of at least 12 feet is also recommended.

The ball and net are standardized by rule, but the racquet or paddle may be of any material. The paddle is generally 4½ to 5 ounces in weight and has a rubber or sandpaper surface.

Adaptations: For play by students in wheelchairs, the table should be situated in an area with sufficient room to accommodate the movement of the chairs. The table should be made stationary by nailing or screwing the legs to the floor. This enables wheelchair players to grasp the table for support while moving their chairs into position for stroking the ball.

A paddle developed by the author, useful to blind or partially seeing players, may be constructed from a rectangular board 2 or 2½ feet by 1½ feet in size with handles attached at each end. A Space Ball net, which is made of a rectangular frame and netting and designed to be held in the hands, may also be substituted for the regulation paddle.

For blind beginning players, play may be limited to half of the table

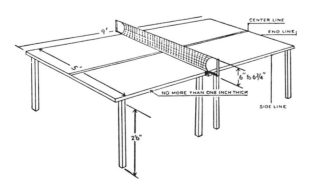

FIGURE 34.   Table tennis.

on each side of the net. Paper is placed on the half of the court not being used so that players will be able to tell by the difference in the sound of the ball striking the surfaces if the ball is good or out of bounds. If a sighted player is the opponent for the beginning blind player, the former may be required to play his full court while the latter plays half of his court. Badminton nets or other finely meshed nets attached to standards may be placed along the sides of the table to help keep the ball on the table where it can be more easily located by blind players.

PLAYING THE GAME.   A score is made each time an opponent fails to return the ball legally or when he commits a fault. Faults are made when a player:

(1) does not return the ball;

(2) does not make a legal serve that lands fairly;

(3) touches the net or support;

(4) moves the playing surface while the ball is in play;

(5) touches the playing surface with his hand while the ball is in play;

(6) is touched by the ball before it bounces on his side of the court;

(7) hits the ball before it bounces on his side.

Adaptations: Touching the table for purposes of supporting the body or moving the wheelchair is not called a fault. However, deliberate banging against the table should be considered a fault.

A game is 21 points. In case of a tie at 20–20 points, the winner of the game is the one who first wins 2 successive points.

GRIP.   The tennis grip is the preferred grip for table tennis. The racquet is grasped as if shaking hands with the handle. The thumb and forefinger are placed on either side of the surface of the racquet. The side of the thumb rests gently on the racquet where the handle and the face meet. The forefinger is separated slightly from the rest of the fingers and extends across the face at its base. The rest of the fingers are closed around the handle.

Adaptations: Double-arm amputees will have the paddle taped to a stump. Blind players using the special paddle described previously will grasp a handle in each hand and hold the paddle in front of the body ready for play.

SERVE.   For the serve the ball is held in the open flat palm of the hand; the fingers must be held straight. The server puts the ball into play by tossing it into the air. The ball is struck with the racquet so that it bounces first into the server's court, then passes over the net and lands on the receiver's side. When the ball is struck in serving, it must be completely free of the serving hand. At the moment of impact the ball must be behind the end line and between the side lines (if they were extended beyond the end line).

Many different kinds of serves may be employed. The serve may be backhand or forehand. Either of these may be combined with one of the following: top spin, side spin, or chop. Top spin is acquired by turning the face of the paddle (the side with which the ball is struck) slightly downward and dragging the face of the paddle over the ball in the direction of the intended flight. Side spins are achieved by dragging the paddle across the ball from one side to the other as it is hit. Dragging the paddle from right to left will cause the ball to bounce to the receiver's left side; dragging it from left to right has the opposite effect. The chop is made by hitting the ball with the paddle face held slightly upward and striking the ball while the paddle is dragged downward.

Each player serves until 5 points have been scored. The serve then passes to the opponent, unless the score is tied at 20–20; in this situation the serve alternates until one person is two points ahead.

In doubles the server starts from the right side of his court and must serve the ball to the receiver in the right court. He serves until 5 points have been made; then the service passes to the former receiver who serves to the partner of the previous server.

Adaptations: Players who are on crutches and use the table for support are allowed to serve in front of the end line if it is necessary to maintain body balance. Players with one hand serve by grasping the ball between the extended forefinger and thumb after the grip has been taken. The ball is tossed into the air and served either before or after it bounces. Serving by players with taped-on paddles is accomplished by balancing the ball on the face of the paddle and then tossing it into the air with an appropriate movement of the paddle. The ball is stroked after it bounces. Beginners may be permitted to hit the ball over the net without its bouncing again; skilled players may be required to allow the ball to bounce on their side of the table after it is hit and before it passes over the net.

A ball can be picked up on the face of the paddle by placing the face of the paddle on the ball. The paddle is then drawn quickly toward the player. In the same movement, the paddle is slipped under the rolling ball, which is brought to balance on the face. If the ball is resting on the table, it may be picked up by pushing it close enough to the edge of the table to be reached by the player's head. The paddle is placed parallel with the table and the ball rolled onto its face with the forehead. The ball may be carried by pressing it between the forehead and the paddle.

Blind players using the two-handled paddle may start the game by gently tossing the ball over the net to the opponent.

FOREHAND AND BACKHAND.   The forehand is employed for all balls that are driven more than one foot to the right side of the player (for right-handed players). As soon as it can be determined that the ball is going to land so it can be played by a forehand stroke, the backswing is made: the paddle is brought to the right side about table height, the wrist is slightly superextended, and the paddle is held so that the handle is parallel to the table and the head faces the right. As the swing forward is made, the weight shifts to the left foot. The paddle is brought forward and upward to strike the ball at its highest bounce. If top spin is desired, the face of the racquet is slanted slightly downward as it makes contact with the ball and is dragged over its top. In either case the paddle follows through forward and upward.

The backhand is used on balls that bounce on the left side of the body, in front of the body, or within one foot on the right side of the body (for a right-handed player). The paddle is turned so that the opposite face from that used in the forehand is facing the ball. If the ball is on the left side of the player, the arm crosses the body. If the ball is in front or not over one foot from the right side, the paddle is held in front of the on-coming ball. In all cases the head of the paddle points to the left and the handle is parallel to the ground. The backswing is very short, but the wrist is flexed to add power to the stroke. The backswing should bring the paddle in front of the approaching ball slightly above table height. The paddle is brought forward and upward; at the same time the wrist is superextended to meet the ball at the height of its bounce.

For a forehand or backhand chop the paddle is held above the point where the ball will reach the height of its bounce. With the paddle tilted slightly upward, the head is dragged downward on the ball as it is hit forward.

Adaptations: Beginners and those who have difficulty in making coordinated arm movements will depend chiefly upon forehand and backhand strokes without spin. If the paddle head is not dragged on the ball, the tilt of the paddle face will dictate how high the ball will go into the air. A player who consistently knocks the ball into the net will need to tilt the face up, while one who knocks the ball too high into the air will need to tilt it down.

The blind player who is using the two-handled paddle will hold the paddle in front of the body with both hands and move it to the right or left as he hears the ball bounce. If he knocks the ball consistently into the net, he will need to tilt the face of the paddle upward. Conversely, if the ball bounces too high, the board must be tilted downward. Beginners should be encouraged to bounce the ball high to make its return easier.

PLAYING THE BALL AND STRATEGY.   After moving to play a ball, the player should return to a position near the center of the table 2 to 4 feet from the end line. The weight should be carried on the balls of the feet, and the knees should be slightly flexed so that the body may move readily in either direction to play the ball. The ball cannot be hit until after it bounces in the receiver's court, so it is undesirable to be too close to the table as this makes it difficult to return a hard-hit ball that bounces off the table.

The safest shot for most opponents is a long shot to the receiver's backhand.

In the doubles game, the players on the same side must alternate in returning the ball; therefore, the safest shot is on the side opposite that of the player whose turn it is to return the ball.

Adaptations: Wheelchair players will keep the center position as just described but will stay closer to the table. One hand is rested on the table to manuever the chair into position to play the ball. Some players prefer office chairs with free-rolling casters to wheelchairs because they are more maneuverable.

A fault is not called if a blind player inadvertently holds his two-handled racquet in such a way that the ball is struck before it bounces. However, if there is intent to hit the ball, the act becomes a fault.

CORNER PING PONG

Corner ping pong is a game developed at the University of Connecticut by the author for use in the adapted physical education program by those who are limited in movements of the legs. The game utilizes the skills of table tennis and might be used as a practice drill as well as an adapted game.

PLAYING AREA AND EQUIPMENT.   A corner area with smooth walls for a height of 6 feet by 6 feet on each side of the corner is needed. The floor and wall markings are shown in Figure 35. Table tennis paddles and ball are used.

Adaptations: If smooth walls are not available, plywood may be cut the required size and placed over rough walls or attached to the floor to create a corner for playing.

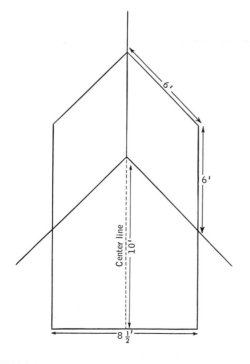

FIGURE 35.   Corner ping pong court.

To decrease the amount of movement required of the players, the court size may be reduced, with the size of the wall surface kept in the same proportion to the floor area.

PLAYING THE GAME. One player stands on each side of the center line. The ball is dropped by the server and stroked against the floor to the forward wall. The ball must rebound to the adjacent wall, then bounce onto the floor of the opponent's area. If the server fails to deliver a good serve, one point is recorded for the opponent.

The ball may bounce only once on the floor before the opponent returns it. He must stroke the ball against the forward wall in his section of the playing area so that the ball rebounds to the adjacent wall and onto the floor in the server's playing area. Failure to return the ball is scored as a point for the server.

Scoring is similar to table tennis. Each player gets five serves. A ball that is stroked out of bounds is scored as a point by the other player. Game is 21 points, and the winner must win by 2 points.

Adaptation: To decrease the speed of play, the served ball is required to strike the floor before it hits the wall. In each subsequent play, the ball must be hit so as to strike the floor first before it hits the wall.

SHUFFLEBOARD

Shuffleboard is played on a hard-surface court with long-handled cues and eight disks, four of which are of one color and four of another color. The object of the game is to push the disks with the cue so that they will land in the scoring area of the court and to prevent the opponent from scoring by knocking his disks out of the scoring section.

PLAYING COURT AND PLAYERS. The shuffleboard court is 52 feet long and 6 feet wide, laid out on a hard surface. The court may be located either inside or out of doors. The scoring areas are marked as shown in Figure 36.

The game may be played as singles by two or as doubles by four players. In singles, both players begin play at the same end of the court; they then move to the opposite end of the court to total the score and play the disks from that end. In the doubles game, partners play at opposite ends of the court, remaining there throughout the entire game.

Adaptations: The length of the court may be shortened for those who do not have sufficient strength to propel the disks the total distance on the regulation court. It may also be shortened in length for mental retardates who are poorly coordinated, to insure success in scoring.

A strip of tape placed on the floor to show the direction of the court is helpful to blind students. By feeling the tape, they are able to locate the court and to adjust their aim accordingly.

The doubles game is, of course, preferable for players with limited locomotion. If there are not enough players for a doubles game, singles

FIGURE 36. Shuffleboard court.

may be played with opponents stationed at opposite ends. The opponent, in this case, counts the score and returns the disks by pushing them back to the other player for his next turn. Playing the game this way eliminates the challenge and excitement of preventing the opponent from scoring, but it does provide fun and exercise for those whose range of locomotion necessitates adaptation of the game.

PLAYING THE GAME. A player in a singles game uses disks of one color only, and in doubles the partners use the same disks of one color. At the start of the game the four disks of each player are put on the side of the 10-off area. Players play the disks alternately from the 10-off area. A disk which fails to reach the farther dead line is removed before the next disk is played.

To shoot, the player faces the disk, with the head of the cue resting on the court squarely behind the disk, the cue forming a straight line with the disk and the target. The player stands slightly at the side so that the arm is in a straight line with the cue. The cue is grasped in the fist with the **V** formed by the forefinger and thumb on top.

The delivery is made (by a right-handed player) by taking a step forward on the left foot as the arm with the cue swings forward, pushing the disk evenly and smoothly forward. The head of the cue slides along the floor. In the follow-through the arm is fully extended, with the cue pointing in the direction of the moving disk.

The first disk may be played as a block or pilot shot. In this shot the disk is placed so that a second shot can be made to rest behind it in the scoring zone (see diagram in Figure 37). This is an offensive tactic designed to protect the scoring disks from the opponent.

A game may be set at 50, 75, or 100 points. After all the disks have been played, the score is tallied by counting the disks that are in the scoring area and not touching a line. Each disk has the value of the number in the section of the court in which it lands. Ten points are subtracted from the score for each disk in the 10-off area.

Adaptations: A wheelchair patient should place his chair facing the court and slightly to the side so that the arm with the cue can be dropped to the side of the chair to make the shot.

Players on crutches must shift the body weight to the crutch of the opposite arm to free the playing arm to make the shot.

For those seated in straight chairs for playing, it may be easier to move

FIGURE 37. Pilot or block shot.

FIGURE 38. Orthopedically handicapped players make their own specific adaptation for a game of shuffleboard.

the disks along the 10-off line to put them in the proper position than to move the chair to place the player in the proper position for shooting.

Bed patients can play shuffleboard if they are able to lie on the stomach or sit in a partially reclined position and extend an arm over the side of the bed to push the cue.

Players who are spastic may achieve better results in playing the disk by making several repetitive movements with the cue behind the disk before actually pushing it forward. The athetoids, on the other hand, have greater success if no preliminary movements are made. They should place the cue behind the disk and push forward immediately.

To simplify scoring for the mentally retarded, the score may be based on the number of disks which land within the scoring area of the count: each disk then counts one point.

QUESTIONS

1. Justify a severely handicapped student's learning to play tennis even though the necessary adaptations make the game so different from the original game of tennis.

2. Discuss ways of decreasing the amount of rapid locomotion in the games of badminton and tennis.

3. How can a double amputee learn to play a racquet game?

4. Describe the adaptations that would be necessary for a blind player to play any of the racquet games.

5. Which of the dual games can be played from a wheelchair? What adaptations are necessary?

SELECTED READINGS

AAHPER: *Physical Education for High School Students,* ed. 3. Washington, D.C., American Association for Health, Physical Education, and Recreation, 1963.

Ainsworth, Dorothy S., *et al.: Individual Sports for Women,* ed. 4. Philadelphia, W. B. Saunders Co., 1963.

Cartland, Douglas: *Table Tennis Illustrated.* New York, The Ronald Press Company, 1953.

Fait, Hollis F., *et al.: A Manual of Physical Education Activities,* ed. 2. Philadelphia, W. B. Saunders Co., 1961.

Haslam, Charles:*The How to Book of Shuffleboard.*St. Petersburg, Fla., Great Outdoors Association, 1955.

Vannier, Maryhelen, and Fait, Hollis F.: *Teaching Physical Education in Secondary Schools,* ed. 2. Philadelphia, W. B. Saunders Co., 1964.

Vannier, Maryhelen, and Poindexter, Hally Beth: *Individual and Team Sports for Girls and Women.* Philadelphia, W. B. Saunders Co., 1960.

20
TEAM GAMES

Team games are important in the physical education program because they provide big-muscle activity necessary for developing and maintaining a desirable level of physical fitness. Since handicapped children are likely to be less physically fit, their participation in team games is especially important for this reason. Team games are important, too, for the opportunities they give these children to demonstrate their ability to contribute to the group effort. Their fellow team members are likely to gain an understanding and respect for the handicapped they would not otherwise develop, while the handicapped themselves are likely to acquire greater confidence in their abilities and to accept themselves as they really are. That some of the team games are among our most popular spectator sports is still another reason to include team games in the curriculum; in learning to play them, students become more intelligent spectators.

ORGANIZING THE INSTRUCTION

The team games, because of their vigorous nature, cannot be adapted to all types of exceptional players. However, even though the game as a whole may not be adaptable, specific skills involved can be adapted for play by nearly all types of handicapped students. For example, those whose locomotion is restricted because of leg disabilities may still engage in modified basketball shooting and football passing drills.

In the school situation, then, the teacher may plan to include the handicapped in the drills which are used for improving the skills of the team sports. Some slight modifications may need to be made, as, for example, in a drill which requires rapid movement from one position to another; the student who is incapable of moving rapidly may be permitted to omit this phase of the drill and continue on to his place in line.

Unless severely restricted in arm and leg movements or greatly lacking in physical fitness, handicapped students may also be included in the lead-up games and in the actual competitive play of the team sports, subject to the adaptations required by the physical condition. Frequent rest periods should be planned because the strenuousness of competitive team play may tax even the most physically fit player, and, as noted elsewhere, handicapped youngsters are likely to be lacking in physical fitness. For students unable to participate in these phases of the class instruction, the teacher may plan continued work on the drills. The drills should be varied whenever interest wanes. Injecting a competitive element into a drill makes performing the drill more interesting and often more satisfying to a handicapped student, because it provides him with a tool for evaluating his progress. Rather than drilling on passing by throwing the football to a receiver, for example, a competitive element may be introduced by drawing a target on the field at which the thrower may aim in the hope of scoring a bull's eye.

If students will be working on drills and drill-like games while the teacher is engaged in instructing and supervising the rest of the class in team play, the teacher must organize student helpers to retrieve balls and otherwise assist the handicapped players who cannot work entirely on their own. No student should be allowed to serve so frequently as a helper, however, that he is deprived of his own physical education.

BASKETBALL

Basketball is played by two teams on a court which has a basket located at a designated height above the floor at each end. A score is made when a player successfully throws the ball into the basket assigned to his team. The team which has possession of the ball attempts by passing and dribbling the ball to bring it close to its basket for possible scoring while the opposing team tries to prevent the score from being made and to gain possession of the ball for itself.

PLAYING COURT AND PLAYERS. The regulation basketball court is 50 feet by 94 feet. It is marked with boundary lines, a mid-court line, a center circle, and two free throw circles and lanes. The height of the baskets for official play is 10 feet. A height of 8 feet is recommended for players below the ninth grade.

In boys' play there are five players on a team: two guards, two forwards and one center. A girls' team has six players: three forwards and three guards.

FIGURE 39. Basketball shooting practice with an improvised ball-return arrangement. (National Recreation Association.)

Adaptations: Because basketball is a strenuous game requiring speed and endurance, it cannot be adapted readily to a large range of handicapped students. For those who are able to participate in moderate exercise, however, play may be confined to half the court. The number of players per team may also be increased to reduce the physical demands upon individual players.

The baskets may be lowered for modified activities designed for students with restricted arm movement and for students who must shoot from a sitting position in a chair or wheelchair. For those who cannot move about readily, a device such as the one shown in Figure 39 can be made to help in retrieving the ball.

A light string hung from the back side of the hoop so that it is low enough to be reached with the hand and yet high enough to be above the head is of great assistance to the blind player in determining the location of the hoop before he shoots. A bell attached to a length of twine may be hung from the hoop so that it will be made to ring when the ball enters the hoop and notify the shooter of his success.

PLAYING THE GAME.   Playing time for a basketball game is divided into halves of specified length. The team with the higher number of points at the end of the game is the winner. Two points are scored each time the ball is thrown through the basketball hoop, and one point is scored for a successful free throw. The latter is awarded as the result of a rule infraction by the opposing team.

The rules governing play differ somewhat for boys and girls and are subject to change each year. Therefore, it is recommended that the teacher who includes basketball for either sex in the program secure a copy of the rule book after each revision.

Adaptations: While the game of basketball is not readily adapted to a large range of handicapped students, drills and games of passing, catching, and shooting the ball can be performed by nearly everyone. Generally, these students will not be able to participate in regular basketball play and should, therefore, be provided with a basket especially for their own use.

CATCHING THE BALL.   In catching, the fingers are spread to receive the ball. When catching a high ball (above the waist), the thumbs are together. If the ball is below the waist, the little fingers are together. The ball is caught on the cushions of the finger tips, not with the heels of the hands. As the ball is caught, the arms give with the ball as the elbows are flexed. The ball is brought back toward the body. The eyes follow the ball throughout the catch.

Adaptations: A one-handed player may catch the ball by trapping it between the lower portion of the arm and the body, with the upper arm cradling the ball as it is brought into the body.

Those on crutches may find it easier to bring the ball to the side of the body rather than toward it when giving with the ball, as this permits the balance to be kept on the crutches placed under the arms.

Blind players will catch the ball by extending both arms forward, with elbows slightly flexed. The passer must throw the ball into the open arms. The ball is cradled in the arms as the fingers come in contact with the ball to control it.

PASSING.   Whether the teammate is standing or moving and how great the distance is from the passer to receiver will determine how hard the ball should be thrown. The ball should be thrown hard enough to reach the teammate, without being thrown so hard as to cause it to be fumbled when caught. The passes most commonly used are the two-handed chest pass and overhand pass.

In the *two-handed chest pass*, the ball is brought chest high with the elbows flexed. The arms are extended sharply and the ball is released from both hands with an outward snap of the wrists. As the pass is made, the weight is brought forward.

For the *overhand pass*, the ball is brought back behind the shoulders about head high, with one arm, as in throwing a baseball. Then the arm is brought forward, and the ball is released with an abrupt snapping of the wrist. The ball should be thrown without imparting a spin, because this makes it difficult to catch.

Adaptations: One-armed players will make their passes with one arm.

In long passes the overhand pass will be used, while in short passes the ball will be thrown underhanded.

Players on crutches will have to have a greater wrist snap than otherwise in making the two-handed chest pass. Generally the most effective pass for those on crutches will be the one-hand pass.

SHOOTING.   The two shots most used are the one-hand push shot and the two-hand set shot.

In the *one-hand push shot* (with the right hand), the ball is brought up in front of the body with both hands. The right hand is under and in back of the ball, and the left hand is under the ball. The right arm is extended up and in the direction of the basket, with the left hand holding the ball against the fingers of the left hand. As the ball is brought to shooting position in front of the right shoulder, the ball is rolled onto the right hand. The right arm is extended full length, and the left arm is removed from the ball. The ball is released with a wrist snap and leaves the hand from the finger tips. The ball must go high enough, with sufficient arch, to drop straight into the basket.

In the *two-hand set shot,* the ball is held chest high with the finger tips covering its upper portion. The knees are flexed, with the weight brought forward. The elbows are held close to the body. The wrists are straightened, the knees and the elbows extended, and the ball released toward the basket with a snap of the wrist.

Adaptations: Players on crutches are more successful with one-hand shots than with two. Most of the body weight must be taken on the crutch to free the shooting arm. A combination of one regular crutch and one Canadian crutch[1] often provides sufficient means of getting around on the floor, and, with the use of the latter on the shooting arm, that arm is freed for shooting while the weight is borne on the other crutch.

WHEELCHAIR BASKETBALL

Students confined to wheelchairs cannot be accommodated readily in a regulation game, but, if there are several wheelchair patients who are not so severely handicapped as to prevent the use of the arms in throwing, a special adaptation of the game known as "wheelchair basketball" may be played. The game is started by one team at the end of the court. The ball is passed from one player to the next in an attempt to move it near enough to the basket to score. Defensive play has the same objective as in regulation basketball. Dribbling is permitted, but usually only skilled wheelchair players are able to control the ball sufficiently to make this feasible. Jump balls are eliminated. A loose ball is given to the opposing team at the point where it was last touched. Contact between

---

[1]The Canadian crutch is a crutch that is strapped to the arm and is only about half as long as an ordinary crutch, since it need not come up under the arm.

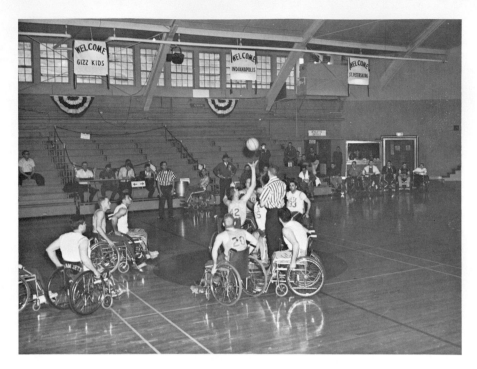

FIGURE 40.   Wheelchair basketball. (The National Society for Crippled Children and Adults.)

wheelchairs is treated the same as contact between players in a regular game. Complete rules for playing wheelchair basketball may be secured from the National Wheelchair Basketball Association, Student Rehabilitation Center, University of Illinois, Urbana, Illinois.

SOFTBALL

Softball is a team sport which closely resembles baseball, after which it was patterned. It is played with a bat and ball on a diamond-shaped field with bases located in each corner of the diamond. The teams alternate turns at bat. The members of the team not batting take certain designated positions on the field. The batters attempt to score by hitting the pitched ball and running safely around all the bases. The team with the highest number of scoring runs after a specified number of innings is the winner.

PLAYING FIELD AND PLAYERS.   An official softball diamond consists of four bases 60 feet apart. The distance of the pitching box from home plate is 46 feet for boys and 38 feet for girls. A team is composed of nine players: pitcher, catcher, first baseman, second baseman, third baseman, short stop, left fielder, center fielder, and right fielder.

Adaptations: The size of the diamond may be reduced and the distance of the pitching box from home plate decreased as needed to accommodate the abilities of the players.

For blind players, the diamond should be small in size and located inside the gymnasium or within a fenced area so that balls will be more easily retrieved. Only one base is used, and a run scores when the player has run to the base and returned home safely.

More fielders may be added to reduce the work and the amount of movement required of any one fielder.

PLAYING THE GAME. A game consists of seven innings. An *inning* is the period during which both teams have been up to bat and have been retired after three outs. An *out* is made at bat when:

(1) The batter has three strikes (except on the third strike when the catcher fails to catch the ball and there is no one on first base).

(2) A foul ball is hit and caught.

(3) An infield fly is hit and there are runners at first and second base with less than two outs.

A *strike* is a ball, legally thrown above home plate in the strike zone, which the batter either fails to strike at or strikes at and misses. The *strike zone* is the area over the plate between the batter's knees and shoulders.

A batter becomes a runner when he has hit a fair ball. He is out when:

(1) An opposing player reaches first base with the ball before the runner touches the base.

FIGURE 41. A teammate prepares to run bases for a batter in braces. (The National Society for Crippled Children and Adults.)

(2) A runner is touched with the ball while going to and from any base.

(3) A runner leaves the base before the ball leaves the pitcher's hand in a pitch to the batter.

(4) A runner runs to the next base on a fly ball that is caught if he leaves before the ball is caught.

Pitched balls which do not legally enter the striking zone and are not struck at are called *balls.* After four balls the batter is permitted to advance to first base.

Adaptations: Strikes may be called only when the batter strikes at the ball and misses. Balls are not called, and the batter is not permitted to advance on balls.

If a batter is able to bat but unable to run bases, another player on his team may do the base running for him. Where the runner starts from will depend upon the ability of the batter. If the batter is especially good, the runner should be required to start on the opposite side of home plate from first base. For weaker batters, the runner may start closer to first base.

SLOW PITCH SOFTBALL

Recently a form of the game of softball known as slow pitch has become popular in physical education classes. The difference between softball and slow pitch is that the ball is pitched to the batter underhanded at moderate speed with an arc of not less than one foot before it reaches the plate. The arc must not be any higher than 10 feet above the ground. Bunts are not permitted.

Adaptations: The following modifications may be made to eliminate injury from base sliding or bat throwing and increase the success of the batters.[2]

1. The hitting team provides its own pitcher. He must remain on the mound during any play, and may in no way interfere with any fielders. Hitter is retired as penalty for interference. (Note: The pitcher is relieved by another member of the hitting team to take his regular turn at bat.)

2. The batter receives a maximum of two pitches. If he accepts the first pitch and swings, he must hit a fair ball or he is out. The hitter may elect to let the first pitch pass, but he must then hit a fair ball on the second pitch or he is out. (Foul balls are out; a swing and miss is out.)

3. No bunting is allowed. The hitter must take a full swing at the ball, or he is called out.

4. Stealing bases is not allowed.

5. Sliding is not allowed (because of the lack of proper equipment).

---

[2]George Wigton: "Ideas that Score (Softball Modified)." *Journal of Health, Physical Education, and Recreation,* Vol. 33, No. 8, Nov. 1962, p. 61.

A base runner is out as a penalty for sliding (regardless of whether or not the slide was accidental).

6. All members of the hitting team, with the exception of the batter, pitcher, base runners, and the "on deck" batter, must be on the bench. If benches are not available on the field, an area is marked off with chalk lines, and the hitting team is confined to that area.

7. The batter must drop his bat entirely within the area chalked off along the first-base line. Batter is out as penalty for infraction. Note: In case of infraction of rule 6 or 7, after or concurrent with the third out, the penalty is carried over to the next inning.

For the blind, only one base is needed, the first base. The fielders are spaced to cover the diamond adequately. The ball that is used should be an inflated one the size of a soccer ball or volleyball. The ball is rolled to the batter so that it bounces on its way to home plate. The batter will depend upon hearing the ball in order to hit it.

The batter is out after three strikes. A foul ball is counted the same as a strike except on the last strike. In this case, another ball is rolled.

In a fair hit the instructor remains quiet. If a fair hit is made, the first baseman makes an intermittant sound loud enough to be heard by the runner to first base and the fielders and yet not so loud as to interfere with the ability of the fielders to hear where the ball is rolling. If the ball is fielded successfully, the fielder rolls the ball to the first baseman. If it comes into the first baseman's possession before the runner gets to first base, the runner is out. If the runner gets safely to first base, his team scores and he returns to where his team is waiting to bat. Three outs retire the side.

CATCHING. Softball can be played without gloves, but a glove does provide protection to the hand and makes catching easier. In catching the ball, the body should be placed in line with the ball. The player should watch the ball throughout the catch. If possible, the ball should be caught in both hands. If the ball is above waist level, the thumbs will be together; if it is below the waist, the little fingers will be together. If a ball is far to the side, it may be necessary to reach with one hand to catch the ball. In either case, the ball is caught in the palm of the left hand (for right-handed players). As the ball strikes the hand, the hand should give slightly to cushion the ball. If both hands are used in catching, the right hand is brought over the top of the ball to hold it in the palm as the ball strikes the palm of the left hand.

Adaptations: In most cases, players who lack skill in catching should be provided with gloves to increase their efficiency and protect their hands.

Players with one hand can catch the ball without a glove and so be ready immediately to throw the ball; however, these players can learn to use a glove if a functional joint at the shoulder and a portion of the upper arm remains on the disabled arm. In this case, as soon as the ball is caught with the one hand, the glove with the ball in the pocket is placed under the opposite arm and the hand slipped out of the glove so that the ball stays in the pocket. In one continuous movement, the ball is grasped with the hand and thrown.

The ball may be caught by players on crutches or in wheelchairs with a little practice of the proper techniques. On crutches the body is propped in position by the crutches, with one arm bearing most of the body's weight, thereby freeing the other arm to catch the ball. The participation of players on crutches will usually be limited to throwing and catching and perhaps batting.

Blind students playing modified softball will face the direction from which the ball is coming as determined by hearing it move along the ground. If it is a rolling ball, the feet are spread apart to cover as much ground as possible. The hands with fingers spread are placed between the legs. As the ball rolls forward, the hands are positioned to grasp the ball. If the ball is to be thrown through the air by seeing or partially seeing players, the catcher turns toward the thrower and extends his arms with the palms up to make a basket to catch the ball. The thrower aims for the "basket." He lets the catcher know when the ball is thrown.

THROWING.   Pitching in softball is done underhanded. However, the overhand throw is used almost exclusively in the rest of the game. In making an overhand throw, the player holds the ball with the first and second fingers on top of the ball and the thumb under it. The arm is raised to the back of the head at about ear level. The wrist is super-extended, and the elbow is held back on the level of the shoulder. The left foot is placed forward in the direction of the throw (for a right-handed player). The ball is brought forward past the ear until the arm is fully extended at about shoulder height. In a continuous motion, the wrist is flexed and the ball is released. The trunk is simultaneously rotated to the left. The arm follows through, coming to rest down near the knee on the opposite side of the body. The body weight shifts from the back foot to the front foot as the throw is made.

Adaptations: Very young children may need to grasp the ball by placing three fingers on top of the ball. Individuals with missing fingers will need to adjust the grip so they are able to place at least the thumb or one finger on one side of the ball and one finger on the other side.

Those players who are throwing from a sitting position or from a propped position on crutches will, of course, use the upper part of the body in throwing. The twist of the trunk will come from the hips only. Those who are unable to or should not twist in this manner will make the throw completely with the arm, keeping the body relatively motionless.

One blind player in throwing the ball to another blind player makes the throw underhanded so that it rolls along the ground, bouncing in very short bounces, and can be heard as it rolls.

BATTING AND BASE RUNNING.   The (right-handed) batter should grip the bat firmly near the end with his left hand, placing the right

FIGURE 42. Batting while on crutches requires learning new techniques, but it opens up many new opportunities for play with peer companions.

hand above and as close to the left as possible. The top hand should be aligned with the bottom hand so that the third joint of the little finger rests between the second and third joints of the index fingers of the lower hand as it encircles the bat. The batter takes a position at the plate so he faces it, with his left side toward the pitcher; the corner of the plate near him splits the center of the body. The distance from the plate should be such that, when the bat is swung, the heavy part of the bat will come over the center of the plate. The bat is held back of the body and not rested on the shoulders. Both elbows and right wrist are flexed. The elbows are held away from the body, with the left elbow in line with the wrist and hand. The batter watches the ball as it leaves the pitcher's hand and continues to watch it until it is hit or has passed by the batter.

When the player swings to strike the ball, his front foot moves forward in a shuffle step. The step is completed before the ball is hit. The bat is swung parallel to the path of the oncoming ball. The ball is contacted in front of the plate, and the bat should follow the ball after it is hit until the swing of the body at the hips changes the direction of the bat. After the ball is hit, the first step toward the base is taken by the right foot with a short step. This is followed by one or two short steps to speed the acceleration, and then the runner goes into full stride toward first base. He runs through the base rather than attempting to stop exactly on it.

Adaptations: In slow pitch ball, in order to swing parallel with the thrown ball the swing must be more upward than for a fast pitched ball.

Batters on crutches will need to depend more on their arms for power in hitting than on the twist of their bodies. Consequently, they should probably concentrate more on placement than on distance. For those who are unable to run to first base, a substitute runner may be provided as described earlier in this chapter.

A blind batter in the adapted game takes a stance with the left side to the batter (if right-handed). He kneels on his left knee with his weight partially on his right foot. The left hand grasps the bat near the end. The right hand is four to five inches above the left. The bat is brought back in preparation for the swing. It is parallel to the floor and two or three inches above it. Before the pitch, the batter notifies the pitcher that he is in position to bat. As the batter hears the ball roll into the striking zone, he swings the bat forward to strike the ball, keeping the bat parallel to the floor.

FOOTBALL

Football is a strenuous competitive game in which two opposing teams strive to advance the ball to their respective goal lines to score. The goal lines are located at each end of the playing field. The team with the higher number of points at the end of the designated playing period is declared the winner.

PLAYING FIELD AND PLAYERS.   The size of the official playing field is 360 feet by 160 feet. The field is marked at five-yard intervals in either direction from a line in the center of the field which is called the fifty-yard line. The last mark on each end is the goal line, and beyond this is the end zone, on the outer boundary of which the goal post is located.

A team is composed of eleven players. They are referred to by the positions they play: linemen (center, guards, tackles, and ends) and backfield men (quarterback, halfbacks, and fullback).

Adaptations: Because football is a sport which requires body contact, its strenuousness cannot be modified by reducing the size of the playing area or by increasing the number of players as is possible with the other games presented in this chapter. Consequently, only those whose handicaps do not impose restrictions on the range or amount of movement, such as the deaf [3] and mentally retarded, can participate in regulation football. For others, modifications must be made in the way the game is played. For example, arm amputees are able to play football in the position of linemen by substituting blocking for tackling. In a regular game they may be used as place kickers.

Modification of the game to eliminate end runs makes possible play by teams of blind and partially sighted players. They cannot play suc-

---

[3] There is a slight modification for the deaf in that the signals are made with hand signs.

FIGURE 43.   Armless boy is the place kicker for his team. (Providence Journal-Bulletin.)

cessfully against teams of normal players but are able to compete against other blind teams. (Partially sighted boys in a normal school situation cannot usually be worked in as players in a regulation game of football.) On the blind team, those who are totally without vision play the center, guard, and tackle positions while the partially sighted play as ends and backs. The linemen play their positions by meeting force with force. If the opponent attempts to block from a certain direction, this is taken as a cue by the linemen that the play is going in the opposite direction; and they fight their way in that direction. They grab any opponents who attempt to run by them.

PLAYING THE GAME.   Because so few of the handicapped will be able to participate in regular football, rules and complexities of play will not be discussed here. It is suggested that teachers who wish to include football in their programs but are unfamiliar with the rules secure the rule book from their state high school athletic associations.

PASSING.   In a forward pass, the ball is grasped so that the index finger is about two inches from the tip. The thumb is placed opposite the index finger, with the fingers spread. The ball is brought up and back near the ear with the end that is being grasped pointing back over the shoulder. For a right-handed thrower, the right shoulder is thrown back and the left foot is placed forward with the weight on the back foot. The arm is then brought forward close to the head. A step is taken forward in the direction of the throw. The weight is brought forward on the front foot as the arm is brought forward. The ball is released with a wrist snap, making the ball spiral as it goes forward.

Adaptations: All passes that are made to partially seeing players will of necessity be very short distances of about four or five feet. This enables the receiver to tell where the ball is by the movement of the thrower. Passes should be thrown to the mid-section of the receiver.

For those players who because of limitations cannot participate in football but are able to throw the ball, games of accuracy can be devised for participation. Tires hung by ropes can be used as targets. The tire may be swung to increase the difficulty of the game. A pass receiver may be used to create another game of throwing accuracy. The passer's accuracy is measured by how far the receiver has to move in order to catch the ball. Throwing for distance can be used as another competitive activity.

RECEIVING PASSES.   Passes are caught on the fingers. Both hands should be used in catching the ball. The fingers are spread wide and the hands give as the ball comes in contact with the fingers. As in all catching, the ball is watched until it is caught.

Adaptations: One-arm catchers catch the ball with the palm and fingers. As the ball comes in contact with the hand, it is drawn to the body and trapped between the body and hand.

The partially seeing and the blind can catch a football thrown without great force from short distances to the receiver's mid-section. The totally blind person must be told that the ball is coming and place his arms in position with one arm above the other with the palms facing each other in readiness to catch the ball as it comes in contact with his mid-section. The ball must, of course, be thrown accurately. The player with partial sight watches the thrower, which helps in judging when the ball will arrive, even though he does not have sufficient sight to see the ball coming.

KICKING.   In *punting* the ball is held by both hands. For a right-handed kicker, the right hand is under the ball and the left hand is on the left side. A step is taken forward with the left foot. The right foot starts the swing with the knee slightly bent. The ball is dropped so that in kicking the ball will be partially on the instep and partially on the toe. The toe is pointed slightly inward. The foot meets the ball about knee high, continues to follow through, and rises above the head.

In the *place kick* the ball is held by another player. He should be on his knees. If he is to receive the pass from center, he should be back 10 to 12 yards from the center. A mark should be made by the holder at the place where he will put the ball. If the kicker is kicking with his right foot, the holder will be on his right side. When he receives the ball, the holder places the point of the ball on the ground, with the fingers of his right hand on the top of the ball. The kicker stands in front of the ball. As the ball is placed on the ground, he steps forward with his left foot so that it is six to eight inches behind and slightly to the left of the ball. He keeps his eye on the ball at all times. He then swings his right foot forward so the toe meets the ball slightly below its center. He follows through with his leg. His head remains down, watching the ball, as he follows through.

Adaptations: One-arm amputees in kicking the football will hold the ball in one hand by placing the hand under its center and balancing it or grasping the point of the ball with the fingers and thumb. Double-arm amputees are limited to place kicking.

Boys who because of physical limitations cannot play football or touch football may participate in kicking contests for distance. Contests of kicking accuracy can also be devised for these students. For this purpose, several concentric circles are laid out on the field, with each circle given a number value, much like an archery target. The points achieved by each of a designated number of kicks are totaled to determine the winner.

VOLLEYBALL

Volleyball is a team game played on a court which is divided into two playing areas of equal size by a net. One team occupies each half of the court. Each team attempts to score the higher number of points by hitting the ball legally over the net so that the opposing team is unable to return it.

PLAYING COURT AND PLAYERS. An official playing court measures 60 feet by 30 feet in area. The net which divides the court is 8 feet high for men and 7½ feet high for women. A height of 6 feet is recommended for players in the elementary school and a height of 6½ feet for junior high school age players. Teams consist of six players each.

Adaptations: The net may be lowered to less than the stated heights if the abilities of the players indicate the need for this. However, the net should be high enough so that no player is able to reach over the top of it.

On a regulation court, it is possible to increase the size of the teams to 8 or 10 players. If some of the players are on crutches, the area assigned to them to defend will need to be smaller than the areas defended by players who have normal locomotion.

If wheelchair patients are playing the game, the court may be increased or decreased in size, depending upon the number of players. In any case, the area that each wheelchair player is responsible for in playing will need to be small enough so that he can readily cover it.

For the blind or partially sighted, the court may need to be larger.

PLAYING THE GAME. In assuming playing positions, three players on each team are net players. They face the net about an arm's length from it and at equal distances from each other. The other three players are in the backcourt. The players here are directly behind the net players and about two or three strides in from the back line.

The game begins by serving the ball from anywhere behind the back boundary line. In serving, the ball is held in the open palm of one hand and struck with the closed fist of the other hand so that the ball rises into the air and goes over the net.

Each team member serves in turn and may have one trial to serve the ball over the net. The server continues to serve until his team fails to return the ball; then the serve passes to the opposing team. All offensive players rotate clockwise one position when a new player begins to serve.

In returning the ball, the player must bat it; it cannot be momentarily caught. Each team is allowed three hits to return the ball over the net. No player may hit the ball twice in succession. One point is scored if the receiving team fails to return the ball. The receiving team gets the ball to serve but does not score if the serving team fails to return the ball. Usually the game is played to 15 points, provided that the winner has won by 2 points. If such a margin does not exist, the game continues until one team wins 2 points in a row.

Adaptations: If more than six players are used, the distribution of players may be made so that they will be equally divided between the net and the backcourt, or three players may be placed at the net with three in the backcourt and three others placed in between.

Those who have insufficient power to get the ball over the net in the serve may be permitted to move up a specified distance to the net. A one-armed server must throw the ball high into the air and bat it with the same hand. An overhand stroke is made.

Players lacking sufficient coordination to strike the ball to return it over the net may be permitted to catch the ball and return it by throwing it back inbounds on the other side of the net. The net in this case should be higher than usual, and a score is made when the ball is not caught or when it is thrown out of bounds or into the net. Throwing the ball over the net may be substituted for serving, if necessary.

This adaptation may be used also by the blind with the addition of permitting the ball to bounce. A score is made:

(1) when the ball rolls out of bounds before it is trapped;

(2) when it is thrown and does not land in the opponents' court;

(3) when it goes into the net.

Wall volley is an activity that can be used with good results as a game for the blind and as a drill with other handicapped students learning to play volleyball. Players volley the ball against the wall. The number of times a player volleys the ball successfully constitutes the score. Blind players will need to be allowed to stand closer to the wall than other players. For sighted students, the ball is volleyed above a line 6 feet high which is marked on the wall. Players should control the ball on their fingers throughout the volley rather than on the palms.

Students on crutches will need to balance themselves with their crutches in such a manner as to free at least one hand for striking the ball. The ball may be served as described for the one-handed player.

The wheelchair player may serve underhand by leaning to the side of the chair, or the ball may be tossed high into the air with one hand and stroked underhand with the other. The wheelchair player will need to develop, as must the player on crutches, the ability to return the ball with one hand. However, if he skillfully maneuvers his chair, he will be able to use both hands a large portion of the time. A one-hand return executed to the side of the body, or in the case of the wheelchair player to the side of the chair, can be made by reaching straight out with the arm to the side. The ball is allowed to drop to shoulder height and the ball is struck and lifted into the air by hitting it with the palm.

QUESTIONS

1. What part can team games play in developing physical fitness in the handicapped? What are their limitations?
2. What modifications are necessary to enable a blind player to shoot baskets?
3. Discuss the basic rules for playing wheelchair basketball.
4. In what ways may a player who is in braces and unable to run participate in softball?
5. What adaptations are necessary in volleyball so that a player on crutches can participate with normal teammates?
6. What place does football have in the adapted physical education program?

SELECTED READINGS

AAHPER: *Basketball Selected Articles.* Washington, D.C., American Association for Health, Physical Education, and Recreation, Division for Girls and Women's Sports, current edition.

AAHPER: *Official Basketball Rules and Guide.* Washington, D.C., American Association for Health, Physical Education, and Recreation, Division for Girls' and Women's Sports, current edition.

AAHPER: *Official Softball Rules and Guide.* Washington, D.C., American Association for Health, Physical Education, and Recreation, Division for Girls' and Women's Sports, current edition.

AAHPER: *Physical Education for High School Students*, ed. 3. Washington, D.C., American Association for Health. Physical Education, and Recreation, 1963.

Athletic Institute: *How to Improve Your Basketball.* Chicago.

Fait, Hollis F.: *Physical Education for the Elementary School Child.* Philadelphia, W. B. Saunders Co., 1964.

Fait, Hollis F., *et al.*: *A Manual of Physical Education Activities,* ed. 2. Philadelphia, W. B. Saunders Co., 1961.

Lawrence, Helen, and Fox, Grace: *Basketball for Girls and Women.* New York, McGraw-Hill Book Co., Inc., 1954.

Meyer, Margaret H., and Schwarz, Marguerite M.: *Team Sports for Girls and Women,* ed. 4. Philadelphia, W. B. Saunders Co., 1965.

Mitchell, Viola: *Softball for Girls,* rev. ed. New York, The Ronald Press Company, 1952.

National Federation of State High School Athletic Associations: *Official Basketball Rules.* Chicago, published annually.

Noren, Arthur T.: *Softball,* ed. 3. New York, The Ronald Press Company, 1959.

Vannier, Maryhelen, and Fait, Hollis F.: *Teaching Physical Education in Secondary Schools,* ed. 2. Philadelphia, W. B. Saunders Co., 1964.

Vannier, Maryhelen, and Poindexter, Hally Beth; *Individual and Team Sports for Girls and Women.* Philadelphia, W. B. Saunders Co., 1960.

21
SWIMMING

Swimming ranks high among the physical education activities which can be most successfully taught to those who are handicapped. The success is due in a large part to the buoyancy of the water, which, in providing support for the body, is both helpful and reassuring to the handicapped student engaged in learning a new skill. Sustained by the water, a crippled body can perform otherwise impossible movements; even those students who are incapable of walking, as is the case with those who have severe cerebral palsy, are frequently able to learn to swim. Mentally handicapped students find the buoyancy of the water comforting, and this fact is a great help to the teacher in allaying the fears which often prevent successful learning of an activity by the retarded.

Swimming is also high among the activities which are most beneficial to the handicapped. Swimming, of course, provides the handicapped student with important skills for his safety on, in, or near the water. It also makes possible participation in a recreational activity which is popular with the nonhandicapped and so opens opportunities for socialization. In addition, the handicapped swimmer reaps important physiological benefits.

The beneficial effects upon the body result from the amount and nature of the work performed in swimming. Even mild activity in the water has a good effect upon those whose movements are severely restricted. Improved circulation and increased strength are likely to occur in most participants. Those who have restricted movements in the joints caused by pain and stiffness often benefit greatly from the increased movement of the joints made possible in the water. Likewise, cerebral palsy patients often find they are able to make movements in the water that they are not otherwise able to make because of the water's buoyancy.

ORGANIZING THE INSTRUCTION

Swimming instruction should be scheduled regularly for students who are to be in the swimming program. Class size will vary with conditions. If the students' disabilities are not severe, the teacher will be able to handle larger numbers in a single period. Those with moderate deviations may possibly be included in a regular swimming class for normal students. When the disabilities of the students are more severe, the size of the class for one teacher must be reduced proportionately to retain teaching effectiveness and maintain the safety of the participants. For some individuals with severe disabilities it may be necessary to provide individual instruction. In the school situation, individual instruction may be provided by student helpers. In a community swimming program, volunteers may be recruited from throughout the community.

Before organization of the class and methods of instruction are developed, the instructor must determine for each student his present level of skill, the movements he is capable of making, and his attitude toward his handicap. Different kinds of disabilities impose different limitations. The kind of movements an individual can make will determine the approach used by the instructor to teach him. Analysis of movement will provide information for deciding which strokes should be taught and what modifications are necessary. The student's acceptance or lack of acceptance of his disability determines to a considerable extent the way in which the instruction, particularly in its initial phase, is presented.

OVERCOMING FEAR OF THE WATER

Most nonswimmers feel some anxiety about entering the water in the beginning. This is especially true of handicapped nonswimmers because they lack confidence in their physical abilities. Consequently, the teacher should strive to make the introductory activities to the water as much fun as possible so that the student will begin to feel secure in the water before he has time to be frightened.

Fun is most likely to occur if the teacher's manner is sincere and friendly, if his instructions are clearly stated and calmly spoken, if his attitude conveys understanding and appreciation of each student as an individual, and if his own enthusiasm for water activities is conveyed to the participants.

Developing special techniques for getting out of the pool unassisted may give handicapped beginners additional reassurance. Special devices such as ramps and steps with hand rails are especially useful in developing

FIGURE 11.   A special handrail makes descent into the water easier for the disabled swimmer. (Journal of Health, Physical Education and Recreation.)

such techniques. For some severely handicapped students it may not be possible to develop a way of leaving the pool unaided. These students must be given physical assistance by the instructor or by a student who is both gentle and strong enough to do so.

The teacher should seek to provide experiences that will lead the student from that to which he is accustomed and readily accepts to new experiences that will lead to complete acceptance of the water. Sitting on the side of the pool splashing with the feet is one example of an activity that is generally accepted without anxiety and which can be directed toward the objective of complete acceptance of the water. Ambulatory students may progress from dangling the feet to standing in waist-deep water and from this to bobbing up and down to their shoulders and eventually to their chins. The final step would be ducking completely under the water and opening the eyes.

Adaptations: Those who are not ambulatory or have severe limitiations in motor movement may need support in the water. Support may be provided by the instructor if this seems necessary or desirable. There are a number of flotation devices such as tubes, canisters, and water wings which may be used to support or stabilize the body in the water. The students should be held in such a manner as to relieve all fear and anxiety that may develop. Slowly, as their confidence increases, the amount of support can be reduced and finally withdrawn.

For students with cerebral palsy it is an absolute necessity that anxiety be kept at a minimum to allow muscular relaxation. For these students, as well as for others who experience difficulty in relaxing in the water, relaxation exercises such as floating the arms and legs while in a sitting position in shallow water are very helpful. Maintaining the water temperature in the low 90's, which is somewhat higher than the 78-degree temperature recommended for normal usage, also aids in muscular relaxation.

During the introductory activities, care should be taken to prevent fearful, cautious individuals from being suddenly and unexpectedly splashed by the more adventurous. A good rule to establish firmly in everyone's mind before entering the water is no deliberate splashing of other people.

ESTABLISHING BREATHING RHYTHM

As soon as the students show sufficient confidence, they may proceed to place their faces in the water while holding their breath. This is done by bending over from a standing position in chest-high water. Students should be encouraged to repeat the action until they are able to hold their faces under the water 15 to 20 seconds.

The next step is to exhale through the mouth while the face is submerged. The final step is to establish a definite rhythm pattern of breathing. To achieve this the students bob the head up and down in the water, taking air in through the mouth while the head is above the water and exhaling through the mouth while the head is down.

Adaptations: Those who cannot stand may take a sitting position on the bottom of the pool if the water is shallow enough. A steel chair may be used where the water is not sufficiently shallow to permit sitting on the bottom. The seated student performs the above activities in the sitting position. If a student must be wholly supported by the instructor or helper, he may be held in a prone position to enable him to lift his head above the water and lower his face into the water.

Cardiac cases should not be allowed to practice breath holding. For these students, instruction in how to expel air while the face is under water must accompany the instruction in how to place the face in the water. Or, if their conditions are moderate to severe, they may be taught floating and swimming techniques that do not require submersion of the face.

BEGINNING SWIMMING SKILLS

THE TUCK FLOAT.   Learning the float helps greatly to promote self-confidence in the beginning swimmer. The tuck float is an easy float for the beginner to learn; moveover, in the process of learning it, the student develops the ability to regain his feet in the water. To learn the tuck float, a nonswimmer should stand in water about chest deep. A deep breath is taken and the face is placed in the water; then the knees are pulled up to the chest and gripped with the arms. Holding this position the body floats to the surface. A return to the standing position is accomplished by releasing the knees and thrusting the feet down. At the same time the head is raised. The hands push down on the water to help regain balance.

THE FACE FLOAT.   The prone face or dead man's float is executed by bending at the hips and placing the face in the water. At the same time the feet are pushed against the bottom of the pool to place the body in a horizontal position face down on the surface of the water. The hands are extended in front. The return to a standing position is made by raising the head and bringing the knees up under the body. The arms are brought forcefully to the sides while at the same time the legs are extended downward into a standing position.

THE BACK FLOAT.   In the back float, a position is taken by extending the head back and pushing slightly with the feet from the bottom. The hips are lifted high and the head is placed back so the ears are under the water. The arms may be held at the sides or extended to the side. A recovery to a standing position is made by bringing the knees toward the chin as the head is brought up and forward. The hands are brought down and past the hips. As the body rights itself, the legs are extended to the bottom.

Adaptations: Tuck and face floats cannot be taught to students who should not hold their breath, such as those with cardiac disturbances and arrested tuberculosis. In these cases the vertical float is used as a substitution. In the vertical float, the body is at approximately a 70-degree angle with the face lifted just enough to clear the water. This will need to be done in water that is chin deep or deeper. A slight movement of the arms may be necessary to keep the chin above water. A helper may support the body until the swimmer gains confidence and skill in using the arms. To give support, the helper places one hand under the swimmer's chest.

Those who cannot support themselves in the water on their feet should be held by a helper until they have acquired sufficient confidence to use the kickboard or hang on to the gutter for support. A hand placed under the chest in the face float or under the head in the back float will provide sufficient support.

Those who do not have use of the arms will need help at first in regaining their feet from a float position, but they can learn to right themselves by a very forceful extension of the legs while simultaneously lifting the head and shoulders. If the swimmer has the use of only one arm, the arm action used to regain the feet should be executed as near to the center of the body as possible for maximum effectiveness.

The ataxic should be watched carefully during attempts to regain the standing position because of his poor sense of balance, particularly when he cannot see his feet.

FIGURE 45.   A beginning swimmer, supported by an inner tube, is given help by an instructor. (Journal of Health, Physical Education and Recreation.)

THE GLIDE AND THE FLUTTER KICK.   After the beginner has learned the face float, he may be taught how to glide in the prone position. The glide is performed much like the face float except that, instead of lifting the feet off the bottom, the feet push off from the bottom to move the body forward into a prone float position.

The flutter kick is the simplest kick to learn. The student assumes a prone position and thrashes the legs alternately up and down. The kick starts at the hip; the knee is relaxed but is not bent. The toes are extended. In the kick the feet are spread vertically from 15 to 20 inches. For younger children, the spread will be less.

Adaptations: If physical abilities permit, the kick may be introduced as a land drill; the student assumes a prone position on a bench with the legs projected beyond the bench. The kick can also be practiced while holding on to the gutter or a kickboard. After the kick is mastered, it is combined with the prone float to propel the body forward.

Anyone who cannot place his face in the water should be assisted by a helper, who takes the swimmer by his extended hands to tow him while he kicks.

Swimmers who have lost the use of one leg must learn to use the remaining leg in the flutter kick. If the leg is paralyzed, it may be helpful to put a small float under the thigh of the disabled leg.

FIGURE 16.   A handicapped beginner is introduced to the water through the same types of activities used to orient nonhandicapped beginning swimmers. (Journal of Health, Physical Education and Recreation.)

THE DOG PADDLE AND THE HUMAN STROKE.   In the dog paddle the head is held above the water. The arms are alternately extended forward and downward and then pulled backward under the chest. At the same time the feet are moved in the flutter kick. The human stroke is executed much like the dog paddle except that the face is in the water as in the prone float and the arms are fully extended in front of the head before pulling down and back. As in the dog paddle, the hands do not leave the water.

Adaptations: Those who are able may practice the arm stroke with the leg kick on a bench before getting into the water. Following this the arm movement is practiced while standing in chest-deep water.

Land practice of swimming strokes is not effective with cerebral palsied swimmers because of the increased tension in the muscles when they are out of the water. Consequently, their practice should all be in the water.

Swimmers who have limited movement of their limbs will need to be supported by a helper who passes a hand under the swimmer's chest. Water wings or inflated tubes may also be used as supports for these students. Those who because of amputation or atrophy of a limb have difficulty balancing in the water must make the necessary movements of the active limbs close to the center of the body to overcome the imbalance.

The best placement of the movements can be determined by experimentation.

INTERMEDIATE SWIMMING STROKES

The side stroke, the elementary back stroke, and the crawl are strokes that are frequently taught on the intermediate level.

THE SIDE STROKE.   The body is turned on its side with the stronger arm on top. The arm under the water is fully extended at right angles to the body while the other arm rests fully extended along the side of the body. The under arm is brought down to a nearly vertical position and then the elbow is bent. At the same time, the top arm is brought up to enter the water near the head. This arm recovers to the starting position with a downward reaching movement. Meanwhile the other arm is recovering with a pulling movement toward the body.

The kick for the side stroke is called the scissors. The legs are bent slightly at the knees as one leg (usually the top leg) is brought in front of the body and the other leg is moved to the rear. The legs are then extended fully and brought together forcefully in a movement resembling the opening and closing of a scissors.

The movements of the arms and legs are coordinated to begin and recover simultaneously. The body glides momentarily in the water before the next stroke begins.

Adaptations: Those who have weak shoulder joints subject to frequent dislocation will find the side stroke the safest stroke for swimming. It will also be the most effective stroke and the most easily learned by those who have lost one limb. When there is a disabled or missing arm, the side stroke is performed with the functional arm on the bottom.

The functional leg, when the other leg is missing or disabled, may be either on the top or bottom, whichever proves better through trial and error. If both legs have been lost, the swimmer will probably have to find a suitable modified position through experimentation; this will usually be a partially prone position rather than wholly on the side of the body.

THE ELEMENTARY BACK STROKE.   The arm movement for the elementary back stroke begins with the arms fully extended at a 45-degree angle between the head and shoulders. The arms are brought to the sides of the body in a sweeping arc. In the recovery the hands are brought along the sides of the body to shoulder height. They are then fully extended to begin the next downward stroke.

In the kick, the knees are brought up and out to either side of the body so the heels are touching. The legs are then extended fully and brought together forcefully.

The straightening of the legs occurs at the same time that the arms are being brought down to the sides. The arms recover along the body to the armpits before the legs start their recovery.

Adaptations: Many disabled students find it easier to swim on the back than in any other position. In the position on the back, almost any kind of movement with the arms or legs will move the body in some direction. If the swimmer does not have use of the arms, the legs may be used in a flutter kick to propel the body; conversely, if the legs cannot be used, the arms may be used as in the back stroke. Finning and sculling movements with the hands may be substituted for the arm stroke if movement of the arms is restricted.

THE CRAWL.   In teaching the crawl, it is necessary only to add the arm movement to the flutter kick and breathing technique introduced in the beginning skills. The arm stroke is made by extending the arm fully in front of the face and pressing downward against the water, with the hand leading the rest of the arm. When the arm is beneath the shoulder, the shoulder is lifted and the elbow is raised until it clears the water. The arm is then brought forward above the water with the fingers near the water, ready for entrance into the water for the next stroke.

The arms stroke alternately, and inhalation should occur as the shoulder is lifted in the recovery. The head may be turned to either side, depending upon which seems more natural for the swimmer. The kick is coordinated with the arms to accomplish a smooth and rhythmical stroke.

Adaptations: The crawl is the most satisfactory stroke for those with loss of movement in the legs. In some cases of leg disability, flexion and extension may be developed to compensate for lack of leg action. Hip impairment may require the swimmer to execute the flutter kick with greater knee bend.

The arm stroke may be modified for those with arm and shoulder limitations by reducing it to less than the full stroke. The crawl should not be swum by those with weak shoulder joints subject to frequent dislocation.

QUESTIONS

1. Why is swimming one of the most important activities in the physical education program for the handicapped?

2. Discuss the techniques which may be utilized in developing confidence in a beginning handicapped swimmer.

3. What special techniques can be developed to help a person who cannot walk to get out of the pool unaided?

4. Discuss ways in which to encourage the cerebral palsied beginner to relax.

5. What precautions need to be taken in teaching someone with a heart disorder to swim?

6. Plan the adaptations that would be necessary to teach a person who had no arms to swim.

SELECTED READINGS

AAHPER: *Aquatics Selected Articles.* Washington, D.C., American Association for Health, Physical Education, and Recreation, Division for Girls' and Women's Sports, 1964.

AAHPER: *Physical Education for High School Students*, ed. 3. Washington, D.C., American Association for Health, Physical Education, and Recreation, 1963.

Ainsworth, Dorothy S., *et al.: Individual Sports for Women*, ed. 4. Philadelphia, W. B. Saunders Co., 1963.

American Red Cross: *Instructor's Manual, Swimming and Diving Courses.* Washington, D.C.

American Red Cross: *Swimming for the Handicapped: Instructor's Manual.* Washington, D.C., 1960.

Armbruster, David A., Sr., *et al.: Swimming and Diving,* ed. 4. St. Louis, The C. V. Mosby Co., 1963.

Connecticut Society for Crippled Children and Adults, Inc.: *Report of the Third Institute on Swimming for the Physically Handicapped.* Hartford, Conn., (740 Asylum Avenue), 1958.

Fait, Hollis F.: *Physical Education for the Elementary School Child.* Philadelphia, W. B. Saunders Co., 1964.

Fait, Hollis F.: *et al.: Manual of Physical Education Activities,* ed. 2. Philadelphia, W. B. Saunders Co., 1961.

Gabrielsen, M. Alexander, *et al.: Aquatics Handbook.* Englewood Cliffs, N.J., Prentice-Hall, Inc., 1960.

National Association for Retarded Children: *Swimming for the Mentally Retarded.* New York, 1959.

Smith, Hope M.: *Water Games.* New York, The Ronald Press Company, 1962.

Vannier, Maryhelen, and Fait, Hollis F.: *Teaching Physical Education in Secondary Schools,* ed. 2. Philadelphia, W. B. Saunders Co., 1964.

Vannier, Maryhelen, and Poindexter, Hally Berth: *Individual and Team Sports for Girls and Women.* Philadelphia, W. B. Saunders Co., 1960.

22
WEIGHT TRAINING

Weight training is the systematic exercise with weights for the purpose of developing the body; when weight training is performed competitively, it is referred to as weight-lifting. Both weight training and weight-lifting have become enormously popular with boys and young men over the past decade. Part of this popularity can be attributed to the acceptance of weight training in the conditioning programs of athletes for sports competition.

Athletic trainers were, for the most part, slow to recognize the value of weight training in conditioning the body. Experiments had shown as early as 1950 that the heavy resistance exercises afforded by weight training and lifting were very efficient means of increasing the strength and power of the muscles without detrimental effects to the neuromuscular action. This experimental evidence was not widely accepted, however, for a number of years. Gradually, the value of weight training in body conditioning was recognized, and today weight training is an important part of nearly all athletic training programs.

In addition to its increased use by athletes, weight training is being used more and more for rehabilitation of the ill and injured. Its use for this purpose was pioneered by DeLorme.[1] He developed a program of exercises using weights which he called progressive resistance exercises,

[1]Thomas L. DeLorme: *Progressive Resistance Exercises.* New York, Appleton-Century-Crofts, 1951.

and it is by this name that programs of weight training for the disabled are generally known today.

Weight training for purposes of rehabilitation is a specialized activity and is usually attempted only in hospital situations under the guidance of a physician. In the school physical education program, weight training is directed toward developing and maintaining a satisfactory level of physical fitness. In addition, for the handicapped, it provides another opportunity to engage with normal peers in a popularly accepted activity.

AREA AND EQUIPMENT

Weight training requires very little space; an area as small as 100 square feet is adequate. The floor must be able to support considerable weight; therefore, a concrete floor is desirable. However, if the floor is wooden, heavy planks may be placed over it.

Equipment consists primarily of barbells and dumbbells (Figure 47). The barbells are used for exercises with two hands, while the dumbbells, which are shorter, are used chiefly for one-arm exercises. Some special pieces of equipment have been devised to expand the exercise possibilities; among these are head straps, iron boots, wall pulleys, wrist rollers, chest springs, inclined boards, and leg press apparatus.

ORGANIZING THE INSTRUCTION

Weight training lends itself readily to incorporation in a dual program. After initial instruction in the lifts, students may proceed on their own or in pairs. For those working alone, the use of a personal progress sheet is very helpful; on it should be recorded at the end of each class period the amount of weight lifted and the number of repetitions made. This will enable the student to know exactly where to begin at the start of the next class.

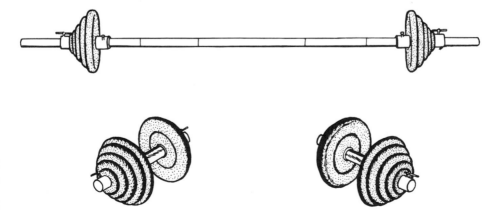

FIGURE 47. Barbell and dumbbell sets.

Regardless of the class organization for instruction on weight training, all students, before they begin, should have a clear understanding of the activities they must avoid, the adaptations they must make, and the safety precautions they must observe.

Safety regulations which should be stressed emphatically by the teacher are:

1. Warm-up exercises should be taken before attempting a heavy lift. The warm-up may consist of the side-straddle hop exercise or running in place with exaggerated arm movements.

2. In moving a heavy weight from one place to another, the lift should be made with the knees flexed and the back straight. No one with back difficulties should ever lift weights by bending at the hips with the legs straight.

3. Collars (the metal pieces which hold the weights to the bar) should be fastened securely. They should be checked before each lift is attempted.

4. A lift should never be made over someone who is sitting, squatting, or lying on the floor.

5. All exercises should have the approval of the handicapped student's physician. Participants with weakened or injured muscles should use light loads as prescribed by the doctor. When exercising those parts of the body which are not injured, the utmost care must be taken to prevent the injured part from being brought into action inadvertently. Special care must be taken so that the lifter will not slip or allow his load to slip, thereby bringing into action a muscle that was being protected. To be absolutely safe, a lifter with an injury should not make an all-out effort even though the injured part is not involved in the effort.

Those for whom lifting weights is contraindicated for the leg area may do their lifting while sitting or lying down, avoiding all lifts involving the legs. Some participants with minor back difficulties may be allowed to take arm and leg exercises if the back is protected against undue stress. To protect the back in such exercises as the two-arm curl, lateral raise, front raise, and military press, these lifts can be made sitting down, with the back held firmly against the back of the chair. Exercises that require heavy weight on the shoulders are contraindicated for those with weak backs. The iron shoe exercise is a possible substitution for the deep knee bends which require heavy weight on the shoulder to develop the quadriceps of the legs. Exercises from the prone position do not place undue stress upon the back and therefore need not be adapted. In the supine position those exercises that have a tendency to hyperextend the back, such as the leg raises and the supine pullover, are contraindicated for those with any type of back difficulties or with exceptionally weak abdominals.

In lifting heavy weights, a deep breath is taken and held to stabilize the thoracic region (chest). When this is done, there is an extreme elevation of the arterial blood pressure because the increased pressure in the thoracic region prevents blood from returning to the heart. If the effort is prolonged, the blood pressure falls after its initial rise. This is known as the Valsalva phenomenon.

Because of the Valsalva phenomenon, lifting of weights is not usually recommended for those with cardiac or circulatory disorders. However, such individuals need developmental exercise, and one of the best ways to get it is weight training. Under close supervision, some of these people can take part in a program of weight training which is confined to certain parts of the body. The objective of such a program is to increase the strength, power, and size of the muscles in these areas. Only a few muscles are working at any one time in a prescribed lift; therefore, it is possible to exercise them sufficiently without placing great demands on the heart and circulatory system as would be the case if the body were more completely involved in exercising.

Before a student with a cardiac or circulatory disorder begins a weight training program, the program should be fully described to his physician and permission secured for each proposed exercise. To avoid the Valsalva phenomenon, the student must never hold his breath while lifting; regular breathing must be continued throughout all exercises. The exercises should be performed in a reclining position to conserve energy. If an exercise cannot be adapted to the reclining position, it should be eliminated. Only one limb should be exercised at a time. The weight that is to be lifted should be well within the range of the muscle strength. The participant should be able to lift the weight 10 to 15 times before being exhausted.

The student with only one arm will perform all the lifts involving the use of the arm with his good arm. The weights should be sufficiently light so that lifting them with one arm will not produce twisting of the body or bending of the spine laterally, for such movements may produce muscular development that will cause postural difficulties. Students with functional stumps may find it possible to do the lifts with a prosthesis.

LIFTING TECHNIQUES

There are many different types of lifts. Many of them exercise different muscles while others exercise muscles in different groups or exercise the same set of muscles. The muscles that are primarily involved in any given lift can be determined with some degree of accuracy even by someone who does not have a thorough knowledge of anatomy. It must be remembered that a muscle does not push but always pulls to move a joint and that a contracting muscle is harder than a muscle not being worked. Consequently, by examining the direction of movement of the part of the body involved and by palpating the muscle or muscles while the lift is being executed, the muscles being used can be located. Then, by referring

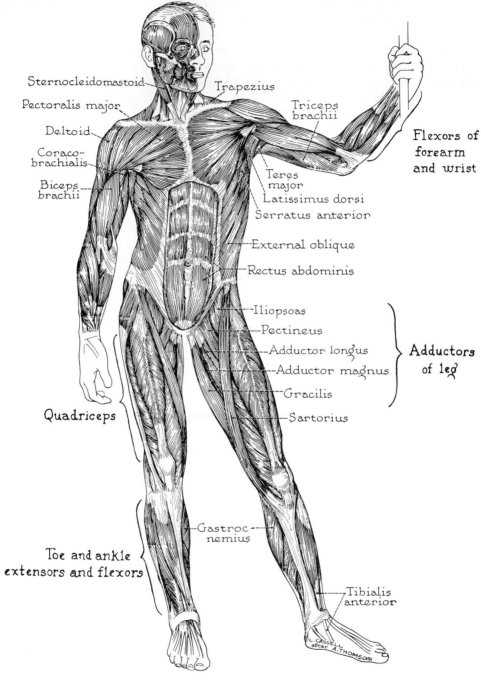

Sternocleidomastoid

Pectoralis major

Deltoid

Coraco-
brachialis

Biceps
brachii

Trapezius

Triceps
brachii

Teres
major

Latissimus dorsi

Serratus anterior

External oblique

Rectus abdominis

Iliopsoas

Pectineus

Adductor longus

Adductor magnus

Gracilis

Sartorius

Flexors of
forearm
and wrist

Adductors
of leg

Quadriceps

Toe and ankle
extensors and flexors

Gastroc-
nemius

Tibialis
anterior

L. CASSELL
after A. THOMSON

FIGURE 48. Surface muscle chart. (King and Showers, Human Anatomy & Physiology, 5th Ed.)

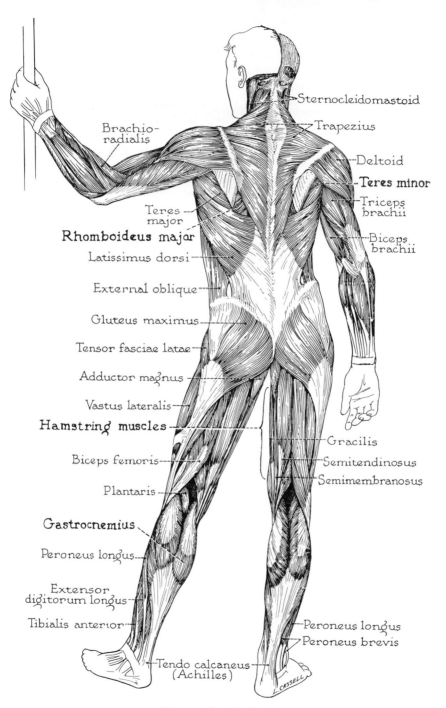

Sternocleidomastoid
Trapezius
Deltoid
Teres minor
Triceps brachii
Biceps brachii

Brachio-radialis
Teres major
Rhomboideus major
Latissimus dorsi
External oblique
Gluteus maximus
Tensor fasciae latae
Adductor magnus
Vastus lateralis
Hamstring muscles
Biceps femoris
Plantaris
Gastrocnemius
Peroneus longus
Extensor digitorum longus
Tibialis anterior

Gracilis
Semitendinosus
Semimembranosus

Peroneus longus
Peroneus brevis

Tendo calcaneus (Achilles)

L. CASSELL

FIGURE 48. *Continued*

to a chart of the skeletal muscles like the one in Figure 48, the muscles can be identified.

The lifts presented here are selected to give a fairly complete workout to the major muscle groups in a minimum number of exercises. All lifts are made from the standing position unless otherwise indicated.

NECK EXTENSION AND NECK CURL.   Neck extension exercises the posterior muscles of the neck (sacrospinalis, cervical muscles, trapezius). A prone position is taken on a bench or on the floor. If a bench is used, the neck extends over the end of the bench. A plate of the barbells is held with both hands on the back of the head. The head is lifted backward as far as possible while the chest rests on the bench or floor. The neck is then lowered to the starting position.

The neck curl is performed in the supine position, and the weight is held on the forehead. The head is brought up and forward until the chin touches the chest.

Adaptations: The exercise may be done without the weights held to the head to decrease the strenuousness of the exercise. If there is extreme muscular weakness or cervical vertebrae injury or malfunction, the neck muscles may be exercised by tightening the flexors and extensors at the same time and holding for a few seconds, repeating until sufficient work has been given to the muscles, as a substitute for the exercise with weights.

MILITARY PRESS OR STANDING PRESS.   The muscles involved in this lift are the deltoid, pectoralis major, and triceps. To make the lift, a pronated grip (back of the hands up) is taken on the bar. The bar is lifted and brought to rest against the chest as in Figure 49. The bar is then raised straight over the head until the arms are fully extended. The bar is lowered to the chest position and the exercise repeated.

Adaptations: Care must be taken to keep the back straight as the weight is lifted above the head. This is especially necessary if the lifter has lower back difficulties. To avoid the tendency to hyperextend the back, the participant may sit in a chair with a high back, holding his back firmly against the chair's back.

FIGURE 49.   Chest rest position.

Two-Arm Curl.   The biceps and the brachialis are the primary muscles used in the two-arm curl. The supinated grip (palms up) is taken. The bar is brought to the thighs. The bar is raised to the shoulders by bending the elbows. The weight is then lowered until the arms are fully extended. The lift may be done by taking a pronated grip. The finger and wrist muscles (extensors of the fingers and wrist) can be exercised by hyperextending the wrist while lifting the weight to the shoulders.

Adaptations: Lifters with back disorders must take the utmost care to avoid pushing the hips forward to help start the lift upward. This movement hyperextends the back, thereby placing undue stress upon it. To avoid this possibility, the lifter should keep the weight light enough to be handled easily with the arms. As additional protection against hyperextension the lifter may stand with his back against the wall so that he is unable to move his hips during the lift.

Straight-arm pullover.   The major work in this lift is performed by pectoralis major and minor, triceps, latissimus dorsi, and serratus anterior muscles. A supine position is taken. The bar is on the floor at arm's length from the head. A grip is taken with the palms up. The bar is pulled and lifted with the arms held straight to a position above the chest. The bar is returned to the starting position and the exercise repeated.

Adaptations: To decrease the difficulty of the lift for those lacking arm strength, the pullover may be done with the arms bent until the bar is above the head, at which time the arms are extended fully. The bar is lowered in a reverse manner.

Those with weak backs should not perform the straight-arm pullover.

Straight-leg dead lift.   In this lift the back muscles and upper posterior leg muscles (erector spinae, gluteus maximus, and hamstrings) are used. The bar is placed near the toes. The body is bent at the hips and the upper back held straight. An alternate grip is taken on the bar (one hand pronated and the other supinated), and the bar is lifted by straightening the back. The knees are locked and the arms are kept straight. The bar is then lowered to its original position.

Adaptations: Those with back injuries should modify the lift to reduce the strain upon the back muscles and yet exercise the extensors of the back, as follows: A sitting position is taken on a bench, with a light dumbbell in each hand. The shoulders are hunched forward, and the chin rests on the chest. The head is lifted, the shoulders thrown wide, and the back straightened. Return to the original position and repeat the exercise.

Sit-ups.   The major muscles involved in the sit-ups are the abdominals and the iliopsoas. A supine position is taken, with the legs straight and the toes hooked under the bar. A weight is held to the back of the head with both hands. The head is brought forward until it touches the chest and then the back is lifted off the floor in a sit-up position. The return is made to the starting position.

To make the exercise more difficult, the knees are bent rather than being held straight in the sit-up.

Adaptations: No weight is placed behind the head. The head is brought forward until the chin touches the chest. Then the shoulders start the raise from the floor. The small of the back remains in contact with the floor throughout the lift. The return is made to the supine position.

DEEP KNEE BEND AND HEEL RAISE.   In the deep knee bend the gastrocnemius, soleus, quadriceps, and gluteus maximus are used extensively. The bar is held across the back of the neck and shoulders, and the body is lowered to a full squat position. The return is made to the original position.

In the heel raise, the gastrocnemius, soleus, and plantar flexor of the feet are developed. The bar is carried on the shoulders as in the deep knee bend. The bar is lifted by raising the heels off the ground until the weight is resting on the balls of the feet. The heels are then lowered.

Adaptations: Some authorities feel that deep knee bends affect the ligaments of the knee to their disadvantage and therefore recommend that only a three-quarter squat be taken.

Those suffering from injured knees should substitute iron shoe exercises for knee bends. Those with back difficulties should not perform the lift with heavy weights on the shoulders. Those with arch problems in the feet should not do the heel raise.

LATERAL, FORWARD, AND BACKWARD LIFTS.   The muscles involved in each of these lifts are: lateral lift—deltoid, supraspinatus, trapezius, serratus anterior; forward lift—deltoid, pectoralis major, coracobrachialis, serratus anterior, trapezius; backward lift—deltoid, teres major, rhomboids, trapezius.

Dumbbells are grasped in each hand with the hands at the sides of the body. In the lateral raise, the arms are lifted directly sideways to the horizontal level. For the forward raise, they are lifted forward. In the backward raise, the arms are raised backward and upward as far as possible without bending the trunk.

Adaptations: In the lateral and forward lifts, a sitting position may be taken to avoid hyperextending the back. Those with weak shoulder joints subject to dislocation should never raise the arms higher than shoulder level. As an additional safety precaution, the exercise should be performed with one arm at a time. The opposite arm is brought across the chest and the hand grasps the shoulder to pull it in toward the body during the lift. In this way it becomes impossible to raise the arm inadvertently above the desired level.

The backward lift is contraindicated for those suffering from weak shoulder joints subject to dislocation.

PRONE LATERAL RAISE.   The deltoid, pectoralis major, infraspinatus, teres minor, and trapezius muscles are brought into play in this exercise. A prone position is taken on a bench, and the hands grasp dumbbells on the floor to each side of the body. The weights are lifted toward the ceiling as far as possible, keeping the arms straight. The dumbbells are then lowered slowly to the floor.

Adaptations: No modification is required except for amputees and cardiac cases.

SUPINE HORIZONTAL ARM LIFT.   The following muscles are used in this lift: deltoid, pectoralis major, coracobrachialis, and serratus anterior. A supine position is taken with the arms extended out from the shoulders. The dumbbells are grasped with the palms facing up. The arms are raised over the chest with the elbows locked and then returned to the original position.

Adaptations: The lift will usually not require adaptation except for amputees and cardiac cases.

SHOULDER ROTATION.   The muscles exercised in the shoulder rotation are: subscapularis, teres major, deltoid, infraspinatus, and teres minor. A supine position is assumed on the floor. The arms are bent at the elbow with hands resting parallel to the ears. Dumbbells are held in each hand. The elbows remain in contact with the floor as the weights are first lifted into the air, then lowered so the arms are resting along the sides of the body, and then returned to the original position.

Adaptations: This exercise is contraindicated for those with weak shoulder joints subject to dislocation. Adaptations for amputees and cardiac cases are given at the end of this section.

QUADRICEPS EXERCISE WITH IRON BOOT.   The lifter sits on a low table with the lower part of one leg at right angles to the thigh. An iron boot is strapped to the foot. The knee is extended until it is straight and parallel to the floor. The leg is then lowered to the original position.

Adaptation: Those recuperating from knee injuries should take a much lighter load on the injured leg than they are able to lift with the normal leg; one half the weight is usually recommended. The lifter should sit so that he may be able to lower the weight to the floor rapidly at any time.

HAMSTRING EXERCISES WITH IRON BOOT.   A prone position is taken with an iron boot fastened to the foot. The leg is bent and the knee raised until the boot touches the buttocks. The foot is then returned to the starting position. No adaptations are usually necessary.

ADAPTATIONS SUGGESTED FOR THOSE WITH CARDIOCIRCULATORY DISORDERS.   *Two-Arm Curl.* A supine position is taken. An appropriate weight is held in one hand. As the elbow remains in contact with the floor, the weight is lifted until the arm is vertical to the floor. The weight is returned to the starting position. The tricep may be exercised as well without adding more work at a given time by bringing the weight past the vertical position to rest upon the shoulder. The weight is then returned to the floor.

Straight-Arm Pullover: The weights are lifted in a bent arm position. Only one arm is exercised at a time.

Sit-ups: No weights are placed behind the head. The head is brought forward until the chin touches the chest and the shoulders start the raise from the floor. From this position the body is returned to a supine position.

Prone Lateral Raise, Supine Horizontal Arm Lift, and Shoulder Rotation: All of these may be done with one arm at a time with appropriate weights.

Iron Boot Exercises: For the quadriceps exercise the subject may lie on a bench with the legs extending beyond the bench and the feet on the floor. With the iron boot on one foot, the knee is straightened. The leg is returned to the original position. The hamstring exercises can be taken as described. One leg is exercised at a time.

CIRCUIT TRAINING

Circuit training is a pattern of exercises that enables a large number of participants to work out at one time. Different exercise stations are placed throughout the exercise area. The participants progress from one station to the next until they have completed the circuit.

Exercises chosen for the circuit should meet the following criteria:

1. They can be performed by participants working on their own.

2. They are strenuous and of such a nature that the work load may be increased from time to time.

3. They are standardized (performed in a specific manner), so that they may be done in the same way each time.

4. They contribute to the sum total of the exercises in accomplishing the objectives of the program.

In arranging a circuit, the teacher should select exercises that develop all areas of the musculature. The following areas are suggested: arm, shoulder, and hand; neck; back; abdomen and hips; thigh, leg, and foot.

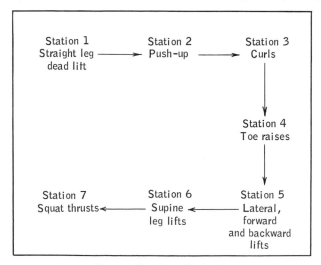

FIGURE 50. Sample circuit.

Care must also be taken to select activities that exercise different sets of muscles, not the same set over and over.

The actual number and kinds of exercises which are included in a circuit will depend upon time available, body areas to be exercised or emphasized, and the amount of equipment and space available.

The number of times that each exercise in the circuit is to be done will depend upon individual ability. It must not be set so high that the performer will stop from exhaustion, but it must be high enough to insure that it is close to the maximum of which he is capable. With experimentation the proper number of repetitions can be determined for each person.

There are two general ways of increasing the work load. One is increasing the number of repetitions, and the other is decreasing the time taken to perform the exercises.

A suggested circuit is shown in Figure 50.

Adaptations: If handicapped students are included with normal students in circuit training, each exercise must be analyzed to determine if it is suitable for each type of handicap. Protection from undue stress on weak areas of the body must be provided. Adaptations must be worked out where possible. The special precautions which have been recommended for students with cardiorespiratory disorders must be observed here as well.

QUESTIONS

1. Discuss the difference between weight training and weight-lifting. Which one is more appropriate for the adapted physical education class?
2. What has caused the growth of interest in weight training in recent years?
3. List all the exercises presented in the chapter that are contraindicated for those with a back difficulty.
4. What precautions must be taken when someone with a heart ailment is engaging in weight training?
5. Develop a circuit which will include activities for developing strength in the arms, fingers, legs, neck, and back.

SELECTED READINGS

AAHPER: *Weight Training in Sports and Physical Education.* Washington, D.C., American Association for Health, Physical Education, and Recreation, 1962.

DeLorme, Thomas L.: *Progressive Resistance Exercises.* New York, Appleton-Century-Crofts, Inc., 1951.

Massey, Benjamin H., *et al.: The Kinesiology of Weight Lifting.* Dubuque, Iowa, William C. Brown Company, Publishers, 1959.

Murray, Jim A., and Karpovich, Peter V.: *Weight Training in Athletics.* Englewood Cliffs, Prentice-Hall, Inc., 1956.

Vannier, Maryhelen, and Fait, Hollis F.: *Teaching Physical Education in Secondary Schools,* ed. 2. Philadelphia, W. B. Saunders Co., 1964.

Woolf, M. H.: *Weight-Lifting Handbook.* New York, Landau Book Co., 1954.

23
OUTDOOR EDUCATION

Broadly stated, outdoor education embraces all of the learning activities which deal directly with the wise utilization and appreciation of the natural environment. It consists of learning by actual performance in the natural laboratory out of doors.

More specifically, however, for purposes of this discussion, outdoor education is defined as one specialized aspect of general education. As such, it is an integral part of the school curriculum. Identified in this way, outdoor education enhances every field in the modern curriculum from pre-school through college.

Outdoor education has been part of human experience since human society began. In primitive cultures almost all learning took place in and was directly related to the natural environment. As civilization developed and human knowledge expanded, learning experiences necessarily became less direct. Inevitably, it was determined that a combination of direct and indirect learning were required if man was to develop culturally, socially, and physically. Educators came to accept the view that both direct experiences—learning through working with real things in life situations—and textbook and laboratory materials are essential for the best possible education.

One phase of outdoor education, camping, has a long history. Camping was fairly well established as an organized activity for normal children by the end of the 19th century. Children who suffered physical and mental disabilities, however, were generally denied admittance to camps, both because those in charge were unable to cope with their disabilities and because the values of camping for the handicapped had not been fully realized. The establishment of camps especially for handicapped children began with what were generally referred to as "summer homes" along the eastern seaboard. The first actual camp appears to have been established around 1900 through the efforts of two Chicago teachers of crippled children. The success of this initial effort led to the establishment of more camps, until today camping facilities are available to thousands of handicapped children.

VALUES OF OUTDOOR EDUCATION

Outdoor education, particularly that phase of it known as camping, offers excellent living experiences to those handicapped participants who might be stifled in a less permissive atmosphere. Here the individual is, for a little while, taken away from the normal routine of school or home and placed in a dynamic situation under the guidance of professional personnel who have an understanding of the psychological problems faced by those who are handicapped.

In an outdoor environment the individual is able to express himself freely. There are no distractions, no noisome cities, no densely populated neighborhoods, no loneliness bred of isolation from one's peers. Here the

Figure 51.   Many kinds of outdoor education activities can be made available to everyone. (The National Society for Crippled Children and Adults.) (Picture taken by Roger C. Larson, Director, Camp Easter Seal, Washington State University.)

needs of the individual are satisfied. The child or adult has an opportunity to live close to nature and in so doing acquires an appreciation of the resources of the land.

Luther Burbank once said:

> Every child should have mud pies, grasshoppers, water-bugs, tadpoles, frogs, mud-turtles, elderberries, wild strawberries, acorns, chestnuts, trees to climb, brooks to wade in, water-lilies, woodchucks, bats, bees, butterflies, various animals to pet, hay fields, pine cones, rocks to roll, sand, snakes, huckleberries and hornets; and any child who has been deprived of these has been deprived of the best part of his education.

If the experiences described by Burbank are so vital to the normal child, how infinitely more important they are for the handicapped child. The healing magic of nature's world may not cure a cardiac condition or alleviate rheumatoid arthritis, but it can do much to soothe an aching spirit, quiet an emotionally disturbed child, and offer a new world to the blind, deaf, or mentally retarded. The therapeutic value of outdoor education comes from simply being out of doors, living at an unhurried and unharried pace, learning whatever new skills one is capable of performing, experiencing an entirely new series of activities, or re-learning valuable skills which have been forgotten through disuse.

OUTDOOR EDUCATION AND THE CURRICULUM

Direct learning in an outdoor environment should be part of the regular school curriculum; particularly is this true for those special classes designed for exceptional children. Short walking tours on the school site may be worthwhile, if the school is located in a rural area, but of more significance is the planned trip to nearby parks, zoos, museums, planetariums, farms, reservations, aquatic areas, or other natural resources of the community. Some schools have a sufficiently large site or have acquired enough additional land that it is possible to create an outdoor nature laboratory. Here students can be taught nature study, horticulture, floriculture, conservation, and earth sciences. A gardening activity begun in the spring can be carried on through the summer months and related to several aspects of the curriculum. Such an experience usually correlates with entomology, ecology, biology, and other sciences. A school fortunate enough to have a heavily wooded area combined with a farm has an ideal setting for instruction, for then it is possible to plan many more experiences, including care of animals, forestry practices, conservation methods, and land use, and to relate these to every phase of the curriculum from mathematics, social studies, and crafts to the earth sciences, health, and physical education.

Whatever the normal child can learn, the exceptional child can learn unless he is handicapped by mental inability. In consequence, there need be no educational adaptation of the programed learning; adaptations will occur only in those educational activities which preclude participation by the handicapped. The environment may need to be modified to meet the needs of the orthopedically handicapped, the blind, etc.; but few of the nature-oriented activities will have to undergo change. Certain outdoor activities such as mountain climbing, spelunking, or tree climbing are obviously going to be beyond the capacities of most handicapped individuals. There are, however, many other activities which can be adapted, so that even those whose handicaps prevent their leaving the wheelchair or stretcher can be included.

GARDENING.   Gardening is an outdoor education activity particularly adaptable for the handicapped. Nonambulatory persons may garden without bending or leaving the bed, stretcher, or wheelchair if light long-handled tools are provided. The bed-ridden patient can have a windowsill or dish garden to bring the outdoors inside.

NATURE STUDIES.   Bird watching, astronomical observations, and the classification of minerals, flora, fauna, and other natural specimens do not require extensive movement. They may be performed by the nonambulatory in sitting, lying, or reclining positions. The materials for classification may be brought by others for manipulation, mounting, or taxonomy. However, if the handicapped person can be provided with a lightweight tool with a long handle and a cutting edge, much like that used by a pruner, he will be able to gather some types of specimens for himself.

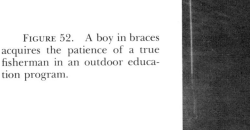

FIGURE 52.   A boy in braces acquires the patience of a true fisherman in an outdoor education program.

FISHING.   Fishing is easily adapted to meet the physical limitations of participants. In the extreme case of a double-arm amputee, the fishing rod may be attached to his waist and harnessed around his upper back so that the rod is at the correct angle. Using a spinning reel, he need only learn to shift his body sharply so that the reel will allow the line to play out. A volunteer will be needed to unhook the catch.

FIELD TRIPS AND HIKES.   A field trip, as the name implies, is a walk taken to explore a field or outdoor area. Its purpose may be simply to enjoy the surroundings, or it may be to search for wildflowers, rocks, or other nature objects or to find materials for use in crafts. Because the pace of a field trip is slow and leisurely, even the most disabled can participate. The distance can be readily adjusted to the physical abilities and endurance of the group.

Hikes are more extensive than field trips and frequently have a specific destination, but this does not mean that anyone need be excluded. Those whose disabilities or lack of stamina prevent their hiking the entire distance may be transported part of the way or the entire distance if the condition requires. Even those who are unable to hike even a short distance enjoy being at the destination when the others arrive, sharing the end-of-the-hike activities and discussions with the hikers. Everyone should be included in the planning and preparations for the hike. Those being transported can be asked to bring the cold drinks for the others or in other ways made to feel they are a part of the entire expedition.

Depending upon the physical conditions of the handicapped, it may be necessary to provide periods of rest during the hike. If only a portion of the hikers will require rest along the way, this group can start earlier and stop to rest when the need becomes apparent.

These are just a few examples of the hundreds of activities which may be adapted to meet the limitations imposed by physical handicaps. A few experiences must be omitted because of environmental impossiblity, but for the most part every tool, device, or activity may be modified in some way to enable the handicapped individual to share in the self-fulfillment of outdoor education.

CAMPING

Camping provides, in addition to the values inherent in any outdoor education activity, a unique experience in group living. In the ideal camp situation the child learns to relax and have fun, to work in harmony with others, to broaden his skills and interests, to develop his own initiative and resourcefulness, and to expand his awareness of himself and the world in which he lives. By camping a youngster may gain skills, interests, and appreciations which will enrich his entire life.

DAY AND RESIDENTIAL CAMPS.   *Day camps* are those which campers attend for the day, returning home at night. The day camp is an ideal arrangement for youngsters who are not ambulatory, who require exceptional help with their braces or with their personal needs, or who for medical or other reasons cannot leave home for extended periods. *Residential camps* are those in which the campers spend the day and night for a span of several days, usually a week or longer. The obvious advantage of the residential camp for those who are able to participate is the added experience of being completely away from the home environment.

SCHOOL CAMPS.   Closely allied to the outdoor educational opportunities described previously is the school-sponsored camping program. The school camp may be one of two distinct operations. As a *summer* camp, it represents an operation of the school system during the months when the school is closed. In this situation (the operation of the camp by the school throughout the summer), the camp becomes by extension a part of the curriculum. The second operational aspect is the *year-round* school camp. Here the camp is, indeed, an integral part of a curriculum which recognizes that many learning experiences can best be undertaken out of doors. It provides firsthand learning experiences close to a natural environment.

The teacher occupies a central position in the school camp program. Through classroom instruction before the class moves into the camp situation, he stimulates his pupils to look forward to the entire outdoor educational experience. He does much to make camping meaningful and serves as a coordinator for relating the camp program to the entire curriculum.

The camping program is generally enriched and comprehensive, specifically suited to meet the needs of the handicapped children who are involved. Months may be spent in planning for the occasion. The school camp is a student's community and all of the usual hazards and problems of sanitation, safety, health, and maintenance of public property are involved. The camper is confronted not only by curriculum subjects but also by the countless offerings of a bountiful nature.

The concepts basic to design, location, and operation of other publicly operated camping facilities apply to school camp properties. In selecting the camp site the following must be considered:

(1) availability of a safe and adequate supply of water;
(2) safe disposal of all sewage and garbage;
(3) climate, topographic features, and general environment;
(4) sources of food supply;
(5) accessibility to good transportation and communication;
(6) natural resources of the camp site;
(7) fire-fighting and protective devices;
(8) adequate cabins and shelters for campers;
(9) facilities for operating a comprehensive camp activities program;
(10) aquatic facilities;
(11) health facilities; and
(12) special facilities for maintenance operations.

All facilities of the school camp should be in accordance with state and local health department rules, ordinances, and regulations. Local building and zoning codes apply to the camp facility and must be followed.

With the camp facility as a base of operations, many experiences proper to the locale can be arranged to offer a meaningful and developmental series of activities. An essential part of programing is that these activities be fun, with plenty of time allowed to complete them. In order to build intellectual appreciation and appropriate skills for lifetime use, the camp should avoid the formal and sometimes regimented procedures of school by offering the most permissive atmosphere possible without anarchy.

SPECIAL CAMPS.   Camps for handicapped children are usually not geared for the medical or therapeutic treatment of the handicap except in special instances. Camps for diabetics and epileptics are examples of the camps established expressly for assisting these condition medically. Most other camps, but not all, are organized for specific types of disabilities, such as the camps for crippled children. In these camps, although the personnel is trained in the understanding of the physically debilitating aspects and the mental and emotional stresses of the young campers, the primary aim is to provide camping fun rather than treatment. This is not to say, however, that the therapeutic effects which result from a good camping program are neglected in either the planning or practice.

In addition to those camps organized to provide medical treatment and those designed specifically for one type of handicap or another, there are many camps attended primarily by nonhandicapped children which also accept children with less severe types of disabilities. In this situation, the child may simply be a handicapped individual going to camp with physically normal children, or he may be one of a group of handicapped attending the same camp as the nonhandicapped but participating in a separate or slightly modified program.

Camps for the Crippled. Under this heading are included camps for the orthopedically and neurologically incapacitated and for cardiac cases. These camps have been established and maintained throughout the country largely through the efforts of the National Society for Crippled Children and Adults. The camps have tried to provide an introductory experience in camping which enables the camper to attend a regular camp after his initial experience in the special camp. In this way the facilities of the special camp can be extended to other crippled children.

A few camps have been established for severely disabled adults, with the program and environment adapted to their special needs. Because such campers have spent much of their lives in hospitals receiving treatment and rehabilitation services, the camp program is deliberately void of medical and vocational therapy. Its aim is rather to provide recreation in a relaxed, friendly atmosphere. There is an emphasis on physical activity in the program offerings because so many disabled adults have given up the thought of ever again participating in active games and dances. The campers are encouraged to get into the water for swimming or just splashing around and to play the adapted sports and games which are offered.

Camps for the Diabetic. Special camps for diabetics, although increasing in number, are not yet widespread, and there are more opportunities for children than for adults. In the diabetic camp, medical treatment and observation are an essential part of the camping experience. Under the direction of a physician a careful check is made of the diet, exercise, and medication of the camper. The diabetic does, in effect, receive the same careful observation and care that he would receive in a hospital at approximately comparable costs but with the tremendous advantage of the relaxed and pleasant surroundings.

In many areas where there is no special diabetic camp, regular camps have arranged to accommodate a group of diabetics in their programs. These camps make available a physician who directs the diet and insulin dosage of the campers and visits them daily. A nurse experienced in handling diabetic cases is on the camp staff and laboratory facilities are provided for the necessary tests.

Camps for the Epileptic. Epileptic children profit greatly from camping experiences. An increasing number of regular camps are providing opportunities for epileptic children to participate in camping activities under the supervision of medical personnel. The children admitted to regular camps are carefully screened, as it has been demonstrated that successful participation is related to personal adjustment to the illness and control of seizures. Those epileptics with serious maladjustments need and deserve the more individual attention which is given at special camps for epileptics. Reasonably good control of seizures appears necessary for satisfactory camping experience with normal youngsters although complete freedom from attacks is not essential unless the camp is totally unprepared for epileptic campers.

Camps for the Blind. Camping for blind children and adults is well established. Special camps have been operated successfully for many years, and in more recent years many regular camps have taken blind children into their programs. Blind campers when given a good program of orientation in carefully planned facilities are able to participate in all camp activities, including boating and swimming.

Camps for the Deaf. Regular camps accept deaf children unless their communication skills or personality adjustment decidedly unfits them for successful participation in the program. Special camps for the deaf are operated by many schools for the deaf.

Camps for the Mentally Retarded. Camps for the mentally handicapped represent another development in the ever-increasing scope of camping for the handicapped. Camping is a particularly enjoyable experience for these youngsters whose participation in so many of the enriching experiences of childhood is limited. The typical program offers all types of waterfront activities, simple recreational games, crafts, group singing, dancing, and story reading. Time is allotted for relaxation and informal get-togethers and for definite periods of rest, all of which are essential to the welfare of the retarded camper.

Because these youngsters lack judgment and control, close supervision is necessary for their physical safety as well as for the preservation of camp unity and harmony. No more than three campers per counselor is the most desirable ratio.

Perhaps the outstanding organizational program established to conduct camping programs for the mentally retarded is that operated under the sponsorship of the Joseph P. Kennedy, Jr., Foundation. The Kennedy Foundation, as it is widely known, is the agency founded by the late President's father to stimulate and support work being performed for retarded children throughout the country. The Foundation, starting with one pilot camp project, now supports some 25 day camps situated throughout the United States. These camps operate sessions lasting between four and eight weeks and are administered through public and private agencies.

Camps for the Aged. In the new emphasis on providing worthy leisure activities for our senior citizens, camping takes on a special significance. The aged take much the same pleasure in nature study, camp crafts, outdoor cookery, singing around the campfire, and cooperative living that those many years their junior find in camp life. Camps for the aged, although not yet extensive in number, include day camps and residential camps. The campers have proven themselves to be extremely adaptable to the lack of home conveniences and the changes in weather which are an inevitable part of camp life.

REFERRING STUDENTS TO CAMPS.   Careful consideration must be given to several factors in recommending students for a nonspecialized camp. A youngster is generally considered to be ready for camping experiences when he:

(1) can take care of his toilet and other personal care needs as well as other youngsters his age;

(2) is able to care for and put on and remove the braces or appliances which he must use;

(3) understands the limitations which his handicap imposes and the safety precautions which are entailed;

(4) has made a reasonable adjustment to his condition;

(5) possesses enough physical stamina to go through the camping period without undue fatigue or recurrent illness.

The type of camp which any particular youngster should attend may be determined by availability, family finances, and other considerations. A few specific suggestions can be made by the physical education teacher, however, based upon his observation and work with the youngster as a student in his program. Children with severe disabilities or personality problems will probably profit most, particularly the first year, from a day camp or specialized camp which is prepared to give special help to those unable to take charge of their personal needs. Wherever the circumstances are favorable, however, the child should be recommended for enrollment in a camp which integrates the handicapped with the nonhandicapped, because of the opportunities for social growth in an atmosphere of acceptance which such a camp cultivates.

The youngster must, of course, be examined and judged able to attend camp by his doctor. The camp will request a medical history of the disability as well as a social history describing his adjustment and personality problems. Recommendations of the kinds of activities which may prove most physiologically and psychologically beneficial may be requested. The medical report should list the activities in which the youngster may not engage and any special precautions which should be exercised. All of this information will serve the camp officials as a medical guide and as a program guide. The care and thoroughness with which the requested information is supplied will determine to a great extent the success with which the camping experience can be directed to meet the needs of the camper.

CAMP PERSONNEL. There are many opportunities for physical education teachers trained in an understanding of the needs of the handicapped to find summer employment in camps for disabled youngsters and adults.

The administrative personnel, more or less standard in all camps for the handicapped, consists of a director, medical staff, counselors, and activity supervisors and instructors. The director is usually responsible for establishing the policies and procedures of the camp as they are set forth by the sponsoring agency. He must have a sound philosophy of camping and understand the goals which the camp is attempting to reach for exceptional children. Among the skills, talents, and knowledge that the camp director must possess are those related to site selection and development, accounting, budget making, selection and education of the camp staff, insurance, construction, maintenance, equipment, program, legal responsibilities, and above all supervision. The camp director is primarily and directly responsible for everything that happens at the camp and for the health and safety of all the campers.

An understanding of the nature of the handicap and the problems in adjustment which it has presented to the youngster is essential for the counselor or instructor in the special camp. This is no less true of those working with handicapped children within the regular camp situation. The specific duties of the cabin counselor are outlined by the director. Often the instructor of a phase of the program, such as crafts or swimming, will also serve as a cabin counselor. The counselor must be prepared to deal with homesickness, failure to conform to the regulations, and similar problems common to any child in an unfamiliar situation, in addition to which he must be equal to the problems, both physical and psychological, arising from the handicap.

The activity instructor (such as the instructor in charge of sports and games) must be ready and willing to meet the challenges of providing a program in which the handicapped campers can participate with success and pleasure. He must learn how to help these children fulfill their needs, how to direct their energies, and how to help them develop their potential within the bounds of their limitations.

SPECIAL FACILITIES. The physical facilities which must be provided for handicapped campers are not extensive. Ramps at entrances to buildings are necessary for children who cannot readily negotiate steps. Obstacles should be removed if they necessitate special assistance to handicapped campers or require considerable effort on their part in overcoming them. However, a limited number of obstacles to overcome can prove stimulating to the disabled campers. Pathways, buildings, and activity areas must be made easily identifiable for those with visual handicaps. For campers who have difficulty standing unassisted while showering, seats may be provided in the shower stalls. Some special medical and therapeutic facilities and equipment may need to be supplied so that the infirmary is prepared to cope with emergencies arising from a specific disability.

PROGRAM. Camps which provide the best possible environment and experience for the handicapped are those which carefully plan and administer their program. Comprehensive and varied nature-oriented activities should be a fundamental part of the program offered in the camp setting; among them are aquatics, astronomy, agriculture, archery, art, crafts, ceremonials, scouting, exploring, hiking, boating, tripping, dances, games, conservation, lapidary work, geology, ecology, hobbies, dramatics, tournaments, music, reading, motor skills, meteorology, pomology, and entomology. There should be both highly organized and free-play experiences for passive and active recreational experiences. There must be opportunities for self-expression through leadership as well as conformity through followership. To the extent that they are capable, the campers should be allowed to plan and assume responsibilities for the success of the program. There should be guidance, counseling, unobtrusive supervision, and enthusiastic leadership. There should also be a minimum of essential regulation and no dogmatism or slavish devotion to a single method of activity presentation.

The program of the school camp for the handicapped must attempt to improve the quality of the camper's education experiences as well as to provide an environment that is conducive to healthful living. The program must be soundly based upon the abilities of the campers to participate, and their interests should be the guidelines for choosing effective activities.

Adaptations: While every effort should be made to offer handicapped campers "normal" games, dances, sports, and camp activities, some modifications are necessitated by the nature of their disabilities. In the special day and residential camps, the activities can be adapted in a general way for everyone, with such attention as is required directed toward individual needs other than the specific handicap. The program activities for the integrated camp will require more careful planning to insure nearly equal participation by the able-bodied and the handicapped. The same considerations which govern successful integration of the handicapped into the regular physical education program will apply in the camp situation. It must be remembered that the handicapped camper has the same basic needs as normal youngsters but some needs are more pronounced than others because of his disability.

A general guide for planning and conducting a program of physical activities for handicapped campers is offered here:

1. Safety precautions must be strictly adhered to, even though the handicapped camper is so anxious to try all the new experiences that he may prefer to ignore restrictions.

2. Lead-up skills must be well mastered before complicated feats are attempted.

3. Campers must be closely observed for early signs of fatigue because handicapped youngsters usually tire easily. Rest periods should be provided as needed.

4. The program should be kept relaxed and unhurried to avoid unnecessary frustrations and anxieties. Competitive events should be prevented from becoming highly emotional.

5. The camper's relationship to others and his acceptance by them should be closely observed, with guidance offered unobtrusively.

6. The camper should be helped to establish realistic goals for his physical development and skill achievement, with full recognition of his potential as well as his limitations.

7. Help should be readily given when actually needed; however, when confidence rather than skill is lacking, the camper should be encouraged to try to do things himself rather than having them done for him.

The camp activities should not follow along the same lines as the city or school recreational program for the handicapped. The campers will, of course, want to play individual and team sports to which they have been introduced in their school and town recreational programs, but these should not form the core of the program.

QUESTIONS

1. What is outdoor education? How does it differ from camping?
2. What is a field trip? What safety precautions need to be taken into consideration for the handicapped?

3. In what ways can participation in camping experiences contribute to the welfare of the handicapped child?

4. What kinds of camps are available to the handicapped?

5. What things must be taken into consideration when recommending camping for a handicapped child?

6. In what ways is the organization of camping for the handicapped similar to that of a regular camp? Different?

7. What special facilities are needed in camp for the handicapped?

SELECTED READINGS

Dimock, Hedley S. (ed.): *Administration of the Modern Camp.* New York, Association Press, 1948.

Freeberg, William H., and Taylor, Loren E.: *Philosophy of Outdoor Education.* Minneapolis, Minn., Burgess Publishing Co., 1961.

Hammett, Catherine T., and Musselman, Virginia: *The Camp Program Book.* New York, Association Press, 1956.

Hunt, Valerie V.: *Recreation for the Handicapped.* New York, Prentice-Hall, Inc., 1955.

Macmillan, Dorothy L.: *School Camping and Outdoor Education.* Dubuque, Iowa, William C. Brown Company, Publishers, 1956.

Pomeroy, Janet: *Recreation for the Physically Handicapped.* New York, The Macmillan Co., 1964.

Shivers, Jay S.: *Leadership in Recreational Service.* New York, The Macmillan Co., 1963.

Smith, Julian W., *et al.*: *Outdoor Education.* Englewood Cliffs, N.J., Prentice-Hall, Inc., 1963.

24

A CORRECTIVE PROGRAM FOR BODY MECHANICS

Concepts of good posture have undergone numerous changes throughout history. At times the exaggerated styles of women's clothing have influenced the concept of good posture, as in the days of the bustle. The ramrod-straight position of the soldier at attention influenced for many years the idea of good body carriage. There is no doubt that the physical education teacher concerned with promoting good posture must take into consideration the esthetics of certain positions, and these, of course, are dictated by custom and tradition. But he should not ignore the effects that a specific posture will have upon the efficiency of the body.

Mastering efficient walking, sitting, and standing postures makes these movements more beautiful as well as more practical from the standpoint of preventing fatigue. Achieving this efficient, graceful posture involves what is currently called body mechanics. This term refers to the alignment of the various segments of the body. Good body mechanics is the most efficient use of the muscles to insure the most effective alignment for the position desired.

Posture cannot be thought of as a single static position, for it changes continually with each movement. Moving the shoulders forward while leaning over from the hips to pick up a small object may be very good posture for that activity, but it is not effective for walking or standing. Consequently, we may say that posture depends upon the type of activity which the body is being called upon to perform.

Good posture also depends upon the structure of the body, which is determined by the relationship of the parts of the body to each other — that is, the relationship of the head to the spinal column and shoulder girdle, and so on. The relationships of the parts, how they fit together, is a determining factor in what constitutes good posture for the individual. People are not built alike, and to force everyone into the same mold of a preconceived idea of good posture is useless. An individual who, because of his body structure, is more round-shouldered than others should not be forced to stand with his shoulders thrust back to the same extent as one whose bone structure permits him to do this without strain. To do so will lower his body efficiency rather than raise it.

Statistics show that from 75 to 85 per cent of all individuals have some deficiency in body mechanics. Only about 1 per cent can be classified as having such good body mechanics that no improvement is possible. Nearly 5 per cent have very marked postural deviations.[1] Consequently, the physical education instructor may expect to find a large number of students in the total enrollment who may profit from instruction in good body mechanics and a small percentage in definite need of such instruction.

The teaching unit in body mechanics should provide exercises for those with good body mechanics as well as those with varying degrees of inefficient body mechanics. For the former, the objective will be the maintenance of strong postural muscles, and the program of exercises and activities will be of a preventive nature. For the others, the program will be corrective in nature and will be directed toward improvement or change in the body mechanics, as individual cases may require.

VALUES OF GOOD BODY MECHANICS

Good body mechanics has a direct relationship with certain aspects of good health. Increased strain upon parts of the body causes pain and discomfort. Some backaches, headaches, foot pains, and neck aches are traced to faulty body mechanics.[2] Consistent misalignment can possibly lead to a structural change in bones which may produce a chronic condition of misalignment.

Some authorities[3] also attribute poor general health to poorly supported vital organs caused by poor posture. Although it would appear that slumped posture and inadequate muscle tone would decrease the space and the support of the vital organs, evidence that would definitely

[1]Charles L. Lowman and Carl H. Young: *Postural Fitness.* Philadelphia, Lea & Febiger, 1960, pp. 26–29.

[2]Hans Kraus and Wilhelm Raab: *Hypokinetic Disease.* Springfield, Ill., Charles C Thomas, Publisher, 1961, p. 19. See also Myrtle G. Scott: *Analysis of Human Motion,* ed. 2. New York, Appleton-Century-Crofts, 1963, p. 396.

[3]Ellen D. Kelly: *Preventive and Corrective Physical Education,* ed. 4. New York, The Ronald Press Company, 1965, pp. 63–64.

link poor general health to crowded and inadequately supported vital organs resulting from poor body mechanics is incomplete.

Aside from its health value, good body mechanics has a social value. Good posture adds to the attractiveness of the appearance and suggests a state of well-being, as contrasted with the suggestion of laziness and poor physical vitality of a slumping posture.

BODY STRUCTURE

The body is held erect by the spinal column. The spinal column of the normal adult is a segmented structure consisting of four curves: the *cervical, dorsal* or *thoracic, lumbar,* and *sacral.* The cervical curve is the curve at the neck; the convex of this curve is forward. The dorsal curve is the curve of the upper back, and the convex of its curve is backward. The lumbar curve is the curve in the small of the back, and the sacral curve is the curve in the inferior (lower) extremity of the spinal column. The convex of the lumbar curve is forward, while in the sacral it is backward.

At birth the spinal column has a single curve, with its convex to the back. During the early months of life, when the baby starts to raise its head and kick its legs, the spine become relatively straight. The cervical curvature develops at the time when the infant sits upright. Later, when the child starts to support his weight on his feet and begins to walk, the lumbar curve comes gradually into prominence. This is accompanied by development of the other curves until the spine adopts the normal curves of an adult. The normal development of the curves is dependent in part upon whether the child is well and active during his early years.

ALIGNMENT.   The upper segment of the body, when in an upright position, must be in alignment with the base of the body (the feet). In perfect alignment the center of gravity of the head, upper trunk, lower trunk, and legs is in a straight line. Looking at the side view, if a plumb line is dropped even with the lobe of the ear, it will pass through the middle of the shoulder, through the middle of the hip, to the side and slightly behind the patella, and fall in front of the outer malleolus. As seen from the back, a line drawn through the body showing the center of gravity would bisect the head and neck and follow the spinal column down between the cleft of the buttocks. The spine should be straight and the shoulders and hips even, but slight variations will occur, depending upon individual differences. The more the body deviates from this alignment, the more energy is needed to hold the body erect because the postural muscles will have less mechanical advantage in maintaining balance. However, in certain cases the structure of the body may be such that there will be more energy expended in forcing the body into the alignment described above than in a less erect position.

STANDING POSTURE.   There has been a tendency to portray good

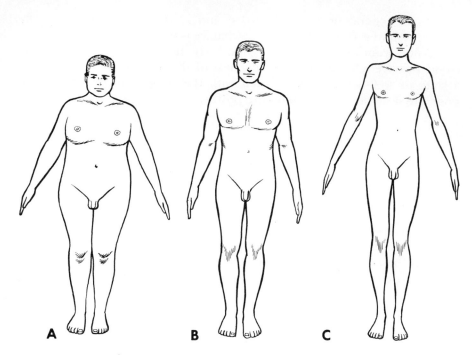

FIGURE 53.   A, Endomorphic body type. B, Mesomorphic body type. C, Ectomorphic
body type.

posture as the proper body alignment for the average body build and
to expect all "good" posture to resemble this. Such expectation fails to
take into consideration the difference in bone structure and body build.

Body builds are usually classified into three categories: *Ectomorphy*,
slender; *mesomorphy*, medium stature with predominance of bone and
muscle; and *endomorphy*, fat and bulky with no muscle definition.[4] Most
individuals are predominantly one type or the other; however, most
people have characteristics of more than one type. One segment of the
body may be predominantly in one classification while another segment
will have more characteristics of another type. This sometimes causes
the individual to appear to have poor posture while actually his body
alignment is the most efficient for his body structure. For example, a
person who has a deep, thick chest with a heavy dorsal area and relatively
slender hip area will appear to have kyphosis (round upper back). To
eliminate this condition would require an exaggerated posture that could
be maintained only by tremendous contraction of the sacrospinalis muscles.
This would entail considerable expenditure of energy and would therefore
be a much less efficient posture than the original one.

The length of the clavicle influences the degree of erectness at which

[4]William H. Sheldon: *Atlas of Men.* New York, Harper & Brothers, 1954, *passim.*

the shoulders will be held habitually by the individual. A relatively long clavicle will force the shoulder girdle back, while a relatively short one will require the scapulae to lie forward and to the side and will cause the shoulders to be brought forward.

The curves of the spine are also influenced by its structure. If the borders of the body of a single vertebra are thicker on one side than on the other, the curve in that area of the spinal column will tend to be increased. There is considerable variation in the thickness of the borders of vertebral bodies in individuals. The difference in thickness will produce a greater or lesser spinal curve than in the average person. To force such a person to assume a very erect position may actually reduce the efficiency of the support of the spinal column. If the vertebrae are in alignment and the edges of the vertebrae cause a larger curve, an attempt to straighten the curve will spread the vertebrae farther apart, causing a probable instability. This cannot be determined by observation of the back, but it can be shown by x-ray.

Differences in the location of the acetabula influence the degree to which the pelvis is tilted, and the tilt of the pelvis determines the size of the angle in the lumbar curve. The acetabula form the pivotal point of balance of the pelvis and the spinal column because of the column's relationship to the pelvis. If the acetabula are situated slightly more to the front than usual, there will be a tendency for the posterior area to drop because of imbalance. The pelvic area rotates upward, causing the lumbar to flatten. If the anterior area drops, the pelvis will rotate downward and the lumbar curve is increased.[5]

WALKING POSTURE.   The mechanics of efficient walking involves a basic pattern, but, like standing posture, the best pattern for any individual is dictated in part by body structure, particularly leg alignment, and variations within limits may be expressions of individual structure and not actual walking faults. Excessive variations which are caused by improper use of the muscles will, in most cases, warrant efforts to modify them. Common walking errors which are frequently caused by improper use of the muscles are:

(1) leaning forward before the lead foot strikes the ground;

(2) carrying the weight on the rear foot until after the lead foot strikes the ground;

(3) exaggerated shifting of the weight to the supporting foot;

(4) swinging the arms in too wide an arc;

(5) exerting force straight up from the rear foot as the step is made;

(6) failing to swing the arms at the shoulders;

(7) looking at the feet;

(8) toeing in or out.

[5]Charles Harold McCloy: *Philosophical Bases for Physical Education*. New York, Appleton-Century-Crofts, Inc., 1940, p. 255.

SITTING POSTURE. A good sitting posture should permit some relaxation, whether one is seated for work or for rest. When sitting in a chair for the purpose of resting, as much of the chair as possible should be used to support the body. A slumping posture which does not utilize fully the support of the chair will be more fatiguing than an erect sitting position. Sitting far back in the chair, with the entire back resting against its contours, permits the chair to aid in holding the body, thereby allowing some muscular relaxation.

For desk work, it is usually necessary to bring the head and eyes over the work; consequently, the back of the chair cannot be used for support. The buttocks are placed far back in the chair, and the weight of the trunk is distributed over the entire area of the buttocks. The trunk leans forward slightly from the hips, and head, neck, and trunk are kept in a relatively straight line. When it is not necessary for the head to be over the working area, the back of the body may be in contact with the back of the chair for support.

The most common errors in sitting are:

(1) failure to place the buttocks against the back of the chair;
(2) permitting the shoulders and back to slump;
(3) shifting the weight of the body to one side;
(4) sitting on one foot.

LIFTING POSTURE. Lifting heavy objects from the floor or ground incorrectly is a common cause of back strain. When lifting heavy objects, the object should be placed as near to the center of the body as possible, as this increases the mechanical advantage in lifting. To pick up the load, the legs should be bent and the lift made by extending the legs with the back held relatively straight. If the object being lifted has a handle, it is possible to keep the back entirely straight during the lift. However, when it is necessary to put the hands under the heavy object on the floor, the trunk may be bent while the hold is being taken. The knees will be flexed during this process. The back is then straightened and the object lifted by extending the knees. In holding a heavy object, the knees should not be locked, as this position has a tendency to cause an exaggeration of the lumbar curve which may place undue stress upon the muscles of this region.

Light objects may be lifted by bending at the hips. However, anyone who has a history of lower back disorder should use the technique for lifting heavy objects in order to protect the back from possible strain.

CAUSES OF POOR BODY MECHANICS

It is frequently difficult to attribute poor body mechanics to any one single cause; in most cases a combination of two or more factors have produced it. For purposes of this discussion, the causes will be divided into two classes: those which are closely associated with fields such as medicine and psychiatry, and those which can be corrected by remedial work in physical education. It is recognized that no hard and fast demarcation can be established between the two, because of factors which overlap; however, a rough line can be drawn between poor body mechanics attributed to such conditions as illness, infection, injury, malnourishment, a feeling of inadequacy, and deformities which are chiefly medical or psychiatric, and faulty mechanics caused by poor neuromuscular habits of the postural muscles, weak musculature, and overdevelopment of one set of muscles at the expense of another, which are more nearly physical education problems.

MEDICAL OR PSYCHIATRIC PROBLEMS.   Debilitating illnesses such as infantile paralysis, rickets, and bone tuberculosis frequently cause deformities which are conducive to incorrect use of the body. Students who suffer from such conditions should be under the care of an orthopedic physician, and postural work with such cases should be under the direct supervision of the physician and the physical therapist. However, in the later stages of recovery, the physical educator may be able to recommend games and activities that will complement the work of the medical team. Such activities need the approval of the physician before the student begins participation.

Injuries which cause a person to shift his weight to avoid pain or ease his work often encourage the development of poor body mechanics. The treatment of the injury must be made by the physician, but the re-learning of postural skills after the healing of the injury may be directed by the physical education teacher in many cases.

Illness often causes an over-all body weakness which lowers the threshold of fatigue. General fatigue is often a contributing factor to poor body mechanics. The fatigued individual doesn't have the energy necessary to hold his body in its proper alignment. The postural muscles are allowed to relax partially, and the various segments of the body gravitate out of alignment (body slump). The longer the fatigue continues, the more habitual the slump becomes. The slumping of the body would appear to be a means of conserving energy. Actually, however, this is not true, for in most cases when the body slumps the center of gravity is no longer in a straight line and the force of gravity will make certain muscles work harder to maintain balance.

Emotions and attitudes influence muscular movement and postural stance. This is readily observed in the child jumping with joy upon receiving a pleasant surprise or the adolescent slumping in his seat with boredom or dejection. There is evidence to support the contention that a habitual feeling of inadequacy and defeat, especially during childhood, encourages postural slumping. In such cases, if the desired outcome is to be achieved from postural training, it is first necessary to rebuild the individual's self-esteem.

PHYSICAL EDUCATION PROBLEMS.   The reasons for neuromuscular habits of the postural muscles which have no pathological basis are difficult to ascertain. It would appear that in some cases the cause is improper use of the muscles: the individual just learned to hold his body incorrectly in much the same way as one sometimes learns a sport skill wrong through trial and error. Just as the error in the sport skill is corrected by a re-learning process, the correction of faulty body mechanics requires a process of re-learning.

Lack of use of the postural muscles contributes to their weakness. Weak muscles, because they are weak, will not be used greatly in maintaining posture; this lack of use contributes further to their weakness. If the muscles are weak, there is greater difficulty in maintaining good body alignment.

In cases where the antagonistic muscles are much stronger than the agonists, there is a tendency for the stronger muscles to pull the body out of alignment. It is possible that a contributing factor to the overdevelopment of one set of muscles is an overspecialization in sports which develop this set of muscles. Evidence for this may be seen in athletes who participate exclusively in sports which require extensive use of the muscles of the chest but little of the back muscles. They may be round-shouldered to some degree because the weak muscles of the back are unable to perform their share of the work in maintaining equilibrium.

POSTURAL DEVIATIONS

There is no precise standard of erectness for measuring normal or abnormal body mechanics. The only possible definition of the normal, or most desired, posture is that it is one in which the center of gravity of each segment of the body is kept in an approximately straight line without decreasing the efficiency of the body elsewhere. The frequently heard postural directive to "stand straight" has given rise to some confusion regarding the position of the spine. The spine is, of course, not straight; it has distinct curves. In some cases in which the curves are too marked, it may be advisable to straighten the curves; but a certain amount of curve is normal and natural. Marked increase in the curvation of the spine does not necessarily indicate a serious handicap. If the various segments of the body are balanced properly, a spine with moderately increased curves may be considered normal for some individuals.

Postural deviations are classified as structural or functional. In the *structural* deviation, the bony structure has changed. A structural deviation is a permanent condition. Because of the change in the bone structure, the deviation cannot be corrected short of surgery or placing the involved area in a cast. Corrective exercise is of little use in this situation. A *functional* disorder refers to a condition in which only the soft tissue such as muscles and ligaments are primarily involved. Functional disorders respond to exercise, and the disorder can be overcome. It should be remembered that it is not always easy to determine the difference between a structural and a functional disorder. Some cases involve a degree of fixation. In the early stages the disturbance may be in the soft tissues alone, but, as the condition persists, bone changes gradually take place.

FORWARD HEAD.   Forward head is a term used to describe a position in which the neck is flexed and the head is held forward and downward, usually with the chin dropped. The condition in which the head and chin are not dropped, frequently called "poke neck" or cervical lordosis, has a high incidence among the nearsighted. It is frequently accompanied by the inability to extend the cervical area and hence does not respond well to postural exercise.

In most cases, forward head accompanies an increased thoracic curve. However, if the thoracic curve remains normal, the efficiency of the body will not be decreased to a great extent, although the neck muscles will of necessity do more work to hold the head in position since it is not well balanced on the neck and shoulders. The chief disadvantage is in appearance. Sometimes a twisting of the neck and/or lateral flexion accompanies the forward head.

ROUND SHOULDERS.   The term round shoulders describes the position that occurs when the scapulae are held to the side toward the axillary area and forward. This is almost always accompanied by an increased thoracic curve. The majority of cases respond well to postural exercises. Some cases of round shoulders, as was pointed out earlier, are not a postural fault in the true sense since they are due to structural differences.

PROTRUDING SHOULDER BLADES.   In the young child protruding shoulder blades or "angel wings" are common. The condition may accompany round shoulders and back. Lack of muscular strength in the back area is a frequent contributor to protruding shoulder blades. Muscles involved in holding the scapulae flat also aid in pulling the shoulders into correct standing posture. Besides the exercises prescribed for the correction of round back and shoulders, hanging and climbing exercises and games are excellent activities to strengthen these muscles in children.

ROUND UPPER BACK.   An increased curve in the upper back causes a round upper back. This is called thoracic or dorsal kyphosis. It is frequently the result of fatigue or inadequate muscular strength in the extensors of the spine. When the upper back is rounded, the sternum is depressed and the rib cage is lowered, resulting in a decrease of chest cavity that may result in distortion of the normal position of the vital organs. As was pointed out earlier, it is not known what effects this may have upon health, although it appears that the normal functions of the vital organs might be restricted. The condition responds well to exercises that strengthen the muscles involved in holding the spine more erect and that stretch their antagonists.

HOLLOW BACK.   An exaggeration of the lumbar curve is called hollow back or lordosis. A functional exaggeration of this curve is caused by increasing the tilt of the pelvic girdle. As the pelvic area is tilted, the symphysis pubis is lowered in front, followed by a forward movement of the lumbar area of the spine, causing an increase in the lumbar curve.

Sometimes lordosis accompanies kyphosis, as an attempt to balance the shift of the center of weight caused by the increased thoracic curve. With the increase of the lumbar curve, the center of gravity in that area is shifted to the back, thus compensating for the shifting of the weight forward in the upper trunk caused by the increased thoracic curve. Also accompanying the increased lumbar curve is the hyperextension of the knees. It is thought that this often precipitates the development of lordosis.

When the lumbar curve is increased, the center of gravity is shifted from near the center onto the back part of the vertebrae, bringing the spinous processes closer together and decreasing the size of the foramina (openings between the vertebrae through which the spinal nerves pass). This decrease in the size of the opening may cause a pressure upon the nerves. The increase of the lumbar curve also necessitates a redistribution of internal organs in the abdominal cavity, causing its contents to be pushed harder against the abdominal wall.

FLAT BACK.   A large decrease in the normal lumbar curve causes a flat back. The action involved in the rotation of the pelvic girdle is the opposite of that in the condition of sway back.

It is difficult to determine just how much a flat back decreases body efficiency. It has been pointed out by some authorities that the extremely straight condition of the back reduces the shock-absorbing mechanism of the spine and causes disturbance in the function of the viscera because of changes in the size of the cavity and in the position of the viscera within the cavity. A flat back does decrease the esthetics of the body.

SCOLIOSIS.   When the body is viewed from the back, the right and left sides of the body should be symmetrical, both shoulders and hips at the same level with the spinal column straight. Most individuals will show a very slight deviation in the spinal column. A slight deviation is usually not noticeable in casual observation and, if it does not become progressively worse, is of no consequence. However, a lateral curvature that is obvious must be considered as an abnormal condition.

The lateral curvature of the spine is accompanied by a twisting of the vertebrae and takes its name, scoliosis, from the Greek word meaning twisting or bending. The lateral curve may be to the right or left or a combination of both. If it is either to the right or left, it is called a **C** curve. An **S** curve is one in which the lower part curves in the opposite direction. In the latter condition, one of the curves is usually the primary curve while the other is a secondary curve developed to compensate for the first curve in the restoration of equilibrium of the trunk as a whole. An uncorrected condition of **C** curve will eventually encourage the development of the **S** curve.

The **C** curve takes its name from the direction of convexity of the curve. A left **C** curve is to the individual's left and causes the right shoulder to be lowered and right hip to be raised. The opposite is true of the right **C** curve. Most **C** curves are to the left. The reason for this is not known, although it may well be connected with dominance.

In most **S** curves the primary curve is to the left. The right shoulder will be held lower than the left while the left hip will be raised higher than the right.

Scoliosis may be functional or structural in nature. If the curve tends to disappear to some degree when a hanging or prone position is assumed, it is probably a functional condition. The causes of scoliosis are varied. A shortened leg, faulty hearing or sight, disease, injury, congenital conditions, and faulty postural habits are the most frequent causes. Seldom does scoliosis in its early stages cause pain or noticeable fatigue. However, in the later stages the muscular pull that is necessitated by the abnormal condition of the spine may cause back fatigue and frequent pains. It is, moreover, a definite cosmetic handicap.

LEG ALIGNMENT.   People do not all walk or stand in the same way because of such differences in basic structure of the body as size, weight distribution, length and shape of the legs, and structure of the pelvic girdle. Leg and foot alignment is said to be proper when a line drawn from the anterior inferior iliac spine bisects the knee cap, ankle joint, and second toe. Some variation will occur due to structure.[6] The location of the acetabulum determines to some extent the alignment. If the acetabulum is located to the front of the center of pelvic gravity, there is a tendency for the person to toe in. Often knock knees accompany this tendency. With the acetabulum to the rear, there is a tendency to toe out. To force one with this structure to toe straight ahead would be to decrease the efficiency in the hip area since the head of the femur would have to change from its customary position in the acetabulum.

FOOT MECHANICS

The feet are the base of the body and bear the entire weight of the body in an upright position. Since the foot is made up of several segments, it is subject to misalignment. The bones of the foot are so constructed as to form two arches: the longitudinal arch and the transverse arch.

The highest part of the *longitudinal arch* is on the inner side of the foot. On the inside of the foot the arch extends from the heel (calcaneus) to the first, second, or third metatarsal (near the ball of the foot). The longitudinal arch is supported by the shape of the bones that fit together, the ligaments, and the muscles.

The chief factor in the stability of the foot is how well the bones

[6]Ibid., p. 254.

involved fit into each other. For example, the calcaneus give the best support to the talus if its contact point with the talus is flat (horizontal) rather than slanting. If it slopes forward and downward, as it does in some individuals, the body weight pushes the talus down the slope of calcaneus, causing a broken arch or flat foot. Muscles involved in maintaining the longitudinal arch of the foot include the plantar muscles of the foot, that have their origin and insertion on the foot, as well as the deep muscles of the calf that pass under the foot and insert in the toes. Variations in bone structure in individuals account for varying degrees of the height of the arch. The highest arch is not necessarily the strongest arch.

The *transverse arch* extends across the foot in the area of the ball of the foot. The five metatarsals form the arch. The fifth and first metatarsals are the base for the arch. It is thought by some authorities that a dropping of this arch occurs when the second and third metatarsals drop down and become weight-bearing. A callus develops under the second metatarsal as a result. There is some disagreement among the authorities[7] about the importance of the transverse arch and the part it plays in creating the callus. Some point out that the callus and pain occur in this area when the second metatarsal is longer than the first and becomes the weight-bearing bone. In either case the problem is accentuated when a person wears high heels, and it occurs less frequently when low heels are worn.

POSITION OF THE FEET.   The preferred foot position with normal structure of the feet and legs is that in which the toes are pointing straight ahead or only slightly abducted (outward). When the feet are abducted to any great extent, the weight of the body is forced over the longitudinal arch instead of over the outer border of the feet with its more stable structure.

Pronation is a movement in which the ankle rolls inward and the body weight is thrown over the longitudinal arch, causing the depressing and lowering of the arch. This is frequently the result of inadequate muscle strength and improper bony structure. Often accompanying this is the eversion of the soles of the feet (turning the outside of the soles upward).

Supination is the opposite condition of pronation. The ankle rolls outward, with the body weight falling on the outer borders of the feet.

OVERWEIGHT AND FLAT FEET.   Extreme overweight is often a factor in flat feet. A person who puts on weight too quickly often overloads foot muscles that have not been strengthened sufficiently over a period of time and cannot do the job of maintaining the arch. Placing a load upon the feet that they are not capable of handling will cause arches to fall. Weak and painful arches are common to the overweight individual.

[7]Dudley J. Morton: *The Human Foot*. New York, Columbia University Press, 1935, pp. 105–112.

TENSENESS AND RELAXATION

Tension is the opposite of relaxation. When we speak of muscular tenseness or hypertonus, we are referring to a muscle that is receiving stimulation from the nervous system above a certain level and is in partial contraction. The amount of contraction is more than that which is normal tonus of the muscle. Relaxation, on the other hand, is the condition that exists when the muscle is receiving a minimum of stimuli from the nervous system.

Muscular relaxation is highly desirable from the viewpoint of good body mechanics. Relaxation helps to conserve energy and retard the onset of fatigue, making it easier to maintain good posture. Moreover, relaxation of the proper muscles improves coordination and makes possible more graceful and efficient movement.

It is valuable, then, for the physical education teacher to have some understanding of the causes of muscular tension and the means of alleviating them in order to achieve relaxation. It is believed that most cases of hypertonus are caused by lack of sleep, overwork, pain, and nervous conditions.[8] If the nervousness arises from anxiety or frustration, temporary relief is often afforded by participation in physical activity, because the activity provides a diversion. Physical activity may also be helpful in that the fatigue produced by the workout may result in needed sleep. Permanent relief may depend on the help of a physician.

An activity which is useful in determining the presence of muscular tension as well as for pointing up the difference between relaxation and tenseness is performed in the following manner.

The subject sits in a chair with an arm resting on the top of a desk or table. He is told to relax his shoulder and arm completely. A helper picks up the arm by the wrist and then immediately drops it. Signs of tenseness are revealed if the subject assists in lifting the arm, resists the movement, holds the lifted position, or lowers the arm gradually when it is released. If the arm and shoulder are relaxed, the hand will "flop" back to the desk or table top. The attention of the subject is brought to the difference in response.

Since relaxation is the opposite of tension, it is possible for the subject to acquire an actual feeling of relaxation by contracting the arm muscles vigorously in moving the arm. Then the subject is told to relax the muscles and note the difference between the two conditions mentally. Alternate tensing and relaxing of the muscles of the arm is continued, in an attempt to make the difference greater each time.

Other parts of the body are then treated in a like manner. When the

[8]Josephine L. Rathbone: *Corrective Physical Education*, ed. 6. Philadelphia, W. B. Saunders Co., 1959.

subject is capable of relaxing all of his muscles at will, he will be able to achieve total muscular relaxation. For total relaxation, a supine position is taken, which can be supported by pillows beneath the back of the neck, under the knees, and on each side of the body for the arm to rest upon. Pillows are not essential, but they add to ease of relaxing. Some authorities[9] recommend that concentration on relaxing be centered on one part of the body at a time, starting at the head and going down toward the feet. It has also been suggested that creating a mental image of a relaxing situation such as sinking deeply in to a soft mattress may be helpful in relaxation of the muscles.[10]

TESTING AND MEASURING
BODY MECHANICS

To develop sufficient muscular strength, endurance, and skill in maintaining the best body mechanics is an objective of the physical education program. Whenever an individual deviates so much that he cannot participate in the regular program to his greatest advantage, or requires special attention to his needs which cannot be given him in the regular class, he should be placed in the adapted physical education program.

Screening Tests. Some schools administer screening tests to select those who require a more extensive examination to determine if they are in need of special consideration in postural education. Every physical education program should provide for some type of screening if it is at all feasible.

There are several different techniques that may be utilized in screening, but subjective evaluation is the one most frequently used. It is less expensive and less time-consuming than other methods. Subjective ratings are made by the examiner of anteroposterior and lateral balance and the alignment of the feet and legs in the standing position. To increase the validity of the observation, the body mechanics of walking can be examined.

For the test, the students are lined up facing the examiner. The students are asked to turn to the left and right and to the back to give the examiner a view of all sides in a minimum of time and to enable the students to change positions frequently to avoid fatigue. The examiner moves along the line about 8 or 10 feet from the subjects to make his observations. It should be mentioned that those with poor static posture usually overcompensate when attempting to assume good posture for the examination. Those who have fatigue slump with the round shoulders

[9]Edmund Jacobson: *Progressive Relaxation,* ed. 2. Chicago, The University of Chicago Press, 1938, *passim.*

[10]Edmund Jacobson: *You Must Relax,* ed. 4. New York, McGraw-Hill Book Co., Inc., 1957, *passim.*

and forward head will throw their shoulders too far back and tilt the head up with the chin slightly elevated, resembling somewhat the "poke head."

As the subject faces the examiner, leg alignment, head and neck alignment, shoulder imbalance, transmission of the body weight to feet, and foot mechanics should be noticed. The feet of the subject are then placed with the heels about two inches apart, and each subject in turn curls the trunk forward with the head, shoulders, and arms relaxed. He reaches down until his fingers are about two feet from the floor and then returns slowly to standing position. The examiner should keep his eyes on a level with the back of the subject, noting any protrusions of one side of the rib cage or a twisting of the back. Either of these indicates muscular imbalance of the back.

As the subject turns to the left and right, notice is taken of evidence of kyphosis, lordosis, flat back, head misalignment, and hyperextension of the knees. The back view should be checked for evidence of hip imbalance and another check made for shoulder imbalance, neck and head misalignment, and faulty foot mechanics.

To make an evaluation of the walking mechanics, the examiner should observe the subjects walking toward him, away from him, and parallel to him. Observations should be made of toeing, leg alignment, use of the foot in heel-ball-toe action, pronation, and movements of the trunk.

The subject's rating on each examination can be recorded on a mimeographed form like the one in Figure 54.

DIAGNOSTIC POSTURE TEST.   Those who are screened out as needing postural work beyond that given in regular class should be examined by a physician before the remedial exercises begin. To assist the doctor in making his recommendations for the kind and extent of activity, diagnostic posture tests may be administered. There are several types. Two of the most effective are the evaluation of postural photographs and anthropometric measurements of the body. Procedures for these tests may be found in test and measurement textbooks. The tests are relatively complex and not recommended for general class testing.

Some schools make a silhouette of each student as a graphic record of his posture. The silhouette, because it shows the student so well his own postural errors, can be a very successful motivator for posture improvement. A series of silhouettes make an excellent record of progress.

The teacher may be able to secure the assistance of the school photography club in making the silhouettes. The process is relatively simple. A bed sheet or similar large piece of material is tacked to a frame to form a screen about 7½ by 3 feet. In a semidark room a light is placed behind the screen so that it will focus on the back of the screen. The subject stands in front of the screen wearing a swimming suit. The picture is taken against the screen.

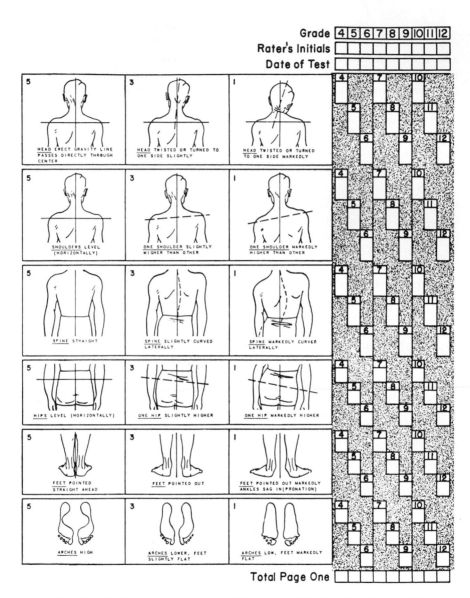

FIGURE 54.   New York posture rating chart. (Vannier and Fait, Teaching Physical Education in Secondary Schools, 3rd Ed.)

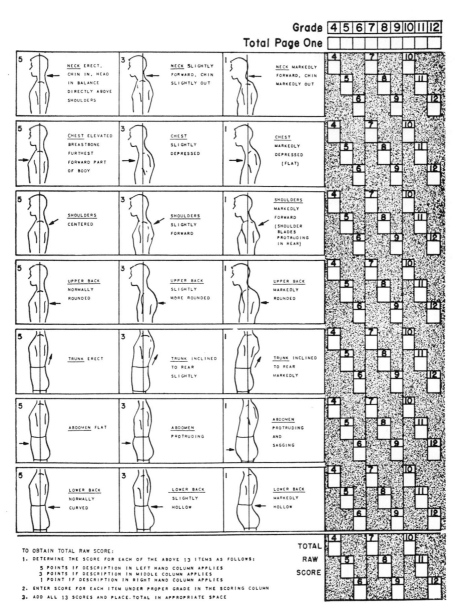

FIGURE 54. *Continued.*

EQUIPMENT

The following items are extremely useful in presenting exercises and activities for the improvement of body mechanics:
(1) free wall space, to flatten the back in standing position;
(2) full-length mirrors;
(3) individual mats;
(4) padded plinths;
(5) pulley weights;
(6) weights;
(7) stall bars and benches.

THE PROGRAM

After the students have been selected for the adapted activity and the medical diagnosis and recommendations are in the hands of the teacher, a conference should be arranged with each student. The body mechanics which need improvement are explained to the student, as are the adjustments and adaptations of activities which are necessary. The student should also be given a clear idea of the improvement which might be expected. The exercise program is then planned with the student, based upon his special needs and his interests. He must be informed about the amount of exercise which is required and the danger signals of too much or improper kinds of exercise. The limitations placed upon him by the examining physician should be explained to him.

For older age groups, a list of activities can be mimeographed, with descriptions of how the activities are performed. The specific exercises for each individual can be checked on this list. A demonstration of the exercises should be given and the possible errors pointed out. The use of special equipment such as mirrors, stall bars, weights, and wall pulleys should be demonstrated and explained. Students above the junior high school level may be permitted to work on their own after this briefing, while the teacher moves about the room to check on individuals. For younger age groups, more direct supervision should be given. For the best possible instruction, the class size should be limited to eight to ten.

It should be emphasized that postural exercises are of little avail if the student does not want to improve his posture. The teacher should continually seek ways to motivate him. An understanding by the student of his needs and the improvement that may be expected is one of the most effective of all motivators.

It is not expected that the time provided in physical education classes is sufficient to enable much significant change to occur in the quality of the body mechanics. Once the student is aware of his problem and knows what can be done for it, he should be encouraged to supplement class activity with work outside the class.

Work in body mechanics should not be done at the expense of partici-

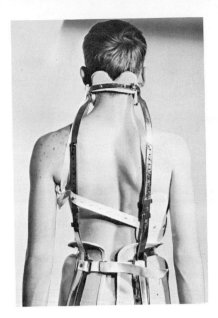

FIGURE 55.   The Milwaukee brace.

pation in other physical education experiences. Additional work in other physical education activities is a necessity in many cases to insure optimum development in organic efficiency and social adjustment. The activities must, of course, be selected with care, particularly for those with severe problems. Reinforcing this concept, Blount and Moe,[11] in speaking of children under treatment for scoliosis with the Milwaukee brace (Fig. 55), state: "Vigorous games such as volleyball, tennis, and bicycle riding are encouraged. . . . Patients (wearing the brace) need not be excused from physical education at school if the authorities will include only the parts of the program that are acceptable."

For a person to assume good posture, he must first know what constitutes good posture for him. In attempting to assume good posture, one who has poor posture is likely to throw his head and shoulders too far back. This is a strained position, and it is no wonder that he cannot maintain it. Before he can achieve a better position, he must first be taught the proper body alignment for his body build. To introduce the student to the new position he should be shown how to assume the desired standing posture with:

(1) the head balanced on neck, neither thrown back nor thrust out, chin slightly tucked in;

(2) the shoulders spread as wide as possible, not thrown back;

(3) the breast bone held up rather than the chest thrown out;

[11]Walter P. Blount and John H. Moe: "Non-Operative Treatment of Scoliosis With the Milwaukee Brace." Milwaukee, W. P. Blount, (2040 West Wisconsin Avenue), 1964, p. 12.

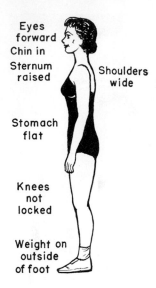

Eyes
forward
Chin in
Sternum
raised

Shoulders
wide

Stomach
flat

Knees
not
locked

Weight on
outside
of foot

FIGURE 56.   Efficient posture.

(4) the pelvis placed under the trunk;

(5) the knees slightly bent, not locked.

This standing position should be one of ease; it should not be strained or difficult to maintain. This position should be assumed frequently and checked for the ease with which it is held.

Postural exercises are designed to strengthen the muscles that are involved in maintaining the correct posture and in stretching their antagonists. Exercise is, of course, to be undertaken only after determining that the deviation is functional and all pathological causes have been overruled.

Exercising should be moderate in the beginning and the work load gradually increased, until the desired results are achieved or it has become obvious that exercise is not going to be effective. Weak muscles will require a very small amount of exercise, while their antagonists that have shortened will not allow a wide range of movement and hence should not be overly stretched in the beginning.

As has been pointed out, the spinal column may compensate for an overcurve by curving in the opposite direction in another area of the spine. In the case of kyphosis, there is usually an increased curve in the lumbar area. When this is so and exercise is given for the round back, care should be taken that the movement does not increase the size of the lumbar curve. The same precaution must be taken with the exercises that are given for forward head and round shoulders and back to avoid increasing the lumbar curve.

The preventive and corrective exercises that follow are frequently suggested for use in postural work. They are divided into three groups: mild, moderate, and strenuous. These are very broad categories, and some exercises do not belong exclusively to group because so much depends on how vigorously the individual performs them. Those exercises for scoliosis that are asymmetrical (exercising only one side of the body) should not be given except under the direction of a physician; they are identified with an asterisk.

PREVENTION AND CORRECTION OF THE FORWARD HEAD

Light Exercises:
1. Assume correct standing position and place light object on head. Walk with weight balanced on head and chin held in.
2. Rotate head in circle with chin held in. The forward movement is relatively passive; backward movement is more forceful.
3. Lie supine on mat; force head down on mat while chin is held in. Do not increase the lumbar curve.
4. Stand with back to wall, heels 2 to 3 inches from the wall. Press the back of the head against the wall with chin held down. Do not increase the amount of curve in the lumbar area.
Moderate Exercises:
1. Interlace fingers behind head, pull down with arms, and push back with head.
2. Throw the head back as far as possible, keeping chin in contact with the muscles in the muscles in the back of the neck.
3. Lying in prone position, raise head as high as possible, keeping chin tucked to chest. (Not recommended when lordosis is present.)
Strenuous Exercises:
1. On the back in a reverse hook position, arch up on back of neck, bearing weight upon the head, hip, and feet. (Not recommended when lordosis is present.)
2. A helper stands in front and locks his hands around subject's head. Helper pulls the head down while subject attempts to push the head back.
3. See exercise for neck extensor with the use of weights (page 278). In using this exercise for the forward head, keep the chin tucked as much as possible.

PREVENTION AND CORRECTION OF ROUND SHOULDERS, ROUND BACK, AND PROTRUDING SHOULDER BLADES

Light Exercises:
1. Stand with feet slightly apart and fists clenched. Cross the arms in front and fling them upward and backward behind the head. Raise up on toes as arms are flung backward.
2. Raise the arms at the sides until they are parallel to the floor. Hold

the palms up. Move the arms with moderate speed so that the hands describe a small circle backward, downward, forward, and upward.

3. Raise elbows to shoulder level, clasp hands and pull, with each arm resisting the other.

4. On the back in a hook position with hands at the side, palms up, move the arms horizontally to a position over the head and return to original position. Do not increase the curve in the lumbar area.

5. Lying supine on a narrow bench with knees bent, feet on floor, grasp dumbbell or weight in each hand. Extend arm sideward, allowing weight of dumbbell to stretch muscles of chest. Bend elbows and return to original position. Do not increase the amount of curve in the lumbar area.

6. Stand in a corner and place a hand on each side of the corner, shoulder height, with arms parallel to floor. Try to touch nose to corner, keeping back straight but allowing elbows to bend.

Moderate Exercises:

1. Lying prone, hands clasped behind the back, raise the head and shoulders off the mat. Keep lower back straight.

2. Lying prone, extend arms over head. Raise head, trunk, and arms, arching upper back. Keep lower back straight.

3. Interlock fingers behind back in lumbar area. Press elbows down and back, trying to bring elbows together. Head is held up. Do not sway lower back.

4. With hands well spread, grasping wand, raise hands overhead. Wand is moved back over the head as far as possible while the arms are kept straight. Do not sway lower back.

5. Lie supine on mat with pad under shoulders and fingers laced behind neck. Helper kneels at the head, grasps subject's elbows, and presses downward slowly.

6. Standing with arms at side, move shoulders in circle by first shrugging them then forcing them backward and dropping them to original position.

Strenuous Exercises:

1. Lie supine and place the hands under the neck; inhale and raise the shoulders off the floor. The head, elbows, hips, and legs remain in contact with the floor. Avoid arching the small of the back. Exhale and return to original position.

2. Sit on the floor. Place the feet in front and the hands behind the body. Raise the weight of the body on the hands and feet and walk forward, backward, and/or sideways.

3. Sitting on the floor, interlock fingers behind the neck, arms parallel with the floor. Helper places knee in back, grasps elbows, and pulls.

4. Perform straight-arm hang bar on rings.

5. Grasping dumbbells or weights in each hand, bend at waist, raise arms to the side, and bring parallel to the body. Return to original position.

6. Lying in supine position with helper holding feet, clasp hands at the small of the back, raise trunk, while pushing on back with hands. (Not recommended when lordosis is present.)

7. See exercises for trapezius, serratus, anterior, and rhomboids with weights (pages 279–281).

PREVENTION AND CORRECTION OF LORDOSIS

Mild Exercises:

1. Standing with feet spread, bend forward at the hips, keeping knees straight with arms hanging down between legs. Relax with bouncing movements; bob the trunk up and down.

2. Tilt the pelvis forward; rotate around and around as in hula dancing. Make a rather passive movement in tilting the pelvis backward since this will increase the lumbar curve.

3. Lie in the supine position. Attempt to force the small of the back to the floor by rotating the lower part of the pelvis forward.

4. In hook position on back, contract abdominal muscles and press lumbar region to the floor.

Moderate Exercises:

1. With feet together, bend forward at the hips, keeping knees straight with arms hanging down between the legs. Bouncing from hips, touch floor. Hold three seconds.

2. Stand as above but spread feet. Touch first between legs, return to original position, then touch on the outside of right foot and then outside of left foot.

3. In supine position, raise knees to chest.

4. On hands and knees, tuck pelvic area in so as to flatten the back. Hold for count of five. Return to original position. Avoid extreme arching of the back when returning to original position.

Strenuous Exercises:

1. Lying in supine position, raise both knees to chest, Stretch both legs into the air. Return to knees on chest position.

2. In a sitting position with knees straight and feet apart, reach forward and grasp ankles and pull trunk forward several times.

3. Lying in a hook position, draw knees up to chest, grasp shins, and pull. Hold for three counts.

4. In a prone position, arms extended to the sides with palms up, raise head and shoulders. At the same time forcibly contract abdominal muscles to prevent lumbar curve from increasing.

Note: Exercises that exaggerate the lumbar curve should be avoided by those with lordosis.[12] Exercises such as back bending, leg raises (lying on

---

[12]Charles L. Lowman and Carl H. Young: *op. cit.*, pp. 173–176.

the back and lifting both legs), and the straight-arm pullover in weight training are contraindicated for those with weak abdominals who are subject to hollow back.

PREVENTION AND CORRECTION OF FLAT BACK

Mild Exercises:

1. On knees, place forehead on floor; rotate hips to increase lumbar curve.

2. Tilt the pelvis backward; rotate around. Make a rather passive movement in tilting the pelvis forward and forceful in tilting backward.

Moderate Exercises:

1. Stand with back against wall; push shoulders against wall and force hips away from wall.

2. Interlock fingers behind back in lumbar area. Press elbows down and back, trying to bring elbows together. Sway in at the back.

Strenuous Exercises:

1. Lie prone and place the hands behind the neck; raise the shoulders off the floor. Arch the back, keeping hips in contact with floor.

2. In a hook position, arch the back, taking the weight on the head and feet.

CORRECTION OF SCOLIOSIS: **C** CURVE

Note: These exercises are for **C** curve to the left; if curve is to the right the exercises should be reversed.

Mild Exercises:

1. Hang from a bar or rings by the hands with the arms fully extended. (This exercise is mild, moderate, or strenuous, depending upon the time the position is held.)

*2. Standing with hands on hips, stretch the left arm down at the side and push down hard. Avoid bending body toward left side.

*3. Standing, facing the stall bars, stretch left arm forward and grasp the opposite stall bar. Raise the right arm overhead and stretch.

*4. Standing with hands on hips, raise the right arm forward, upward, and overhead; raise the left arm sideward to shoulder height. Then raise on tiptoe and lift leg sideward and stretch the whole body. Return to original position.

*5. Standing with hands on hips, stretch the right arm up overhead and press the left hand against ribs at point which forces the spine into the best position.

Moderate Exercises:

*1. Stand with feet slightly apart. Trunk should be inclined forward. Place the right hand back of the neck and the left hand well up against ribs. Bend to left and push in with left hand. Avoid letting right elbow come forward.

*2. Sit on stool with hands on hips. Stretch right leg back of stool, resting foot on toes. Stretch right arm up and left arm back. Keep trunk on line with right leg.

*3. Standing with hands on hips, charge forward with the left foot, keeping right foot back and turned so that the sole rests on the floor. Raise right arm forward and upward. Stretch left arm back. Do not drop the head. Keep trunk in a line with the rear leg.

*4. Standing with hands on hips, charge forward with the left foot. Turn right foot and keep it on the floor. Raise right arm forward and upward. Stretch left arm down and back. Bend forward and touch the floor with the right hand as far out in front of the left foot as can be reached. Keep trunk in a line with the rear foot.

Hint to instructor: Exercise 4 is very much like the preceding one, but the final stretch to touch the floor makes it more difficult. Give exercise 3 first, and when that can be done easily, go on to 4.

Strenuous Exercises:

*1. Hang on stall bars with face toward bars and right arm high.

*2. Face the stall bars, the right hand grasping the top bar, the left hand the second bar, the feet resting on a tool or lower bar. Hang down on the arms and stretch right leg over stool or bar.

*3. Hanging with back to stall bars with right arm high, bend and raise left knee.

*4. Lie on plinth with right knee bent over end, left knee bent, and left foot on plinth; left arm is under the back, right arm bent with elbow at waist. Helper grasps wrist of student's right arm pulling sideward while student resists. When arm is up, student must relax and helper stretches to count of five. Student then brings arm to first position while helper resists.

EXERCISES FOR SCOLIOSIS: S CURVE

Note: These exercises are for **S** curve with left dorsal and right lumbar curve; if curves are opposite, exercise positions should be reversed.

Mild Exercises:

1. Hang from a bar or rings by the hands with the arms fully extended. (This exercise is mild, moderate, or strenuous, depending upon the time the position is held.)

2. Sit on floor with legs straight, keeping back erect. Sit in this position for a short time, relax, assume it again.

3. Lying on floor, draw knees up to chest. Clasp hands firmly around knees and hold this position for one minute.

4. With hands on hips, bend forward from hips until back is flat. Hold head up.

*5. Sit astride chair facing back, hands on neck. Bend to left side and come to straight position. Bend only in the dorsal area.

*6. In a supine position with hands on neck, extend right arm upward and at same time stretch left leg across body.

*7. Lying prone, stretch right arm over head and at the same time stretch left arm downward and across back. Hold this position one minute.

*8. Place on hips, shift weight to right leg, and at the same time stretch up.

Moderate Exercises:

1. Lying prone on table, feet held firmly by helper, clasp hands behind back, straighten arms, and at the same time raise body from the table as far as possible.

*2. Place pad under each knee. Assume position for creeping on hands and knees. Stretch the right arm forward and at the same time slide left knee forward. Stretch left arm forward and slide the right knee forward. Creep in a circle to the left.

*3. Stand erect with feet apart, arms extended sideward. Twist trunk backward to right, trying to touch right toe with left hand. Keep knees straight and return to erect position each time.

*4. Sit astride chair facing back, hands on neck. As helper places knee on convexity of upper curve and grasps elbow, bend sideward over helper's knee.

*5. Same as exercise 4 but against lower curve.

Strenuous Exercises:

1. Stand at bar which comes just to hips. Place hands on bar, push down, stretch spine as much as possible. If possible, lift body weight off floor.

2. Lying supine, feet held firmly, clasp hands in front. Slowly come to the sitting position.

3. Lying supine, feet held firmly by helper, slide body over the edge of the table about half way. Slowly come to the sitting position.

*4. Facing bars, grasp bars firmly with one or both hands as directed; Right hand should be on or two bars above left hand. Slide feet slowly to right side as directed until body hangs in a curved position.

*5. Lie supine with buttocks against wall, hips flexed, knees straight, hands at side. Drop one leg, flexing knee and hip, keeping ankle straight. Straighten leg, sliding it up on the wall. Repeat until the motion of riding a bicycle is secured.

CORRECTION OF MISALIGNMENT OF FEET AND WEAK ARCHES.   In most cases of weak arches, the condition has been developing over a period of time. Poor standing and walking habits may be so thoroughly ingrained into the movement pattern that it will take a period of time to develop the strength of the muscles and relearn proper skills of standing and walking Furthermore, the plantar muscles of the feet are difficult to provide adequate exercises for, and so the feet respond slowly to corrective exercise. Any exercise program undertaken must be continued over a period of time to be of any value.

Prevention of foot problems by exercises is much easier than the correction of foot deviation. The following exercises are for strengthening the muscles that aid in maintaining the longitudinal arch. A transverse arch disorder does not generally respond to exercise and should be treated by the proper medical personnel.

Lowman and Young[13] believe that foot exercises that consist of rising on the toes or walking on the toes should not be performed by those who have weak arches because this kind of exercise shortens the calf muscles and throws additional stress on the balls of the feet.

Light Exercises:

1. Stand with feet slightly apart, press toes against floor, and attempt to rotate the knees inwardly to lift the arches of the feet.

2. In a sitting position, cross one leg over the other. Circle foot, first in, then up, out, and down.

Moderate Exercises:

1. In standing or sitting position, curl the toes as if to grasp the floor. Hold in isometric contraction for a brief period of time. The base of the first phalange (big toe) is not lifted off the floor.

Strenuous Exercises:

1. In a sitting position, place the toes on the edge of a towel. Curl the toes so as to pull the towel under the feet. Do not raise the heel, and keep the base of the big toe on the floor throughout the exercise.

2. Sit on the floor with the knees bent and the balls of the feet touching each other, with the heels slightly apart. Draw the feet toward the body keeping the balls of the feet together and the heels apart.

Note: Exercises should not be given to those with painful feet. These students should be referred to the proper medical personnel.

ELEMENTARY SCHOOL ACTIVITIES

Posture difficulties owing to the improper use of muscles are not as prevalent or obvious in children of elementary school age as in older children. However, exercises are much more effective in overcoming postural deviations if they are given before the improper posture becomes well established. Consequently, body mechanics exercises should be included in the physical education program for young children.

As with children who have less than physical fitness, it is usually wiser not to segregate from the regular class those who need special exercises in body mechanics. Such students can usually be accommodated in the regular class by providing special activity designed to meet their special needs.

[13]*Ibid.*, pp. 174–176.

The best method of doing this is through the use of games[14] in which those who need special exercises perform a type of activity which provides this exercise while others perform another activity. Games, contests, and relays have the additional advantage of providing the strong motivation so often lacking in the performance of exercise as such. A few activities are presented here as examples of the types of games or contests which can be devised from various body mechanics exercises:

1. Mimicking the giraffe. The children stretch their bodies to make them tall like the giraffe by reaching high with the arms and rising on tip-toes. Purpose: to strengthen postural muscles generally (not to be used by those with arch difficulties).

2. Eagle and mice. One student is chosen as the eagle; the others are mice. The eagle spreads his arms to the sides and rotates them back, then up and forward. He pursues the mice, trying to catch them while rotating the arms in this manner. The game may be modified so that all must "fly" in which case the mice become sparrows. Purpose: to strengthen muscles in upper back and stretch chest muscles.

3. Follow the leader. The leader executes various body mechanics exercises. Purpose: see exercises for specific postural difficulties.

4. Seesaw. Two students face each other in a sitting position with the legs extended. They grasp each other's hands and place their feet together. Keeping the knees straight, one pulls the other until he is raised off the floor. Then the procedure is reversed. Purpose: to strengthen muscles of the upper back.

5. Relays using the crab walk, seal walk, or measuring worm walk. The class is divided into two or more separate lines. The first one in each line "walks" to specified goal and returns to his line, where he touches the first one in line and then goes to the end of the line. The one who has been touched takes his turn and so on through the entire line. The line which finishes first is the winner. Purpose: crab walk—to strengthen back muscles: seal walk—to increase lumbar curve in flat back; measuring worm walk—to decrease curve in lumbar area.

6. Crab-walk ball. Using the rules of kick ball with the distances between goals shortened, the ball is played with the feet while all players are using the crab walk. Purpose: to strengthen muscles of the upper back.

7. Basketball with the feet. Using a wastebasket or similar receptacle as the basket, the students attempt to toss a basketball or volleyball into the basket with their feet from a sitting position on the floor 6 to 10 feet from the basket. The ball must be grasped by the soles of the feet. Purpose: to strengthen muscles of the longitudinal arch.

8. Ball-passing overhead relay. Two or more teams can participate. Teams form a straight line by sitting cross-legged on the floor. The first player in line passes a basketball over his head with his two hands, keeping

[14]For description of basic skill games see Chapter 16.

his elbows as straight as possible. The next one in line receives and passes it on. The last one in the line runs forward with the ball and, sitting down, passes the ball back. When the one who started the game again becomes the first in line, the game is completed. The first team to complete the game is the winner. Purpose: to strengthen muscles of the upper back.

9. Over and under ball-passing relay. Two or more teams can participate. The teams form a straight line. The first one in line passes the ball between his legs to the second person who receives it and passes it over his head to the next one in line. The ball is passed, alternating the over and under pass. The first line to complete the relay is the winner. Purpose: to strengthen muscles of the upper back and decrease curve in lumbar area.

10. Overhead ball passing with the feet. Two or more teams may be formed, with the members of each team in a straight line, sitting down with the legs extended. The first player in line takes the volleyball between the feet and rolling backward, keeping the knees straight, passes the ball to the person behind him, who takes it in his hands and places it between his feet and passes it back in the same manner. The last person in line receives the ball, runs forward to the front of the line, sits down, and passes the ball with his feet to the one behind. The game is completed when the one who started the game returns to the head of the line. Purpose: to decrease curve in lumbar area.

QUESTIONS

1. What influences help to shape a concept of good posture in a given period of history?
2. Explain what is meant by good posture.
3. What are the values of maintaining good posture?
4. Name the factors that influence the posture one assumes.
5. Discuss the causes of poor body mechanics. Of these causes, which ones can the physical educator do the most to alleviate?
6. Compare structural and functional postural deviations.
7. What are the common postural deviations and their causes?
8. What is the difference between "screening" and "diagnostic" posture tests?
9. Briefly describe how the equipment listed on page 314 is used in postural work.
10. Make a list of methods or techniques that may be utilized in motivating students to improve their posture.
11. Compare the suggested standing position described in this chapter with that of the most erect position one can assume. Which position makes a better appearance? Which is the most efficient? Explain.
12. List the precautions that must be taken when administering exercises to students with kyphosis, lordosis, and weak arches.

SELECTED READINGS

Broer, Marion R.: *Efficiency of Human Movement.* Philadelphia, W. B. Saunders Co., 1960.
Fait, Hollis F., *et al.: Manual of Physical Education Activities,* ed. 2. Philadelphia, W. B. Saunders Co., 1961.
Kraus, Hans, and Raab, Wilhelm: *Hypokinetic Disease.* Springfield, Ill., Charles C. Thomas, Publisher, 1961.
Lowman, Charles L. and Young, Carl H.: *Postural Fitness.* Philadelphia, Lea & Febiger, 1960.

Mathews, Donald K.: *Measurement in Physical Education.* ed 2. Philadelphia, W. B. Saunders Co., 1963.

Meyers, Carlton R., and Blesh, T. Erwin: *Measurement in Physical Education.* New York, The Ronald Press Company, 1962.

Phelps, Winthrop M., *et al.: The Diagnosis and Treatment of Postural Defects,* ed. 2. Springfield, Ill., Charles C Thomas, Publisher, 1956.

Rathbone, Josephine L.: *Teach Yourself to Relax.* Englewood Cliffs, N.J., Prentice-Hall, Inc., 1957.

Scott, Myrtle G.: *Analysis of Human Motion,* ed. 2. New York, Appleton-Century-Crofts, Inc., 1963.

Selye, Hans: *The Stress of Life.* New York, McGraw-Hill Book Co., Inc., 1965.

Stafford, George T., and Kelly, Ellen D.: *Preventive and Corrective Physical Education,* ed. 4. New York, The Ronald Press Company, 1965.

Steinhaus, Arthur H.: *Toward an Understanding of Health and Physical Education.* Dubuque, Iowa, William C. Brown Company, Publisher, 1963.

Wells, Katherine F.: *Posture Exercise Handbook.* New York, The Ronald Press Company, 1963.

25

A DEVELOPMENTAL PROGRAM FOR PHYSICAL FITNESS

Physical fitness as an objective of physical education has always been an important concern, but the amount of emphasis given to it in our physical education program has fluctuated with the times. Except for the war years, when physical conditioning was being stressed, physical fitness received scant attention from the turn of the century until the mid-1950's. Renewed concern about physical fitness was brought into sharp focus in 1955, when Kraus and Hirschland[1] published the results of their testing of European and American children in certain physical activities. By comparison to their European counterparts, American children were shown to be far inferior in physical performance.

The immediate response to these findings was a renewed interest in the promotion of physical fitness and a re-emphasis on physical fitness as an objective of physical education. At the instigation of President Dwight D. Eisenhower, the President's Council on Youth Fitness was created to spearhead the promotion of physical fitness throughout the country.

When President John F. Kennedy assumed office, he took immediate

[1]Hans Kraus and Ruth P. Hirschland: "Muscular Fitness and Orthopedic Disability." *New York State Journal of Medicine*, January 15, 1954, pp. 212–215.

steps to continue the promotion of physical fitness begun by his predecessor. In 1960 he wrote, "The physical vigor of our citizens is one of America's most precious resources. If we waste and neglect this resource, if we allow it to dwindle and grow soft, then we will destroy much of our ability to meet the great and vital challenge which confronts our people."[2] The American people caught the spirit of this statement and responded with enthusiastic support of various organizational efforts to promote a higher level of physical fitness. Today, physical fitness is an important objective of the physical education program, and a significant portion of the program is directed toward achieving that objective. It is of special interest that, in the present endeavor to plan a program of physical education activities which will make maximum contribution to fitness, the other contributions which physical education can make to the mental and emotional growth of youngsters are not being lost sight of.

THE NATURE AND COMPONENTS OF PHYSICAL FITNESS

What is physical fitness? From the physiological viewpoint, physical fitness may be said to be the ability of the body to adapt to and recover from strenuous exercise. This definition implies a general well-being of the body and a capacity for vigorous work. In personal terms it is a reflection of one's ability to work and play with vigor and pleasure, without undue fatigue, and with sufficient energy left for meeting unforeseen emergencies.[3]

Total physical fitness has many components. In a factor analysis study, C. H. McCloy[4] isolated 36 different factors involved in motor performance. Among these were muscular strength, speed of muscular contraction, cardiorespiratory endurance, muscular endurance, flexibility, and agility. However, in a more recent factor analysis study, Fleishman[5] reported isolating three different kinds of primary strength factors, dynamic, explosive, and static, and two different types of flexibility, extent and dynamic. Other factors isolated were: gross body equilibrium, balance with visual cues, and speed of movement. Although he did not use a cardiovascular endurance test in his factor analysis, Fleishman recognized that such a factor probably exists.

To understand the nature of each of these factors or components of fitness and its special contribution to total physical fitness, each must be examined in detail.

[2]John F. Kennedy: "The Soft American." *Sports Illustrated*, December 26, 1960, p. 15.
[3]President's Council on Physical Fitness: *Adult Physical Fitness.* Washington, D.C., Superintendent of Documents, 1963, p. 5.
[4]Charles H. McCloy and Norma D. Young: *Tests and Measurements in Health and Physical Education*, ed. 3. New York, Appleton-Century-Crofts, Inc., 1954, pp. 3–13.
[5]Edwin A. Fleishman: *The Structure and Measurement of Physical Fitness.* Englewood Cliffs, N.J., Prentice-Hall, Inc., 1964, *passim*.

STATIC STRENGTH.   Static strength is the amount of force which can be exerted by a particular muscle. Strength is related to age and sex. In males, strength increases rapidly from the ages of 12 to 19, at a rate proportionate to the increase in weight of the body. After 19 years of age there is a decline in the acceleration of strength increase until the age of 30, after which there is a slow decrease. The growth in strength of the female parallels somewhat the growth of strength in males, except that the growth spurt starts approximately at the age of 9.[6]

Evidence indicates that the emotional state of the individual is a factor affecting the strength of muscles. Excitement may intensify the nervous discharge to the muscles, as well as liberate adrenalin, which increases the strength and endurance of the muscle.[7] Other factors which influence the amount of strength which a muscle can exert are its mechanical advantage (attachment of the muscle to its lever) and the extent to which it is stretched.[8] Still another factor believed to affect the muscle's strength is exercise.

To increase strength through exercise, the muscle or muscles involved must perform more work per unit of time than is customary. This increased work load and the resultant increase in muscular strength and size are known as the *overload principle*. The term overload may be slightly misleading, since it does not necessarily refer to a work load that is at or near capacity but refers to any work that is more than usual for the area of the body involved.

EXPLOSIVE STRENGTH OR POWER.   Explosive strength has been called power by some authors.[9] It is the ability to release force at a specific moment. A release of force by the muscles involves both speed of contraction and strength of the muscle. Speed and strength must be combined to get power. Fitness for such activities as throwing a ball, jumping, football punting, and sprinting requires power.

DYNAMIC STRENGTH OR MUSCULAR ENDURANCE.   Dynamic strength, which is also known as muscular endurance, is not directly related to cardiorespiratory efficiency but is closely related to the strength of the muscle.[10] With all other things being equal, a stronger muscle can perform longer than a weaker muscle. This is why strength of the shoulder girdle and the arms can be estimated by testing the number of times a person can raise his body up in pull-ups.

SPEED OF MUSCULAR MOVEMENT.   Speed of body movement depends upon speed of muscular contraction. Contraction of a muscle depends

[6]Lawrence E. Morehouse and Augustus T. Miller: *Physiology of Exercise,* ed. 3. The C. V. Mosby Co., 1959, pp. 195–196.

[7]F. A. Compos *et al.:* "Some Conditions Affecting the Capacity for Prolonged Muscular Work." *American Journal of Physiology,* Vol. 87, 1928, p. 680.

[8]Arthur C. Guyton: *Function of the Human Body.* Philadelphia, W. B. Saunders Co., 1959, p. 284.

[9]Charles H. McCloy and Norma D. Young: *op. cit.,* p. 66.

[10]W. W. Tuttle *et al.:* "Relation of Maximum Grip Strength to Grip Strength Endurance." *Journal of Applied Physiology,* Vol. 2, 1950, p. 663.

on the energy liberated during certain chemical reactions in the muscles. It is believed that the rate of the liberation of energy limits speed of muscular contraction. Also, the nature of the molecules of the muscle may influence its speed of contraction. It has been postulated that the ability of molecules to rearrange themselves when the muscle is shortened is the factor involved.[11]

Factors that may influence an increase of the speed of muscular contraction are not completely understood. Inheritance is one factor; maturation is another. Practice of a specific muscular movement decreases the time involved in performing the movement. There is some question, however, whether practice can change the speed of muscular contraction or whether it is rather that improved coordination results in a faster movement. For example, a runner can increase his speed in running by improving his coordination to avoid the lateral sway of the body that decreases speed. How much, if at all, his practice to improve coordination influences the speed of muscular contractions is not known.

There is also some question as to whether or not speed should be classified as a factor of physical fitness. Faster performance does not result in more efficient movement because, actually, efficiency is decreased by faster movement. Speed is a factor in efficiency only if the activity requires maximum speed, as when a situation requires a player or worker to move from one spot to another in a limited amount of time. However, because of its importance to successful performance in sports, speed is generally included as a factor in physical fitness.

FLEXIBILITY.   Flexibility is the range of movement possible in any given joint. Fleishman[12] in his study considered flexibility as being of two types, extent and dynamic. The former is defined as the ability to flex or stretch the trunk and back muscles as far as possible in a forward, lateral, or backward direction, while the latter is defined as the ability to make repeated, rapid, flexing movements.

The range of movement in a joint is determined first by bone structure, as, for example, the hyperextension of the joint of the elbow is limited by the bone structure. Other factors limiting range of movement are the ligaments and muscles. The effectiveness of performance in many physical activities is influenced by the degree of flexibility of the total body or of specific joints. The execution of the swan dive is illustrative of a physical performance in which a lack of flexibility of the spinal column would hinder the ability to perform the skill. A person who can exert force over a longer range, which is possible for those having more flexibility, can generate more force. It is also believed by some authorities that a more flexible person expends less energy in performing

[11]Charles H. McCloy: "The Measurement of Speed in Motor Performance." *Psychometrika*, September, 1940, *passim*.
[12]Edwin A. Fleishman: *op. cit.*, p. 99

certain skills than one who has less flexibility, because energy need not be expended to overcome the limited range of motion.[13]

The range of movement of a joint can usually be extended by forcing the joint over a wider range little by little. This is the technique utilized if muscle shortening is the chief factor in the prevention of full range of movement.

BALANCE.   The ability to maintain total body balance with the eyes closed is called gross body equilibrium. The maintaining of body balance with the eyes open is known as balance with visual cues. There appear to be two varieties of each kind of balance, static and dynamic. Static balance is the ability to maintain balance while stationary; dynamic balance is the ability to do so while moving.

Good balance is important in the satisfactory performance of nearly all movements required by everyday life and by all sport skills, although some sports such as gymnastics and swimming place a higher premium on good balance than do other sports. Not much is known about the ways in which balance can be improved. Practice of skills requiring balance does result in improved balance as related to a particular skill.

AGILITY AND COORDINATION.   In Fleishman's[14] factor analysis, speed in changing direction (agility) did not emerge as a separate factor; rather such performances were accounted for by an explosive strength factor.

Coordination, as well, did not appear as a separate factor. Coordination is not a general factor but appears to be specific to the skill performed. Coordination is the process by which the muscles are used correctly to perform a specific movement. It involves the ability to integrate several different factors and different kinds of movements into one single effective pattern. All the factors which are involved in motor coordination are not well understood.

Coordination involves the lower centers of the brain as well as the highest center. In the process of learning a skill, one needs to be aware of the required movement; therefore the highest level of the brain is involved. After sufficient practice, the integration of all the muscles to produce a specific action is relegated to a lower level of the brain. An expert basketball player may have learned dribbling skills so well that, in the process of dribbling in for a lay-up shot in a game situation, he is not consciously aware of all the muscular movement necessary for performance of the dribbling but is concentrating on other aspects of the game.

The structure of the neurons influences the quality of the coordination of the body and, because inheritance determines this structure to some extent, it may be said that muscular coordination is an inherited

---

[13]Charles H. McCloy: Unpublished mimeographed notes, University of Iowa, 1950.
[14]Edwin A. Fleishman: *op. cit.*, p. 99.

trait. This has given rise to the frequently expressed remark in regard to an individual's coordination that he "has it" or he "doesn't have it." Such an appraisal disregards the improvement in coordination which is possible through practice. Even very poor muscular coordination can be improved by means of exercises which emphasize the factors which constitute coordination.

Different movements involve different patterns of muscular movement. One may be well coordinated in shooting a basket but poorly coordinated in throwing a ball. How much transfer is there, then, of coordination developed for one skill to another skill?

If there is a similarity between the skills, some transfer may occur. For example, the skill of using the wrist in hitting a badminton bird is transferable to using the wrist in hitting a ball in squash. However, evidence is lacking to indicate that there is much transfer of coordination from one type of skill to a different type, even though nearly all the same muscles are involved, as in the case of the different skills of throwing of a football and making a smash in tennis.

RESULTS OF LOW PHYSICAL FITNESS

A person who is below the normal range in strength cannot perform the regular skills of his work and play because he is too weak. To take an example from play, the sub-strength tennis player cannot hold the racket with the regulation grip but must choke up on the handle because he is too weak to control the racket otherwise.

Less than normal endurance manifests itself in the inability to carry a normal work load or to participate in normal play without undue fatigue. Lack of endurance is a contributing factor to lack of interest in vigorous activities. It is also a hindrance in other areas of endeavor, as evidenced by lack of accomplishment in academic subjects and failure to utilize opportunities to develop social skills.

Lacking normal speed and power, an individual is hindered in performing specific types of motor movements. Success in such skills as running, jumping, and throwing is dependent upon sufficient power and speed.

Without a sufficient degree of flexibility, the range of movement is limited. This may be disadvantageous when an activity requires a wide range of movement. Moreover, when the range of movement is limited, the distance over which power can be exerted is cut down, and thus less total power is generated. A thrower who has a limited range of movement in the arm will not throw the ball as far using the same amount of strength, speed, and coordination as one who has a wide range of movement.

If coordination is subnormal, the individual cannot learn motor skills in a reasonable length of time. He will appear awkward and inefficient in the performance of skills. Coordination is fundamental to the learning and successful performance of all motor skills of work as well as play.

Experimental studies have indicated that students who have low scores on tests that measure factors of physical fitness have more social adjustment problems than those who have high scores.[15] The apparent reason for this is that the lack of physical skills has caused these children to withdraw from play and sport activities, and so they have been deprived of certain types of social contacts which are valuable to social development. Such withdrawal has a further disadvantage because it fosters further decrease in physical fitness. It cannot be assumed, in all cases of poor social adjustment coupled with low physical ability, that the latter has been the contributing factor. It is possible that the reverse is true or that neither contributed to the other.

There is a high relationship between certain factors of fitness and specific diseases. Strength and endurance are affected by such disorders as infected tonsils, cancer, ulcers, and certain communicable diseases.[16] However, it cannot be assumed that maintenance of strength and endurance serves as a prophylaxis for these diseases, for the disease is the contributing factor to loss of strength and endurance.

Lack of flexibility and strength in the back area and lack of flexibility in the hamstrings are causes of low back pain. It had been reported that approximately 80 per cent of patients suffering from low back pain who were found free from organic diseases improved when given systematic exercise designed to increase the flexibility and strength of the back and the flexibility of the hamstrings of the legs. The patients regressed when the exercise was reduced or discontinued.[17]

CAUSE OF LOW PHYSICAL FITNESS

There is a tendency on the part of some to think that there is only one cause of low physical fitness: lack of exercise. But there are many factors contributing to subnormal physical fitness. Among these are: physical defects or disorders; faulty nutrition; poor health practices, such as insufficient sleep and rest; psychological weakness, such as the lack of ability or desire to get optimum performance from the muscles involved; inherited factors which influence the development of physical efficiency; and lack of muscular activity. The physical educator must take all factors into consideration when planning a physical fitness pro-

[15]Harold E. Jones: *Motor Performance and Growth.* Berkeley, University of California Press, 1949. pp. 160–163.

[16]Donald K. Mathews: *Measurement in Physical Education,* ed. 2. Philadelphia, W. B. Saunders Co., 1963, pp. 55–56.

[17]Hans Kraus *et al.*: *Hypokinetic Disease.* Institute for Physical Medicine and Rehabilitation, New York University, Bellevue Medical Center, 1955, *passim.*

gram. Success in achieving improved physical fitness often depends upon ameliorating the influence of these factors.

TESTING FOR LOW FITNESS

Students suffering from injury or debilitating disease will frequently have lower physical fitness levels, not only in the area involved but also in total fitness, because of the tendency or necessity of withdrawal from strenuous activity. However, many students suffer from low physical fitness who are not handicapped in any other way. Extensive statistics showing incidence are lacking. Individual reports from several schools would indicate that 1 out of 15 students in elementary schools would benefit from individual attention to physical fitness; 1 out of 10 in high school; and 1 out of 5 in college.[18] This is not meant to infer that the majority of students would not benefit from special attention to physical fitness, but that this portion needs special help beyond that which is necessary for the average student.

Those who are in dire need of special work in the areas of strength, endurance, and coordination frequently stand out because of poor performance in class, so that it is easy to pick them out. There is the girl who puts her arms straight out and closes her eyes when a ball is thrown her way, and the boy who lags far behind the others in a short distance run. Watching students attempting to use various types of skills, the teacher is able to pick out those needing special help.

Tests may be used both for determining those who need help and for identifying specific areas of weakness. In selecting tests it must be kept in mind that there are many factors that make up physical fitness, and fitness for one activity does not necessarily mean total body fitness. It is obvious that the more factors which are tested, the more information can be obtained about the individual's total fitness.

To utilize physical fitness tests adequately, the nature of the test must be understood: what it measures, the relationship of what it measures to physical fitness, and what a specific score means. Moreover, if the scores are to have meaning, the test must be given exactly the same way each time for each subject. If norms are to be used, the test must be given in exactly the same way it was given to collect data for the norms.

MEASURING STATIC STRENGTH.   Static strength may be measured effectively with the manuometer, the back and leg dynamometer, and the tensiometer.

The *manuometer* measures grip strength. In the grip strength test, the subject places the convex edge of the manuometer between the first and second joints of the fingers, with the dial toward the palm, and squeezes it. He may use any movement he wishes except supporting the fist against an object.

[18]Hollis F. Fait: "Analysis of Fitness Test Scores of Selected Schools." Unpublished study, Storrs, Connecticut, Physical Efficiency Laboratory, University of Connecticut, 1965.

To measure the static strength of the back extensors, the subject stands on the *dynamometer* with the feet parallel, about six inches apart, and the toes about one inch from the front of the stand. To secure the proper adjustment of the bar, the subject stands erect with the hands hanging loosely in front of the thighs. The bar is connected to the chain at the tip of the subject's fingers. The subject bends forward slightly and grips the bar with one hand forward and the other backward. He lifts straight up, keeping the knees straight throughout the lift. The tester may place his hands over the subject's to prevent their slipping on the bar.

For the leg lift, the subject assumes the same position as for the back lift. A belt is used around the subject's hips to stabilize the bar. The grip is taken at the center of the bar with the palms down at a level just above the pubic bone. As the subject faces the tester in this position, the tester brings the belt around the lower portion of the sacrum to be attached to the right end of the handle and then brought back under the portion of the belt that is in the back. The subject, keeping the head up and the back straight, bends at the knees. The handle is hooked to the chain while the knees are flexed at about 135 degrees. The subject may grip the bar in the middle or at the ends of the bar. He lifts straight up.

A series of static strength tests using the *tensiometer* has been developed by Clarke. These tests are used chiefly in research work but are applicable for class work. Further information concerning the description and use of the tensiometer tests may be found in the reference.

Lifting the weight of the body in pull-ups, push-ups, sit-ups, dips, reverse sit-ups, and leg lifts can be used as a rough measurement of the static strength of the muscle group involved. These tests can separate the students in two categories only: those who can lift their weight in the test, and those who cannot.

MEASURING DYNAMIC STRENGTH.   Dynamic strength is frequently measured by pull-ups, dips, push-ups, sit-ups, leg lifts, and reverse sit-ups.

Pull-ups: To execute a pull-up, a bar which is at a height above the reach of the subject is grasped with the hands and the arms are completely extended, letting the body hand free. Taking the grip while standing on a stool and then stepping off it places the body in the right position. The bar can be grasped with the reverse or regular grip. In the reverse grip the palms face the head; in the regular grip the knuckles are toward the head. When the reverse grip is used, pull-ups are easier; approximately 2½ more pull-ups can be made.[19] The reverse grip should be used by younger children. The American Association for Health, Physical Education and Recreation[20] norms established for the pull-ups show that over

[19]Philip J. Rasch: "Effect of Position of Forearm on Strength of Elbow Flexion." *Research Quarterly*, 26, 1956, p. 333.

K. A. Provins and N. Slater: "Maximum Torque Exerted About the Elbow Joint," *Journal of Applied Physiology*, Vol. 7, 1955, p. 393.

[20]American Association for Health, Physical Education and Recreation, *Youth Fitness Test Manual*, rev. ed., Washington, D. C., 1965, p. 34.

25 per cent of the boys under 10 are unable to do one pull-up with a regular grip. The use of the reverse grip would reduce the number of failures, and hence the test would have greater discriminatory value. If rings are used instead of a bar, the arms will automatically twist to the most efficient position.

In doing the pull-up, the body is pulled up until the chin touches the bar or is even with the bar. The subject may not use his feet to kick up. The body is then lowered until the arms are straight. The subject continues raising and lowering his body until he can no longer continue. One point is scored for each pull-up.

A modified pull-up is sometimes used for girls. In a modified pull-up, the bar is lowered to chest height, so that in gripping the bar the body can be placed at a 45-degree angle to the floor with the arms fully extended. The knees and hips must remain straight during the pull-up. A bent-arm endurance hang has been used as a substitute for the modified pull-up, since the latter has lower objectivity and reliability and is not discriminating. For the bent-arm endurance hang, a stool is placed under the bar. A grip is taken on the bar with the palms out. The head is brought to the bar at the bridge of the nose just below the eyebrows and held there as the stool is removed. The score is the number of seconds that the subject is able to hold the position. Sometimes the hairline, chin, eyebrows, or end of the nose is used as the anchor point for the bar.

Studies by Fait[21] in developing a test for the Connecticut Association for Health, Physical Education and Recreation fitness battery indicated that anchoring at the forehead increased the number of failures by approximately 10 per cent, thereby decreasing the discriminating value of the test. Furthermore, placing the bar at the hairline was difficult because of the many different types of hair styles that girls wear. When the bar was anchored at the chin, the test had less reliability, owing to an inability to keep the head level and at the same angle in repetitions of the test. Anchoring at the tip of the nose was rejected because of possible unsanitary conditions created by testing one person after the other on the same bar.

Dips: Dips also measure arm and shoulder strength but do not measure the same muscles which are measured in pull-ups. The dips measure the antagonistic muscles of those involved in pull-ups. Consequently, the dips can be given in the same testing period as the pull-up or hang tests because the muscle involved will not be fatigued. However, since there is a high relationship between the flexors and extensors of the arm, it is not necessary to give both tests.[22] Generally dips can be executed only by older

[21]Hollis F. Fait: "The Endurance Hang." Unpublished study, Storrs, Conn., Physical Efficiency Laboratory, University of Connecticut, 1962.

[22]H. Brogden *et al.*: "A Factor Analysis of Measures of Physical Proficiency." *Personal Research Section Report 937*, Department of the Army, 1952, *passim*. See also Edwin A. Fleishman: *op. cit.*, p. 67.

boys. For the test, parallel bars are used, and the bars should be shoulder high. The subject mounts by grasping the bars and jumping up to take the weight on his arms. One point is scored for mounting successfully. He then dips to lower his body until the elbows of both arms form right angles. The point is noted by having a helper place his fist at the location. The subject must touch the fist each time he dips. One point is scored for each raising and lowering of the body.

Push-ups: The push-ups test approximately the same muscles involved in the dips. The subject performs the push-up in a prone position with his hands at least shoulder distance apart. The body is lowered, keeping a straight line from head to foot. Only the chin touches the floor. No sagging of any part of the body is permitted. Each full dip scores one point.

Girls who are very strong are able to do this type of push-up. For the other girls and for very young boys, a modification is made by making the knees the fulcrum rather than the toes. This is too easy for many girls and so may not be sufficiently selective. A second modification is possible with the use of a stall bar bench. The techniques of the regular push-up are used except the hands are placed on the bench and the chest is lowered to the bench. This test is more difficult, and many girls will be unable to score in this performance.

Sit-Ups: The sit-up test is performed the same by both boys and girls. The subject is supine with the legs straight and the feet slightly apart. The hands are clasped behind the head and the feet are held down. The subject rolls up to touch the right elbow to the left knee and then lowers the trunk to the floor. The trunk is raised again to touch the left elbow to the right knee. One point is counted for each time the subject sits up and touches the elbow to the knee. The knees may be bent if necessary to touch the elbows.

Sometimes sit-ups are given by having the subject cross his arms across the chest and bring his body up to a 90-degree angle. This makes the sit-up easier to perform. Sit-ups are made more difficult by having the subject bend his knees. The feet are held by the tester while the legs are in the bent position.

Leg Lift: The subject lies on his back, hands behind his neck, with his elbows held to the floor by an assistant. He raises his legs until they are vertical and then lowers them to the floor. The tester may hold his hand above the subject at ankle height when the legs are held vertically to keep the subject from bending his legs or failing to bring them completely to a vertical position. In the leg lift the hips maintain contact with the floor at all times. This test is usually timed for 20 seconds, and the number of times the legs are lifted during that time is the score.

Leg Raise: The subject is supine, with the hands behind the neck and the legs extended. He lifts his legs 10 inches off the floor with the knees held straight. The tester may hold his hands at a point 10 inches above the floor as a guide to the subject. The score is the number of seconds the subject holds his legs in this position.

Reverse Sit-Ups: The subject is prone with his hands behind his neck. An assistant holds the subject's feet down. The subject raises his head and chest and shoulders up as far as possible. The height is noted, and the subject returns to the original position. On the command "Go," the subject makes as many reverse sit-ups as possible in 20 seconds. The tester may hold his hand at the height the subject reached in the trial to insure that the subject lifts to his limit of flexibility each time. The score is the number of lifts in 20 seconds.

In Fleishman's study[23] it was pointed out that the ability to perform a dynamic strength test as fast as possible for 20 seconds depends on the same factor as that which determines the ability to hold a position as long as possible or do as many repetitions as possible. Therefore the three types of tests could be used interchangeably.

MEASURING POWER OR EXPLOSIVE STRENGTH.   The power of leg muscles relative to body weight can be measured by a vertical jump or a standing broad jump; the power of arm and shoulder muscles by the softball throw; agility by runs and dashes.

Vertical Jump: For the vertical jump the subject faces the wall and reaches over his head with both hands. The height of his reach is marked. The subject then turns his side to the wall, crouches, and jumps as high as possible with one hand touching the wall at the height of his jump. The difference between the reaching and jumping heights is the score. To eliminate the effects of coordination of the arm in the jump, the first measurement may be taken at the height of the head while the subject stands against the wall. The subject then jumps without the use of the arm in a preliminary jump. The tester places a yardstick vertically to the wall at the height of the jump. On subsequent jumps the tester adjusts the stick to the highest point reached. The score is taken when an accurate measurement is achieved.

Standing Broad Jump: The subject puts his toes on the line and then without preliminary movement of the feet jumps forward as far as possible. The score is the length of the jump measured from the line to the point nearest to which the subject landed.

Softball Throw: The power of certain muscles of the arm and shoulders is sometimes measured by the softball throw. It appears that skill is a more important factor in getting a good score in the softball throw than it is in the tests measuring explosive power that have already been described. However, Fleishman[24] found that the softball throw using a 15-inch ball and requiring the subject to keep his feet in place while throwing was highly related to the factor of explosive strength that was

[23]Fleishman: *op. cit.,* p. 64.
[24]*Ibid.,* pp. 67, 72.

isolated in his study. Fleishman's subjects were males, and among boys throwing is such a universally well-developed skill that it is likely that the power of the arm was more dominant in determining the distance thrown than the skill level attained. If this assumption is correct, the softball throw would not be as good a measurement for girls, since their skill in throwing is usually not as well developed.

There are two common ways of administering the softball throw. In one, the participant throws from between two lines 6 feet apart. The subject is allowed to run from the back line to the forward line while throwing. In the other method, the throw is made from a stationary position. The subject must keep his feet in place throughout the throw; no follow-through with the feet is allowed. The score in both cases is the distance the ball is thrown.

In his factor analysis, Fleishman[25] found no factor of agility or running speed as such; movements that require change of direction or short bursts of speed were highly related to explosive power. If this is true, the AAHPER shuttle run and the short dashes can be used as a measurement of explosive power.

Shuttle Run: For the shuttle run, two parallel lines are marked on the floor 30 feet apart. Two wooden blocks are placed behind one of the lines. The subject starts from behind the other line, runs to the blocks, picks up one, runs back to the starting line, and puts the block behind the line. He then runs back and picks up the second block, which he carries back across the starting line. The score is the time it takes to carry the two blocks over the starting line.

Short Dashes: In administering the 35-, 50-, or 60-yard dash, a standardized starting technique should be used to eliminate the influence of skill in starting, as follows: The back foot is placed parallel to a wall, or to a board 2 inches by 4 inches by 3 feet secured to the ground, if outdoors. The forward foot and the upper body are turned in the direction of the run. The knees are slightly bent, and the hands rest gently on the knees. The time as measured by a stop watch is the score.

MEASURING BALANCE.   To measure balance with the eyes closed, the stork stand or static balance test can be used. The subject places his hands upon his hips. One of the feet is brought up and placed against the inside of the knee. When the subject closes his eyes, a stop watch is started. The score is the number of seconds balance is maintained with the eyes closed.

Balancing on a beam is frequently used to measure static balance. The beam should be from ¾ to 1 inch wide. One foot is placed lengthwise on the beam. The other foot is raised off the floor. The time that the subject balances on the beam with his eyes closed constitutes his score.

[25]*Ibid.*, p. 99.

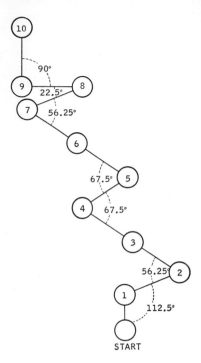

FIGURE 57. The layout for the Bass test of dynamic balance. Distance between the start and circle 1 is 18 inches. The distance between each of the other circles is 33 inches.

Dynamic balance with the eyes open can be measured by the Bass Test of Dynamic Balance.[26] This test is a good measurement of balance while moving for older children. For the testing, eleven circles each 8½ inches in diameter are drawn on the floor. The subject stands with his right foot in the starting circle and leaps into the second circle, landing on his left foot, and into the third circle on his right foot, and so on through the circles, with the feet alternating. The heel should not touch the floor in the landing. The subject must remain stationary in each circle 5 seconds before leaping to the next circle. The score for the entire test is 50 plus the number of seconds required to complete the test, minus three times the errors committed during the test. The errors are: (1) touching the heel to the floor, (2) moving the foot while standing in the circle, (3) hopping upon the supporting foot, (4) touching the floor outside the circle, (5) touching the floor with the other foot, (6) touching the floor with any other part of the body.

For very young children, dynamic balance may be tested by drawing a line 10 feet long on the floor. The child hops on one foot along the line to the end. The score is the number of times the child steps off the line. The center of the toes must always be on the line. Dynamic balance for young children may be tested by rail walking. A rail 2 inches wide is placed a few inches above the floor. The length of distance walked before stepping off is the score. Measurement is taken from the foot nearer the starting point.

MEASURING FLEXIBILITY.   The flexibility test most frequently administered is toe touching with knees straight, which measures the flexibility of the hamstring muscles. The subject stands erect, hands at his sides. With the feet together and the knees straight, he bends down slowly in an attempt to touch the floor with his finger tips. The subject is not permitted to bounce. The tester places his hands on the subject's knees to detect bending. A modification of this test which affords greater discrimination is placement of the subject on a stall bar bench to perform the test. This permits measurement of the distance beyond the toes which the subject can reach.

A flexibility test recommended by Fleishman[27] is the twist and touch. This test measures how far the subject can rotate his spine. The subject stands with his side toward the wall, an arm's length away with the fist closed. His feet are together, and his toes touch a line drawn perpendicular to the wall. A horizontal scale marked off from 0 to 30 inches extends on either side of a line on the wall which is drawn perpendicular to the line on the floor. Keeping his feet in place, the subject twists back around as far as possible and touches the wall, with his hand at shoulder height and the palm facing the floor. The tester helps the subject keep his feet from moving by placing his own foot against the subject's foot. The subject's score is the farthest point on the scale reached and held for at least two seconds.

Fleishman's[28] test for dynamic flexibility is the bend, twist, and touch. This test measures the speed with which the subject can flex, extend, and rotate his spine. The subject stands with his back to the wall, for enough from the wall so that he can bend over. His feet are approximately shoulder width apart. A mark is placed on the wall in chalk directly behind the middle of the subject's back and at shoulder height. Another mark is made on the floor between the subject's feet. On the signal "Go," the subject bends forward, touches the mark between his feet with both hands, and then straightens up, twists, and touches the mark on the wall with both hands. He then repeats by touching the floor and turning the other way to touch the wall. The score is the number of complete cycles made in 20 seconds.

MEASURING SPEED-OF-LIMB MOVEMENT.   Running in place may be used to measure speed-of-limb movement. The score is the number of times the right foot touches the ground in a period of 20 seconds. Fleishman[29] found that a two-foot tapping test measured the factor of speed of limb movement more satisfactorily. For this test the subject stands

[27]Fleishman: *op. cit.*, p. 130.
[28]*Ibid.*, p. 130.
[29]*Ibid.*, p. 99.

facing a 12-inch-square kick board attached to the wall 18 inches above the floor. On the signal "Go," the subject lifts his right foot and touches the kick board twice before returning it to the ground. He then does the same with his other foot. Two distinct taps are made with each foot each time, and four taps make one complete cycle. The score is the number of cycles completed in 15 seconds. As stated previously, Fleishman believes that running measures explosive power and not the factor of speeed-of-limb movement.

MEASURING CARDIORESPIRATORY ENDURANCE. Distance runs of 300, 440, or 600 yards are frequently used to measure this factor. A drop-off score or endurance ratio may be used. McCloy[30] suggests using the formula of dividing the time of the distance run of 300 yards by the time of the 60-yard dash. The smaller the quotient, the greater is the endurance, the rationale being that the 60-yard run represents the subject's speed of running. If cardiorespiratory endurance does not affect running time for the 300 yards, the time for the total should be only five times greater than the time for 60 yards.

THE KRAUS-WEBER TEST.   A once-popular physical fitness test is the Kraus-Weber battery, which consists of six test items measuring the strength of the abdominal and psoas muscles, certain back muscles, and the flexibility of the back and hamstrings.

For testing the abdominals plus the psoas, the subject is supine with the hands behind the neck; his feet are held down. Holding his hands behind his neck, the subject attempts to roll up into a sitting position; he must not perform a stiff back sit-up. If the subject is unable to perform the test, he has very weak abdominals. A twisting of the upper body during the sit-up may indicate an unequal development of the back muscles.

To test the strength of the abdominals without the psoas, the subject is supine with the hands behind the neck and the knees bent. The feet are held down during the test. The subject rolls up to the sitting position as in the first test item.

For the testing of the psoas, the subject is in a supine position with the hands behind the neck and the legs extended. He lifts the legs 10 inches off the floor and holds for 10 seconds. The knees are straight. If the subject arches his back extremely in performing the test, this may indicate very weak abdominal muscles. It may also be an indication of postural habits contributing to lordosis.

In the test for strength of the back, the subject is prone with a pillow under his abdomen. The pillow must be large enough to supply actual support to the body, and it must be placed so that it becomes a fulcrum for the body. The subject places his hands behind the neck and raises his chest, head, and shoulders while his feet are being held down. He holds the position for 10 seconds. The observer should check for pro-

[30]McCloy and Young: *op. cit.*, p. 184.

nounced muscular development on one side of the spinal column, as this is possible evidence of the development of scoliosis.

For another test of the back area, the subject assumes the same position as above except that the hands are placed so the head can rest on them. With his chest held down, the subject attempts to raise his legs without bending the knees and to hold them in the raised position for the count of 10 seconds. Failure to do so indicates a weak back area.

In the test of the flexibility of the back and hamstrings, the subject stands erect with the hands at the sides. He should not wear shoes. With the feet together and the knees straight, he bends down slowly in an attempt to touch the floor with his finger tips. He remains as far down as it is possible for him to reach for the count of three. The subject is not permitted to bounce. The tester places his hands on the subject's knees to detect bending. Inability to touch the floor indicates short hamstrings and an inflexible spinal column.

PHYSICAL FITNESS INDEX.   The physical fitness index is more frequently used in New England and in the Northwest than elsewhere in the country. The test consists of seven items: pull-up, push-up, leg and back lifts on the dynamometer, and left and right grip on the manuometer. A complete description of the test items may be found in Mathews.

AAHPER FITNESS TEST.[31]   The American Association for Health, Physical Education and Recreation includes seven items in its physical fitness test battery. The items follow, with any variations or special directions required by the battery.

1. Pull-ups for boys (regular grip); flexed arm hang for girls (the chin is brought above the bar).

2. Sit-ups (hands behind the head; when the body is brought up to the 90-degree angle, the trunk is turned and the right elbow is brought to the left knee; a return is made to the supine position and the trunk raised to touch the left elbow to the right knee).

3. Shuttle run.

4. Standing broad jump.

5. Fifty-yard dash.

6. Softball throw (made from between the restraining lines; run between lines permitted).

7. Six-hundred-yard run-walk (running may be interspersed with walking at subject's discretion).

FLEISHMAN'S FITNESS TEST.[32]   Based upon his scientific analysis of the physical fitness factors, Fleishman recommends the ten following tests. Any variations or special methods of performance are noted.

1. Twist and touch.

2. Bend, twist, and touch.

---

[31]American Association for Health, Physical Education, and Recreation: *op. cit., passim.*
[32]Edwin A. Fleishman: *Examiner's Manual for the Basic Fitness Tests.* Englewood Cliffs, N.J., Prentice-Hall, Inc., 1964, *passim.*

Item

	10 yrs.	11 yrs.	12 yrs.	13 yrs.	14 yrs.	15 yrs.	16 yrs.	17 yrs
			BOYS					
Pull-up (regular grip)	—	—	—	—	—	—	1	1
Sit-up	6	6	10	12	15	15	18	20
Shuttle run	14.3	14.0	14.0	13.2	12.5	12.9	12.6	12.5
Broad jump	3'4''	3'7''	3'10''	4'0''	4'6''	4'9''	5'0''	5'5''
50 yd. dash	10.8	10.2	9.6	9.3	8.8	8.5	8.0	7.9
Softball throw	54	63	75	73	90	102	102	115
600 yd. run-walk	3:48	3:48	3:50	3:39	3:33	3:16	3:2	3:5
			GIRLS					
Modified pull-up	2	2	5	6	3	1	2	2
Sit-up	4	5	5	5	4	4	4	3
Shuttle run	15.0	15.0	15.0	14.8	14.0	14.4	14.0	14.2
Broad jump	3'2''	3'3''	3'5''	3'6''	3'6''	3'8''	3'10''	3'7''
50 yd. dash	10.8	10.5	10.4	10.5	12.5	15.1	12.3	13.
Softball throw	26	30	35	39	33	42	44	43
600 yd. run-walk	4:16	4:19	4:25	4:31	4:30	4:14	4:32	4:45

FIGURE 58.   Score of Fifth Percentile.

3. Shuttle run (between two parallel lines 20 yards apart; the runner runs to the opposite line, touches the ground on the far side of it with either foot, returns to the starting line, and repeats; on the last lap he is to go all out to cross the finish line standing up).

4. Softball throw (from a stationary position; no follow-through with the feet is allowed).

5. Hand grip on the manuometer.

6. Pull-ups (reverse grip).

7. Leg lifts.

8. Cable jump test (a rope about 20 inches in length is held in front by the subject, who must jump over it without losing his grip; the score is the number of correct jumps out of five attempts).

9. Balance (one foot is placed lengthwise on beam 1½ inches high by ¾ inch wide by 24 inches long).

10. Six-hundred-yard run-walk.

ADAPTED PHYSICAL FITNESS TESTING

TESTS FOR PHYSICALLY HANDICAPPED CHILDREN.   Some students cannot be given physical fitness tests, either because their disabilities render them incapable of performing the tests or because their conditions may be aggravated in attempting them. However, a good many of the handicapped can be included in the testing if proper precautions are taken. In some instances, this will mean eliminating those tests which involve the part of the body which is injured or disabled. A subject with only one arm, for example, would not be required to do pull-ups but could be expected to take the running tests, as these would not be dangerous for him. In certain cases, the nature of the disability will not be such that safety is a major factor of concern. For example, missing fingers on a hand will not prevent safe participation in the pull-ups. It would not be meaningful, however, to make an evaluation of this subject's score by comparing it to scores achieved by students able to take a normal grip. His score is likely to be less because he has less grip strength and not because of less muscular endurance of the arms, as would be indicated by a low score by normal students. A meaningful measurement for each handicapped individual can be devised, however, by using a progress chart on which scores are recorded each time the test is taken.

TESTS FOR MENTALLY RETARDED CHILDREN.   Physical fitness tests designed for normal youngsters are not valid measurements of physical fitness for the mentally retarded because they are for the most part too complex, and many times the scores are lowered because of the subjects' inability to comprehend and respond immediately with the proper muscular movements. This contention is supported by studies which show that when physical fitness tests commonly given to normal children are given to mentally retarded subjects, the scores demonstrate a high relationship to the I.Q.'s of the subjects.[33] Fait and Kupferer[34] demonstrated that, when the physical fitness test items were simplified, the relationship of the scores to I.Q. was greatly diminished. The Burpee or squat thrust test serves as a good illustration. The scores of retarded children, when given a modified Burpee test which required them to squat and return without thrusting, fitted a fairly normal curve, whereas the scores from the performance of the full Burpee test produced a curve skewed to the left. The inability of the mentally retarded to perform well on the Burpee test appears to be caused more by their inability to remember the movement sequence than by poor agility.

Subsequent to this study, Fait adapted physical fitness tests for the mentally retarded from those given to normal children. Although most of the original tests were highly related to I.Q., none of the adapted tests were. The adapted tests and the original tests were both given to normal youngsters. A high correlation was shown to exist, indicating that the adapted tests were measuring the same factors of fitness as the original tests. The adapted tests are used as test items in the following battery of physical fitness tests for the mentally retarded.[35]

These tests may be used for the educable and for a majority of the medium and high trainables, if the youngsters do not have other handicaps

[33]Lawrence Rarick and Robert J. Francis: "Motor Characteristics of the Mentally Retarded." *Cooperative Research Monograph*, No. 1, OE-35005, U.S. Office of Education, 1960, *passim*.

[34]Hollis F. Fait and Harriet Kupferer: "A Study of Two Motor Achievement Tests and Its Implications in Planning Physical Education Activities for the Mentally Retarded." *American Journal of Mental Deficiency*, Vol. 60, 1956, pp. 728–732.

[35]Research study, financed by the Joseph P. Kennedy, Jr., Foundation, in progress at the Physical Efficiency Laboratory at the University of Connecticut under the direction of Hollis Fait in conjunction with the Mansfield State Training School. Information about norms may be obtained by writing to Hollis Fait, School of Physical Education, University of Connecticut, Storrs, Connecticut.

which prevent safe performance of the test. (See Chapter 13 for discussion of educables and trainables.)

Bent-Arm Hang or Straight-Arm Hang:[36] For the bent-arm hand, a horizontal bar or doorway bar may be used. A stool approximately 12 inches high is placed under the bar. The subject steps onto the stool and takes hold of the bar with both hands, using a reverse grip (palms toward the face). The hands are shoulders' width apart. The subject brings his head to the bar, presses the bridge of the nose to the bar, and steps off the stool. He holds this position as long as possible. The timer starts the watch as the subject's nose presses to the bar and the body weight is taken on the arms. The watch is stopped when the subject drops away from the bar. The tester should be ready to catch the subject in the event that he falls. The number of seconds the subject held the position is recorded on the score card.

For the straight-arm hang, the subject steps on a stool, grasps the bar with a regular grip (palms away from the face), and steps off the stool. When the subject steps off the stool, taking his weight on his arms, the timer starts the watch. When the subject releases his grip, the watch is stopped. The subject should not be allowed to take a new grip during the hang. The tester may cup his hands lightly over the subject's to prevent "re-gripping." The time is recorded to the nearest tenth of a second.

Three or Five-Chair Zigzag Run: Three or five chairs[37] are placed 5 feet apart in a line. (The distance is measured from the back leg to the back leg of each chair.) The starting line is at a distance of 3 feet from the first chair and the finish line at a distance of 3 feet from the last chair. A line is drawn on the floor to mark the zigzag course between the chairs which the runner is to follow. Starting at the right of the first chair, the subject runs in and out of the line of chairs as rapidly as he can. For the starting position, the subject places one foot slightly forward and places the hands on the knees. The subject starts at the command, "Ready: go!" and the watch is started on "Go!" The watch is stopped as the runner passes the last chair. The purpose of the finish line is to prevent the runner from slowing up at the end of the run. The number of seconds to the nearest tenth of a second is recorded on the score card.

Leg Lift: The subject lies flat on his back with his hands clasped behind the neck. A helper should hold the subject's elbows to the ground. The subject raises his legs, keeping the knees straight, until they are at a 90-degree angle. Another helper, who stands to the side of the subject, extends one hand over the subject's abdomen at the height of the ankles when the legs are fully lifted. This serves as a guide to the subject in achieving the desired angle and to encourage him to keep his legs straight.

---

[36]Both tests measure the factor of muscular endurance, but they test different muscle groups. The straight-arm hang is usually easier to administer to the trainable.

[37]Five chairs make a better test; however, if the subjects become confused, the number may be reduced to three to insure a successful run.

FIGURE 59. The course of the agility run may be marked for the mentally retarded. (Mansfield [Conn.] State Training School and Hospital.)

The subject is to do as many leg lifts as possible in the 20-second time limit. He begins on the command of "Go" and ceases on the command of "Stop." The score is the number of leg lifts performed during the 20 seconds.

Static Balance Test: The subject places his hands on his hips, lifts one leg, and places the foot on the inside of the knee of the other leg. He then closes his eyes and maintains his balance in this position as long as he can. The watch is started the moment he closes his eyes. As soon as the subject loses his balance, the watch is stopped. The score is number of seconds to the nearest tenth of a second.

One-half Burpee: The subject is in a standing position at the command of "Go." He squats, touches his hands to the floor, and returns to a standing position. The movement is repeated as rapidly as possible for 20 seconds. The subject must return each time to a complete standing position, i.e., knees straight and the body not bent over 160 degrees. The number of complete squats performed in 20 seconds is recorded on the score card.

Thirty-five-Yard Run and One-Hundred-Forty-Yard Run: The subject places the back foot against the wall[38] with the foot parallel to the wall. He then takes a semicrouch position with the hands resting lightly on the knees. His forward foot and trunk are turned in the direction he is to run. His head is held up so that he is looking toward the finish line. At the command of "Ready: go!" the subject begins the run. The watch is

[38]A board 2 inches high by 4 inches wide and 2 or 3 feet long secured to the ground may be used when testing out of doors.

started on the "Go!" and is stopped as the subject passes the finish line. However, the subject is directed to run to a second line which is about 5 feet beyond the finish line, to prevent his slowing down as he approaches the true finish line. The time of the run is recorded to the nearest tenth of a second. The score is calculated by the following formula to give the cardiorespiratory endurance ability: Time of 140 yards minus (Time of 35 yards × 4).

THE ADAPTED PHYSICAL FITNESS PROGRAM

The development of physical fitness is limited by the structure of the organism. Inheritance may establish a certain capacity for an individual. Accidental injury, disease, or other debilitating factors further influence the limitations for the development of total fitness. Such students require special concentration and attention to their needs and should be placed in the special adapted physical education class for activities that are planned to build up specific factors of physical fitness. Included among those who are to be placed in the adapted class should be those who because of their inability to participate successfully in the regular class have withdrawn or desire to withdraw from activity and those who owing to general low fitness are unable to keep up with class instruction.

Those who are only slightly handicapped by their lack of fitness or are low in just one factor may be included in the regular class if certain modifications are made to give special emphasis to strengthening the weak areas and, if necessary, to offer protection to these areas of weakness.

In the special class there should be special emphasis on the areas that need work. This does not mean that the physical education program must consist only of activities designed to overcome deficiency, for the program should provide activities that will aid in the achieving of the broad general objectives of physical education.

Before much improvement can be expected in strengthening specific weak areas, the students must be convinced of the values of such improvement. Students may be motivated by helping them establish goals that can be obtained and are desirable for the age in question. Such goals as a better-looking body, a more efficient body in everyday work skills, or an improvement in sports skills may act as motivators.

INCREASING STRENGTH.   Special exercises and activities for lack of strength may be given to those who are in special need of such a program. The most effective way to build strength is to apply the overload principle by resistive exercises or by participation in games that require an additional work load to be carried.

In setting a work load for the student who has below normal strength, one must take into consideration his initial capacity and adjust the work load accordingly. Any area of the body that has a past history of injury should be protected, and the overload given this area should be very slight initially and slowly increased over a period of time. Students who have no organic lesions or history of injury but who are generally weak exhibit a tendency to select too small a work load and need to be encouraged to take more in order to achieve the desired results.

Weight training is a good activity for applying the correct amount of overload to any set of muscles. Contrary to popular opinion, there is no danger of getting the muscle so strong that it becomes "muscle bound." If the special class for increasing strength is rather large, weight training may be contraindicated because of lack of space and available weights.

Research studies[39] have shown that strength improves just as rapidly in isometric contraction (pulling against an immobile object) as in isotonic contraction, which is the type of muscular contraction employed in weight training. To provide an immobile object, screws are placed in the floor, wall, and ceiling and straps attached to them. The participant pulls upon the straps with full effort, utilizing the muscles he wishes to strengthen, for a period of 5 to 6 seconds. This is done two or three times for each set of muscles.

Another activity for promoting the development of strength, especially suitable for large classes, is the dual resisting exercises, in which two people work together giving resistance to each other. Some examples of exercises that can be utilized are given below; others can be worked out using the same basic principles applied here.

1. Students face each other, upper arms against the body with elbows bent and forearms extended to the front. They place their palms against each other and push. One person exercises the triceps; the other, the biceps.

2. Students face each other with arms fully extended and proceed as above.

3. Facing each other, the students extend their arms forward and upward with the fingers interlocked with each other. The hands are brought down, keeping the arms straight and flexing the wrists in an attempt to force the opponent to superextend his wrists.

4. One student carries the other piggyback and takes quarter or half squats, depending upon his strength.

5. Contests such as leg wrestle, arm wrestle, or Indian arm wrestle can be utilized to apply overload.

Increase in muscular strength will also increase muscular endurance and power. General muscular strength increase will influence scores on the pull-ups, push-ups, dips, sit-ups, and vertical jump tests.

There is insufficient evidence to indicate one special way to train for muscular endurance, explosive power, or static strength. It is the general practice at this time to develop explosive power by increasing the static

[39]Henry H. Clarke: "Development of Volitional Muscle Strength as Related to Fitness" in *Exercise and Fitness.* Chicago, The Athletic Institute, 1960, pp. 200–212.

strength by means of overloading the muscle, using a heavy load with a fewer number of repetitions. However, in increasing muscular endurance, it is the common practice to use a smaller weight and a greater number of repetitions. A study done at the University of Connecticut[40] indicates that muscular endurance increased more rapidly in exercises using heavy weights and fewer repetitions than in those with light weights and more repetitions. Static strength development paralleled the development of dynamic strength, regardless of the method used.

INCREASING CARDIORESPIRATORY ENDURANCE.   Those who are below par in strength, even though they are free from pathological disturbances, are also often very low in cardiorespiratory endurance; therefore, activities designed to develop cardiorespiratory endurance should be given along with those designed especially for increasing strength. The body appears to respond to an "overload" upon the cardiorespiratory system by improving the function, as it does when an overload is applied to a muscle.

Those with low endurance levels who have been selected from the regular class for special work will need to be introduced very slowly to endurance activities, since their lack of endurance is frequently connected with an attitude that has made them shun such activities. If there are no pathological causes present, there is little physical danger of giving too much work. However, more can usually be accomplished with this group by starting out very slowly and increasing the length of time of participation in the activity at a slow rate.

Games and sports that require running are excellent for developing endurance. However, with this group, interest may be very low because of past unsuccessful experiences in these activities. If games are used, modifications may be necessary so as to make the participation within the range of their abilities.

Some examples of modified games and activities related to team sports are listed below:

(1) three-court basketball;

(2) line soccer with distance between goal line shortened;

(3) basketball dribble relays;

(4) dribble length of basketball floor and shoot; and

(5) football throw over goal post (thrower throws high enough so he can run forward and catch ball; score is distance run if ball is caught).

The work load that affects endurance can be more easily controlled when giving specific exercises than in game situations. Exercises such as side-straddle hop, squat thrusts, and rope jumping are ones in which the work load can be easily controlled.

INCREASING FLEXIBILITY.   Flexibility can be increased by extending the range of motion. If there is no pathological reason for lack of flexibility,

[40]Donald Minton: "Comparison of Two Types of Weight Training for the Development of Muscular Endurance." Unpublished study, Storrs, Connecticut, Physical Efficiency Laboratory, University of Connecticut, 1960.

exercises that require stretching can be given. Each time the exercise is given, the joint should be moved in a wider range. Usually it is not desirable to segregate those who lack flexibility, because this usually does not hinder them to the extent that they cannot participate successfully with the other students. Flexibility exercises that are given to the entire regular class are appropriate for those who lack a wide range of movement. Such exercises are usually given as warm-up exercises preceding more strenuous activity. Some suggestions are:

(1) touch floor without bending knees;

(2) raise arms laterally and rotate at the shoulder in as wide an arc as possible;

(3) with hands on hips, rotate trunk in as wide a circle as possible (same procedure for the head);

(4) hold arms in front of body, crossed at wrists and at belt level, then throw arms upward and backward as far as possible.

INCREASING BALANCE.   Developing better balance requires practice in balancing activities. Activities such as walking on beams and one-leg balances will be of value.

SPECIAL ELEMENTARY SCHOOL ACTIVITIES

In the elementary school it is usually not desirable to separate the children with low physical fitness from the regular class. As a rule, unless there are pathological disturbances, the difference between the normal group and the less physically fit group is relatively small compared to the difference in these groups in older children. Moreover, segregation at this age level may have psychological repercussions that may be difficult for the teacher to minimize. The most satisfactory method of teaching such children appears to be to keep them with the regular class and to include numerous games and activities which will encourage an improved condition of physical fitness.

Many of the activities already discussed are good for young children, but some will be too difficult for them to perform or too complex for their comprehension. Certain special exercises are valuable in the physical education program for the young child. Hanging, walking with the hands on a low parallel ladder, and climbing should be included in the elementary program to increase shoulder and arm strength. However, when the desired movements and exercises are incorporated into games and activities, they become more meaningful to the child and more fun for him to do. The dual resisting exercises can be used effectively as games and contests with children beyond the second grade, although some are appropriate only to boys. The piggyback-ride exercise should be used with discretion, since it may be too strenuous for many.

The teacher must keep in mind that the sub-strength child should not be placed in game situations where he is always last. An attempt should be made to equalize the competition so that he can achieve some success. Attitudes of the class should be so shaped that any member of the team is readily accepted for the contributions he can make, even though he is not as strong or as efficient in the performance of skills as others on the team.

Following are some suggested activities for use in increasing strength, muscular endurance, and power; cardiorespiratory endurance; flexibility; and balance. Most of the activities contribute to more than one factor of physical fitness, but they are listed here under the factor to which they appear to make the greatest contribution. The lists are not intended to be exhaustive; they are, rather, suggestions for planning the program on the elementary level. The activities are listed according to their degree of difficulty and interest appeal.

ACTIVITIES FOR INCREASING STRENGTH, MUSCULAR ENDURANCE, AND MUSCULAR POWER

Race on tiptoes
Seal walk
Jumping jack
Crab walk
Squat thrust
Modified push-up
Leap frog
Dual rocker

Chinese stand-up
Walking chairs
Wheelbarrow
Tug pick-up
Hand wrestle
Indian wrestle
Indian leg wrestle
Frog tip-up

ACTIVITIES FOR INCREASING CARDIORESPIRATORY ENDURANCE

Midnight
Drop the handkerchief
Bronco relay
Circle relay
Cowboys and Indians

Line relay
Cross tag
Chain tag
Rope-jumping contest
Post ball

ACTIVITIES FOR INCREASING FLEXIBILITY

Bird flying
Dry-land swimming
Twisting at hips
Bending at hips, forward,
   backward and to the sides
Wring the dish rag
Measuring worm
Elephant walk

Snail
Rocker
Touch floor, knees straight
Sit-up, touch toes
Grape vine
Forward roll
Backward roll

ACTIVITIES FOR INCREASING BALANCE

Stork stand

Hopping backward and forward

Hopskotch

Pyramid building

Walking on toes or heels

Turk stand

Beam walking

QUESTIONS

1. Define physical fitness.
2. What do you consider the most important factors in physical fitness?
3. Define: strength, endurance, speed of movement, power flexibility, and coordination.
4. What are the values of the physical fitness tests? What are the limitations?
5. Briefly describe a test for measuring each of the following: strength, speed, muscular endurance, cardiorespiratory endurance, power, flexibility, and coordination.
6. What determines the level of physical fitness for any one person?
7. Briefly discuss what factors one must take into consideration in interpreting the results of only one test of fitness.
8. In what ways may students be motivated to increase their level of fitness?
9. How much emphasis should be placed upon increasing physical fitness in the low fitness group in comparison to the other objectives of physical education?
10. Discuss the techniques that may be utilized in developing strength in physical education classes.
11. Discuss the feasibility of placing those with subnormal endurance and flexibility in the adapted class.
12. What is coordination? How is it developed?
13. In what ways do children of low fitness in the elementary school differ from those who are subnormal in fitness at the secondary school or college level?

SELECTED READINGS

AAHPER: *Youth Fitness Test Manual*, rev. ed. Washington, D.C., American Association for Health, Physical Education, and Recreation, 1965.

Clarke, Henry H. and David H.: *Developmental and Adapted Physical Education.* Englewood Cliffs, N. J., Prentice-Hall, Inc., 1963.

Fleishman, Edwin A.: *Examiner's Manual for the Basic Fitness Tests.* Englewood Cliffs, N.J., Prentice-Hall, Inc., 1964.

Latchaw, Marjorie, and Brown, Camille: *The Evaluation Process in Health Education, Physical Education and Recreation.* Englewood Cliffs, N.J., Prentice-Hall, Inc., 1962.

Mathews, Donald K.: *Measurement in Physical Education.* ed. 2. Philadelphia, W. B. Saunders Co., 1963.

Meyers, Carlton R., and Blesh, T. Erwin: *Measurement in Physical Education.* New York, The Ronald Press Company, 1962.

Willgoose, Carl E.: *Evaluation in Health Education and Physical Education.* New York, McGraw-Hill Book Co., Inc., 1961.

APPENDIX

ENRICHING THE PHYSICAL
EDUCATION PROGRAM FOR
THE MENTALLY GIFTED CHILD

Mentally gifted children, who are usually classified as those with intelligence quotients above 130 to 140, constitute about one per cent of the total population. Their unusual capabilities are demonstrated in high scholastic achievement, originality, creativity, and intellectual interests. Their superiority is usually not limited to mental activities, however. They tend to develop faster physically and to be heavier, taller, and better coordinated than other youngsters of the same chronological age. Moreover, they generally demonstrate greater emotional maturity than the average youngster.

There is currently considerable effort on the part of educators to provide these youngsters with a program of educational experiences which will challenge their intellects and cultivate their abilities. Enriched and accelerated programs for the intellectually gifted have become fairly common in our schools. While the physical education teacher is usually not directly involved in these special programs, he is in a position to make certain contributions to increasing the scope of knowledge and appreciations of gifted students. These students, because they are generally both physically and mentally superior to most other youngsters, are often less challenged and more easily bored by the play activities which hold interest for their contemporaries. When a game lacks challenge and interest, they innovate to increase the complexity of the play; this tends to antagonize the other players, who consequently react by excluding them from future play. The gifted, then, are likely to withdraw and seek their pleasures in mentally satisfying sedentary activities or in daydreaming. Neither of these recourses is, of course, desirable, because the youngsters are deprived of the beneficial effects of participation in strenuous physical activity as well as the wholesome results of successful social intercourse with others in play. The physical educator's contribution to the total education of the gifted student is that of keeping him active in the kinds of sports and games which benefit him and at the same time hold his interest. Strategy and play formations may be introduced to him to provide additional breadth in his game experiences. He should be encouraged to devise new plays and formations for the games being played in physical education class. Whenever possible, he should be permitted to teach some of the more feasible ones to the class. Interest may be heightened further by giving reading assignments to increase his knowledge of specific sports and to broaden his appreciation of the place of sports in ancient and modern cultures. Other reading assignments might be made to introduce him to the more technical physiological and psychological aspects of the influence of exercise upon the human body.

Although many mentally gifted youngsters do develop faster physically and are larger than the average child of the same chronological age, many of them are smaller and more physically immature than their classmates. This is caused by acceleration of gifted students, which permits them to skip one or more grades. Physical development, although faster than average, does not keep pace with mental development, and, consequently, the gifted student who has been accelerated finds that he is inferior in physical performance to his classmates. If he is considerably younger chronologically than the others in his class, he is likely to have less strength, endurance, and coordination than they. His failure to keep up with them physically may cause him to withdraw from physical activities and to pursue only those mental activities in which his success is assured. Such students need special help from the physical educator in gaining an understanding of their own worth, regardless of physical attributes, and an appreciation of the importance of participation in the play activities.

SUGGESTED FILMS AND FILMSTRIPS
FOR ADAPTED, CORRECTIVE, AND
DEVELOPMENTAL PHYSICAL EDUCATION

Allergies. EBF:[1] 16 mm., 12 minutes.
> Understanding nature of allergies.

The Asthmatic Page in the Family Album. CIBA, 1959: 16 mm., 24 minutes.
> Therapy for different types of asthma.

[1] For complete source references, see the next section of the Appendix.

The Auditorially Handicapped Child: The Deaf. Net, 1957: 16 mm., 29 minutes.
    Problems of the deaf child: teaching techniques, needs, and characteristics.
Beyond the Shadows. CSDH, 1959: 16 mm., 26 minutes.
    Steps in establishing diagnostic, educational, and vocational facilities for mentally retarded children in a community.
The Cerebral Palsied Child. NET, 1957: 16 mm., 29 minutes
    The nature of cerebral palsy.
Class for Tommy. BAF, 1952: 16 mm., 20 minutes.
    Teaching mentally retarded children in a class.
Common Heart Disorders and Their Causes. MGHT: 16 mm., 17 minutes.
    Functions of circulatory system and common heart disorders.
The Community and the Exceptional Child. NET, 1957: 16 mm., 29 minutes.
    The community's role, contributions, and problems in helping the exceptional child.
The Crippled Child. NET, 1957: 16 mm., 29 minutes
    Social, physical, and therapeutic needs of the crippled child.
The Deep Well. H&WMC, 1957: 16 mm., 36 minutes.
    Care and treatment of disturbed children in foster boarding homes and institutions.
Diabetic Coma. CDC, 1950: 33-frame filmstrip, 5 minutes.
    What to do for diabetic coma, and how to prevent it.
Diabetics Unknown. PUAC, 1961: 16 mm., 29 minutes.
    How to help find undiagnosed cases of diabetes.
Evaluating Physical Abilities. CUE, 1958: 16 mm., 18 minutes
    Appraisal of physical fitness factors of speed, strength, coordination, agility, etc.
Eyewitness to a Miracle. MSBH: 16 mm., 19 minutes.
    A patient's stay at a tuberculosis hospital.
Foods and Nutrition. EBF: 16 mm., 11 minutes.
    What good posture is, and how to achieve and maintain it.
Guard Your Health Against Tuberculosis. VEC: filmstrip.
    How tuberculosis is transmitted, and how to build resistance against it.
Guard Your Heart. BRAY, 1950: 16 mm., 26 minutes.
    What takes place in arteriosclerosis, coronary thrombosis, and other heart diseases.
Heart Disease—Its Major Causes. EBF, 1954: 16 mm., 11 minutes.
    Causes and treatment of heart disease.
How to Avoid Muscle Strain. MSBH: 16 mm., 13 minutes.
    Correct ways of lifting objects.
The Human Machine. MIS, 1955: 16 mm., 15 minutes
    Physiology of the human body.
Improving Your Posture. CORF, 1949: 16 mm., 11 minutes.
    What good posture is, and how to achieve to maintain it.
In Time to Help. CSDH, 1961: 16 mm., 14 minutes.
    Hearing conservation program: how deafness occurs, how it is remedied.
Iowa Test of Motor Fitness. SUI, 1960: 16 mm., 12 minutes.
    How to administer the Iowa Test of Motor Fitness.
Journey Back. NF, 1949: 16 mm., 20 minutes.
    Rehabilitation of a hemiplegic patient.
The Key. CAROUF, 1958: 16 mm., 30 minutes.
    Adjustment of a deaf girl to life with normal people.
Mentally Retarded: Trainable. NET, 1957: 16 mm., 29 minutes.
    Problems of and training methods for severely mentally retarded children.
Nancy Goes to School. SUI, 1955: 16 mm., 30 minutes.
    A day at school for a handicapped child.
Naval Standard Physical Fitness Test. NF: 16 mm., 20 minutes.
    Physical fitness tests to measure strength, endurance, stamina, and agility.
New Experience for Mentally Retarded Children. V-DE, 1958: 16 mm., 31 minutes.
    Camping for severely retarded children.
Nutrition: Energy, Growth, and Repair. FSMC, 1962: 41-frame filmstrip.
    Relationship of nutrition to energy, growth, repair, and techniques for measuring energy content of foods.
Opportunity to Learn. SUI, 1958: 16 mm., 28 minutes.
    Problems of the severely handicapped child in communicating with the world.

Parents of a Stranger. CAROUF, 1958: 16 mm., 30 minutes.
    Successful family life with a deaf child.
Pay Attention: Problems of Hard-of-Hearing Children. PCR, 1946: 16 mm., 29 minutes.
    Teaching techniques appropriate in class including deafened children.
The Perkins Story. CAMPF, 1958: 16 mm., 40 minutes.
    Blind children at a school for the blind.
Posture and Exercise. EBF: 16 mm., 11 minutes
    Corrective exercises.
Proud Years. CMC, 1956: 16 mm., 28 minutes.
    Methods of physical rehabilitation used with elderly patients.
Reach into Silence. H&R, 1957: 16 mm., 13½ minutes.
    Training teachers to help deaf children speak.
Recreational and Occupational Therapy. NF, 1945; 16 mm., 13 minutes.
    Therapeutic activities suited to patients' conditions.
Testing Multiply Handicapped Children. NEWS, 1963: 16 mm., 29 minutes.
    The testing of children with more than one handicap.
There Was a Door. CON, 1960: 16 mm., 38 minutes.
    Care and treatment of mentally retarded.
This Year, Next Year, Sometime. . . . . NYU, 1962: 16 mm., 19 minutes.
    Treatment of children with severe emotional disturbances.
Thursday's Children. CON, 1956: 16 mm., 22 minutes.
    Methods for teaching deaf children.
The Visually Handicapped Child: The Blind. NET, 1957: 16 mm., 29 minutes.
    Problems encountered by the blind child.
The Visually Handicapped Child: The Partially Sighted. NET, 1957: 16 mm., 29 minutes.
    Problems of and methods of training a child with defective vision.
The White Cane. GYP, 1963: 16 mm., 13 minutes.
    Specialized teaching techniques for blind children.
Who's Handicapped? PCEH: 16 mm., 22 minutes.
    Adjustment of handicapped people to normal life.
Wonder Engine of the Body (The Human Heart). BRAY, 1951: 16 mm., 10 minutes.
    The physiology of the heart.

FILM SOURCES

Bailey Films, Inc., 6509 DeLongre Avenue, Hollywood, California 90028.   (BAF)
Bray Studios, Inc., 729 Seventh Avenue, New York, New York 10019.   (BRAY)
   Attn: Mrs. B. D. Hess.
Campbell Films, Academy Avenue, Saxtons River, Vermont 05154.   (CAMPF)
Carousel Films, Inc., Suite 1503, 1501 Broadway, New York, New York 10036. (CAROUF)
   Attn: David B. Dash.
Center for Mass Communication of Columbia University Press,   (CMC)
   1125 Amsterdam Avenue, New York, New York 10027.
   Attn: M. J. Bours, Business Manager.
CIBA Pharmaceutical Co., 556 Morris Avenue, Summit, New Jersey 07901.   (CIBA)
   Attn: R. H. Roberts, M.D., Director of Medical Information.
Communicable Disease Center, Atlanta, Georgia 30322. *Attn:* National   (CDC)
   Medical Audio-Visual Facility.
Contemporary Films, 267 West 25th Street, New York, New York 10001.   (CON)
   Attn: Leo Dratfield.
Coronet Films, 65 East South Water Street, Chicago, Illinois 60601.   (CORF)
Colorado State Department of Health, Health Education Section,   (CSDH)
   4216 East 11th Avenue, Denver, Colorado 80220.
   Attn: Norma Johannis, Chief.
Encyclopedia Britannica Films, 1150 Wilmette Avenue, Wilmette, Illinois 60091. (EBF)
Filmstrip-of-the-Month Clubs, Inc., 355 Lexington Avenue, New York,   (FSMC)
   New York 10017. *Attn:* Mr. Stone.
Gypsy Enterprises, RFD #2, Simsbury, Connecticut 06070. *Attn:* Mrs. Harry   (GYP)
   Knapp.

Harper & Row. Publishers, 49 East 33rd Street, New York, New York 10016.   (H&R)
Health and Welfare Materials Center, 10 East 44th Street, New York,   (H&WMC)
    New York 10017. *Attn:* Victor Weingarten.
McGraw-Hill Textfilms, 330 West 42nd Street, New York, New York   (MGHT)
    10036. *Attn:* Barbara Josephson
Mississippi State Board of Health, Box 1700, Jackson, Mississippi 39205.   (MSBH)
    Attn: Mary Ann Elkin, Assistant Director.
Moody Institute of Science, Educational Film Division, 11428 Santa Monica   (MIS)
    Boulevard, West Los Angeles, California 90025. *Attn:* Hedley J.
    Parker.
National Educational Television, (NET) Film Service, Audio-Visual Center.   (NET)
    Indiana University, Bloomington, Indiana 47405.
Newsfilm, USA, 250 West 57th Street, New York, New York 10019.   (NEWS)
New York University Film Library, 26 Washington Place, New York,   (NYU)
    New York 10003. *Attn:* Daniel Lesser.
Norwood Films, 926 New Jersey Avenue N. W., Washington, D.C. 20001.   (NF)
President Committee on Employment of the Handicapped, Washington,   (PCEH)
    D.C. 20025. *Attn:* J. Roland Hayes, Information Assistant.
Psychological Cinema Register, Pennsylvania State University, Audio-Visual   (PCR)
    Aids Library, University Park, Pennsylvania 16802. *Attn:* I. C. Boerlin,
    Business Manager.
Public Affairs Committee, Inc., 22 East 38th Street, New York, New York   (PUAC)
    10016. *Attn:* Adele Braude.
State University of Iowa, Bureau of Audio-Visual Instruction, Extension   (SUI)
    Division, Iowa City, Iowa 52240. *Attn:* Lee W. Cochran.
University of California Extension, Educational Films Sales Dept.   (CUE)
    Berkeley, California 90201.
Virginia Department of Education, Film Production Service, State Office   (VDE)
    Building, Richmond, Virginia 23219.
Visual Education Consultants, Inc., 2066 Helena Street, Madison,   (VEC)
    Wisconsin 53704. *Attn:* Margaret W. Dewey.

RECORD SOURCES

Black Mountain Records, 4247 Walnut Street, Long Beach, California 90807.
Childhood Rhythm Records, Chartwell House, 112 East 19th Street, New York, New York
    10003.
Ruth Evans, 326 Forest Park Avenue, Springfield, Massachusetts 01108.
Folkraft Record Company, 1159 Broad Street, Newark, New Jersey 07114.
Folk Dancer, P. O. Box 201, Flushing, Long Island, New York 11352.
Imperial Record Company, Inc., 137–139 North Western Avenue, Los Angeles, California
    90004.
Lloyd Shaw Recordings, Inc., P. O. Box 203, Colorado Springs, Colorado 80901.
RCA Victor Record Division, New York, New York 10010.
Square Dance Associates, Freeport, New York 11520.
Western Jubilee Master Record Service, 708 East Garfield, Phoenix, Arizona 85006.
World of Fun Records, Methodist Publishing House, Nashville, Tennessee 37202.

PROFESSIONAL ORGANIZATIONS

American Association for Health, Physical Education, and Recreation (a department of
    the National Education Association), 1201 Sixteenth Street, N.W., Washington,
    D.C. 20036.
American Medical Association, 535 North Dearborn Street, Chicago, Illinois 60610.
American Occupational Therapy Association, Inc., 3310 East 42nd Street, New York, New
    York 10017.
American Physical Therapy Association, 1790 Broadway, New York, New York 10019.
American Psychiatric Association, 1700 18th Street, N.W., Washington, D.C. 20036.

American Psychological Association, 1333 Sixteenth Street, N.W., Washington, D.C. 20036.

American Speech Correction Association, Speech and Hearing Clinic. (headquarters changes annually to location of elected secretary-treasuer.)

International Council for Exceptional Children. 1201 Sixteenth Street. N.W., Washington, D.C. 20036.

National Foundation, 1790 Broadway, New York, New York 10019.

National Rehabilitation Association, 1025 Vermont Avenue, Washington, D.C. 20005.

SOCIETIES AND ASSOCIATION

American Federation of the Physically Handicapped, Inc., 1376 National Press Building, Washington, D.C. 20004.

American Hearing Society, 817 Fourteenth Street, N.W., Washington, D.C. 20005.

American Heart Association, Inc., 1790 Broadway, New York, New York 10019.

American Legion National Rehabilitation Committee, 1608 K Street, N.W., Washington, D.C. 20006.

Association for the Aid of Crippled Children, 345 East 46th Street. New York, New York 10017.

Children's Bureau, Department of Health, Education, and Welfare, Washington, D.C. 20014.

Comeback, Inc., 16 West 46th Street. New York, New York 10036.

Goodwill Industries of America, Inc., 744 North Fourth Street, Milwaukee, Wisconsin 53201.

Institute for the Crippled and Disabled, 400 First Avenue, New York, New York 10010.

Muscular Dystrophy Association of America, Inc., 1790 Broadway, New York, New York 10019.

National Association for Mental Health, 10 Columbus Circle, New York, New York 10019.

National Council on Rehabilitation, 1790 Broadway, New York, New York 10019.

National Epilepsy League, 208 North Wells Street, Chicago, Illinois 60606.

National Organization for Mentally Ill Children, 171 Madison Avenue, New York, New York 10010.

National Society for Crippled Children and Adults, Inc., 11 South LaSalle Street, Chicago, Illinois 60603.

National Society for the Prevention of Blindness, Inc., 1790 Broadway, New York, New York 10019.

National Tuberculosis Association, 1790 Broadway, New York, New York 10019.

United Cerebral Palsy Association, 50 West 57th Street, New York, New York 10019.

United States Office of Education, Department of Health, Education, and Welfare, Washington, D.C. 20202.

Vocational Rehabilitation Administration, Department of Health, Education, and Welfare, Washington, D.C. 20201.

Volta Bureau, 1537 Thirty-fifth Street, N.W., Washington, D.C. 20007.

PERIODICALS

American Heart Journal
American Journal of Hygiene
American Journal of Occupational Therapy
American Journal of Physiology
American Journal of Public Health
Archives of Pediatrics
Archives of Physical Medicine and Rehabilitation
Child Development
Journal of the American Dietetic Association
Journal of the Association for Physical and Mental Rehabilitation
Journal of Bone and Joint Surgery
Journal of Exceptional Children

Journal of Health, Physical Education, and Recreation
Mental Hygiene
Physical Educator
Physical Therapy Review
Physiotherapy
Recreation
Recreation in Treatment Centers
Rehabilitation Record
Research Quarterly
Today's Health

INDEX